V.9   0015342

SINGLE VOL   3/10/—
SET RATE   2/16/—

COMPREHENSIVE BIOCHEMISTRY

SOLE DISTRIBUTORS FOR THE UNITED STATES AND CANADA:

AMERICAN ELSEVIER PUBLISHING COMPANY, INC.

52, Vanderbilt Avenue, New York 17, N.Y.

SOLE DISTRIBUTORS FOR GREAT BRITAIN:

ELSEVIER PUBLISHING COMPANY LIMITED

12B, Rippleside Commercial Estate, Ripple Road, Barking, Essex

Library of Congress Catalog Card Number 62–10359

With 58 illustrations and 36 tables

COMPREHENSIVE BIOCHEMISTRY

COMPREHENSIVE
BIOCHEMISTRY

SECTION I (VOLUMES I–4)
PHYSICO-CHEMICAL AND ORGANIC ASPECTS
OF BIOCHEMISTRY

SECTION II (VOLUMES 5–11)
CHEMISTRY OF BIOLOGICAL COMPOUNDS

SECTION III
BIOCHEMICAL REACTION MECHANISMS

SECTION IV
METABOLISM

SECTION V
CHEMICAL BIOLOGY
GENERAL INDEX

COMPREHENSIVE
BIOCHEMISTRY

EDITED BY

MARCEL FLORKIN

Professor of Biochemistry, University of Liège (Belgium)

AND

ELMER H. STOTZ

*Professor of Biochemistry, University of Rochester, School of Medicine
and Dentistry, N.Y. (U.S.A.)*

VOLUME 9

PYRROLE PIGMENTS, ISOPRENOID COMPOUNDS
AND
PHENOLIC PLANT CONSTITUENTS

ELSEVIER PUBLISHING COMPANY

AMSTERDAM · LONDON · NEW YORK

1963

CONTRIBUTORS TO THIS VOLUME

J. G. BAXTER, Ph.D.

Distillation Products Industries, Division of Eastman Kodak Company,
755 Ridge Road West, Rochester 3, N.Y. (U.S.A.)

J. E. FALK, M.Sc., Ph.D., F.R.A.C.I., F.A.A.

Division of Plant Industry, Commonwealth Scientific and Industrial Research
Organization, P.O. Box 109, Canberra City, A.C.T. (Australia)

T. A. GEISSMAN, B.Sc., Ph.D.

Professor of Chemistry, Chemistry Department, University of California,
Los Angeles, Calif. (U.S.A.)

C. H. GRAY, M.D., D.Sc., F.R.C.P., F.R.I.C.

Professor of Chemical Pathology, King's College Hospital Medical School,
University of London, Denmark Hill, London, S.E.5 (Great Britain)

A. J. HAAGEN-SMIT, Ph.D.

Professor of Plant Biochemistry, Division of Biology, California Institute of Technology,
Pasadena, Calif. (U.S.A.)

ROBERT S. HARRIS, B.Sc., Ph.D.

Professor of Nutritional Biochemistry, Department of Nutrition and Food Science,
Massachusetts Institute of Technology, Cambridge, Mass. (U.S.A.)

ROBERT HILL, Sc.D., F.R.S.

Department of Biochemistry, University of Cambridge, Tennis Court Road,
Cambridge (Great Britain)

RICHARD ALAN MORTON, Ph.D., D.Sc., F.R.I.C., F.R.S.

Johnston Professor of Biochemistry, Department of Biochemistry, The University,
Liverpool 3 (Great Britain)

C. C. NIMMO, Ph.D.

Principal Chemist, United States Department of Agriculture, Western Utilization
Research and Development Division, Albany, Calif. (U.S.A.)

J. N. PHILLIPS, M.Sc., Ph.D.

Division of Plant Industry, Commonwealth Scientific and Industrial Research
Organization, P.O.Box 109, Canberra City, A.C.T. (Australia)

GENERAL PREFACE

The Editors are keenly aware that the literature of Biochemistry is already very large, in fact so widespread that it is increasingly difficult to assemble the most pertinent material in a given area. Beyond the ordinary textbook the subject matter of the rapidly expanding knowledge of biochemistry is spread among innumerable journals, monographs, and series of reviews. The Editors believe that there is a real place for an advanced treatise in biochemistry which assembles the principal areas of the subject in a single set of books.

It would be ideal if an individual or small group of biochemists could produce such an advanced treatise, and within the time to keep reasonably abreast of rapid advances, but this is at least difficult if not impossible. Instead, the Editors with the advice of the Advisory Board, have assembled what they consider the best possible sequence of chapters written by competent authors; they must take the responsibility for inevitable gaps of subject matter and duplication which may result from this procedure.

Most evident to the modern biochemist, apart from the body of knowledge of the chemistry and metabolism of biological substances, is the extent to which he must draw from recent concepts of physical and organic chemistry, and in turn project into the vast field of biology. Thus in the organization of Comprehensive Biochemistry, the middle three sections, Chemistry of Biological Compounds, Biochemical Reaction Mechanisms, and Metabolism may be considered classical biochemistry, while the first and last sections provide selected material on the origins and projections of the subject.

It is hoped that sub-division of the sections into bound volumes will not only be convenient, but will find favour among students concerned with specialized areas, and will permit easier future revisions of the individual volumes. Toward the latter end particularly, the Editors will welcome all comments in their effort to produce a useful and efficient source of biochemical knowledge.

Liège/Rochester   M. FLORKIN
July 1962   E. H. STOTZ

PREFACE TO SECTION II

(VOLUMES 5–11)

Section II on the Chemistry of Biological Compounds deals with the organic and physical chemistry of the major organic constituents of living material. A general understanding of organic and physical chemistry is presumed, but the reader will find the special topics in Section I of value in the fuller understanding of several parts of Section II. The Editors have made special effort to include a sound treatment of the important biological high polymers, including sections on their shape and physical properties. A number of substances peculiar to plants, certain isoprenoids, flavonoids, tannins, lignins, and plant hormones, often omitted from textbooks of biochemistry, are included. Nevertheless, it is inevitable that some omissions, hopefully minor ones, have occurred. The only intentional omission is the chemistry of the coenzymes and certain components of biological oxidation, which will be covered in connection with their function in Section III.

   The previous policy of dividing the section into smaller volumes has been continued, resulting in seven volumes for Section II. Two of the volumes each contain a complete area, namely Carbohydrates (Volume 5) and Sterols, Bile Acids and Steroids (Volume 10). Comments from readers will be appreciated by the Editors and be most helpful for possible future revisions.

Liège/Rochester   M. FLORKIN
December 1962   E. H. STOTZ

CONTENTS

VOLUME 9

Part A

PYRROLE PIGMENTS

Chapter I. Chemistry and Biochemistry of Porphyrins and Metalloporphyrins

by J. E. FALK

Chapter II. Physico-Chemical Properties of Porphyrins

by J. N. Phillips

Chapter III. Chlorophyll

by ROBERT HILL

Chapter IV. Bile pigments

by C. H. GRAY

Part B

ISOPRENOID COMPOUNDS

Chapter V. Chemistry of isoprenoid compounds

by A. J. HAAGEN-SMIT AND C. C. NIMMO

Chapter VI. Vitamin A

by J. G. BAXTER

Chapter VII. Vitamins E

by ROBERT S. HARRIS

Chapter VIII. Vitamins K

by ROBERT S. HARRIS

Chapter IX. Quinones

by R. A. MORTON

Part C

PHENOLIC PLANT CONSTITUENTS

Chapter X. Flavonoid Compounds, Tannins, Lignins and Related Compounds

by T. A. GEISSMAN

COMPREHENSIVE BIOCHEMISTRY

SECTION III (VOLUMES 12–16)

Biochemical Reaction Mechanisms

Volume 12. *Enzymes - General Considerations*

Chapter I. Introduction, historical, general concepts, isoenzymes by E. C. WEBB (Brisbane, Queensland)
Chapter II. Equilibrium and thermodynamic considerations by R. WURMSER AND R. BANERJEE (Paris)
Chapter III. Oxidation–reduction potentials by R. WURMSER AND R. BANERJEE (Paris)
Chapter IV. Theories of enzyme catalysis by I. B. WILSON (New York)
Chapter V. Enzyme kinetics (optimum pH, optimum temperature, activation energy) by E. A. DAWES (Glasgow)
Chapter VI. Enzyme–substrate relations by J. M. Reiner (Atlanta, Ga.)
Chapter VII. Chelation in relation to enzyme action by B. L. VALLEE (Boston, Mass.)
Chapter VIII. Stereochemical considerations in enzyme reactions by H. HIRSCHMANN (Cleveland, Ohio)
Chapter IX. Structure and function of an enzyme — ribonuclease by C. H. W. HIRS (New York)

Volume 13. *Classification of Enzymes*

Enzyme Commission list and recommendations (revised and annotated by E. C. WEBB, Brisbane, Queensland)

Volume 14. *Biological Oxidations*

Chapter I. Dehydrogenation (Chemistry of NAD, NADP, stereochemistry of hydrogen addition) by S. P. COLOWICK (Nashville, Tenn.)
Chapter II. Pyruvate and α-ketoglutarate dehydrogenases
(a) Thiamine pyrophosphate function by L. O. KRAMPITZ (Cleveland, Ohio)
(b) Lipoic acid function by L. J. REED (Austin, Texas)
Chapter III. Succinate and related dehydrogenases by T. P. SINGER (Detroit, Mich.)
Chapter IV. Flavoproteins in electron transport by Y. HATEFI (Iran)
Chapter V. Cytochromes and cytochrome oxidase by K. OKUNUKI (Osaka)
Chapter VI. Electron transport mechanisms by D. E. GREEN (Madison, Wisc.)
Chapter VII. Oxidative phosphorylation by E. C. SLATER (Amsterdam)
Chapter VIII. Photosynthetic phosphorylation by A. W. FRENKEL (Minneapolis, Minn.)
Chapter IX. Oxygenases by Ll. L. INGRAHAM (Davis, Calif.)
Chapter X. Peroxidases and catalase by A. S. BRILL (New Haven, Conn.)

Volume 9

Part A

PYRROLE PIGMENTS

Chapter I

Chemistry and Biochemistry of Porphyrins and Metalloporphyrins

J. E. FALK

Division of Plant Industry, C.S.I.R.O., Canberra, A.C.T. (Australia)

1. Introduction

The importance of the porphyrins in biochemistry is due mainly to the biological activities of the haemoproteins of which iron-porphyrin complexes form the prosthetic groups, to the photosynthetic activity of the related chlorophylls, and to the great advances in recent years in studies of the biosynthesis of porphyrins. Though some porphyrins and metalloporphyrins occur free in nature, they have no known metabolic functions in normal tissues.

It was not until the synthesis of protoporphyrin and its iron complex, haem, was achieved by Fischer and Zeile in 1929 that the basic structure of the porphin nucleus, as well as the structure of many porphyrins, was proven. The brilliant researches of Hans Fischer and his school in Munich, over the period 1910–1940, have provided an immense body of knowledge of pyrrole and porphyrin chemistry, most of which is summarized by Fischer and Orth[1]. A comprehensive treatise on the more biological and biochemical aspects has been provided by Lemberg and Legge[2].

The biochemistry of porphyrins and their derivatives has had its richest period to date in the decade now closing. During the past ten or twelve years, many steps in the biosynthetic pathway to haem have been elucidated, many new techniques for biochemical analysis in the porphyrin field have been introduced, and the theoretical and physical chemistry of this class of compounds is now undergoing rapid development.

2. Occurrence

The important porphyrins occurring free (not complexed with metals) in nature are protoporphyrin and isomers I and III (see p. 5) of uro- and coproporphyrins. No other isomers are known to occur in nature. Relatively minute amounts of these porphyrins occur normally in blood (copro- and protoporphyrins), urine (copro- and uroporphyrins) and faeces (copropor-phyrin) and much larger amounts are found in certain pathological condi-tions[3] (Table I). Proto- and deuteroporphyrins occur normally in the faeces of carnivores, following ingestion of blood or after intestinal haemorrhage, as the result of modification of protohaem by intestinal bacteria; the por-phyrin phylloerythrin arises similarly from ingested chlorophyll in herbi-vores.

TABLE I

ORDER OF MAGNITUDE OF FREE PORPHYRIN CONTENT OF SOME TISSUES AND EXCRETA[3]

		Uro-porphyrin*	Copro-porphyrin*	Proto-porphyrin*
Normal human	blood (μg/100 ml red cells)		0.5	30
	faeces (mg/day)		0.5	0.6
	urine (mg/day)	0.02	0.1	
Acute porphyria (human)	faeces (mg/day)	2	3	
	urine (mg/day)	50	2	

* For structures, see Figs. 3–7 and Table II.

Free proto- and coproporphyrins occur in relatively large amounts in the root nodules of leguminous plants[4,5] and in some higher plants[1], and traces of free uroporphyrin have been found in the epidermal cells adjacent to the stomatal guard-cells of leaves[6]. Protoporphyrin is excreted by the Harderian gland of the rat, and occurs in the pigmented areas of the egg shells of many species of birds. Uroporphyrin is found in the shells of molluscs. Porphyrins, usually coproporphyrin, are excreted into the growth medium by many microorganisms.

Uroporphyrin III occurs as its copper complex in very high concentra-tion in the wing-feathers of *Turacus indicus*[7,8]. Recent evidence[9] suggests the presence of an Mn-porphyrin in blood.

The haems — the iron complexes of porphyrins — do not occur free in normal tissues, but form the prosthetic groups of the many important, bio-logically active haemoproteins. The known haem prosthetic groups are described in detail below.

3. General chemistry

(a) Structure

The parent nucleus of all the tetrapyrrole pigments is porphin (Fig. 1). Porphyrins are derivatives of porphin in which the β-carbon atoms 1 to 8 of the pyrrole nuclei carry substituents other than hydrogen atoms. Thus, in coproporphyrins (Figs. 3–6), the pyrrole β-carbon atoms all carry as substituents propionic acid or methyl groups.

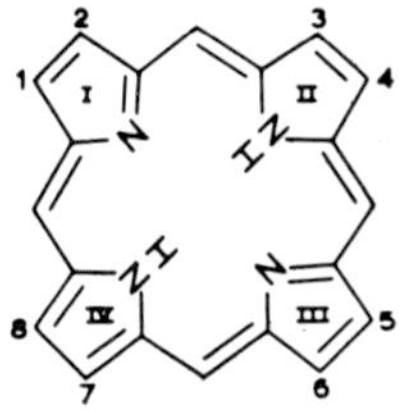

Fig. 1. Porphin. All structural formulae for porphyrins, in this and the following chapter, are drawn to the proportions of the Patterson diagram given for Ni-aetioporphyrin by Crute[15].

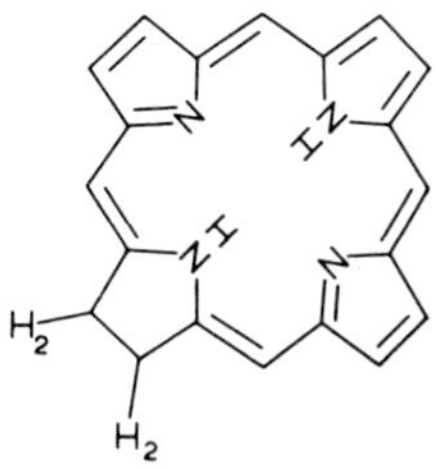

Fig. 2. Chlorin.

Early syntheses of porphin, and some of the controversy over the purity and identity of the products obtained, are summarized by Lemberg and Legge[2]. Several syntheses have been published more recently[10,11] and analyses of the absorption spectrum, which appears somewhat anomalous when compared with those of the simplest porphyrins (*e.g.* octamethylporphin; $\alpha,\beta,\gamma,\delta$-tetraphenylporphin), have been made[11,12].

(*b*) *Isomerism*

Making the tacit assumption that like groups do not substitute in the same pyrrole nucleus, Fischer[1] pointed out that a porphyrin with two different substituent groups could have four position-isomers; he synthesized the four isomers of aetioporphyrin, which has four ethyl and four methyl side chains, and introduced the systematic numbering of the isomers illustrated by the coproporphyrins in Figs. 3–6. Fischer synthesized these porphyrins also. In uroporphyrins I, II, III and IV the methyl side chains of the coproporphyrins are replaced by acetic acid ($-CH_2COOH$) groups; all four uroporphyrin isomers have been synthesized recently by MacDonald (see below).

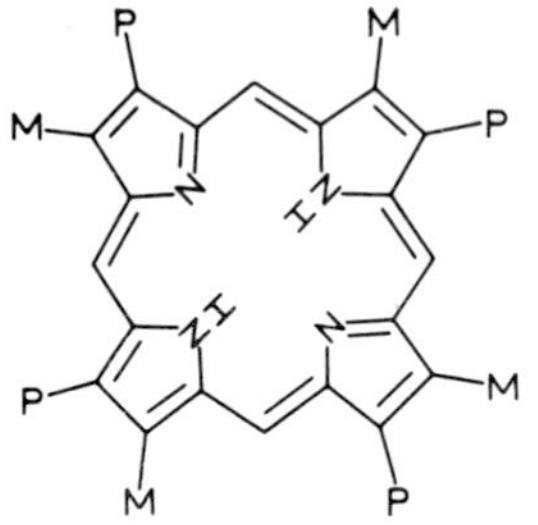

Fig. 3. Coproporphyrin I. For side-chain abbreviations for all formulae, see Table II.

Fig. 4. Coproporphyrin II.

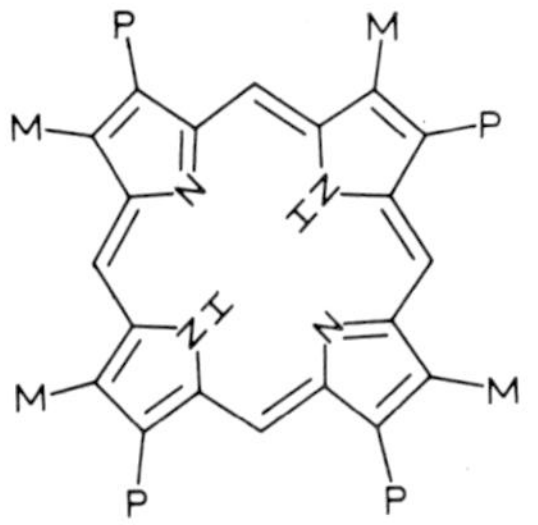

Fig. 5. Coproporphyrin III.

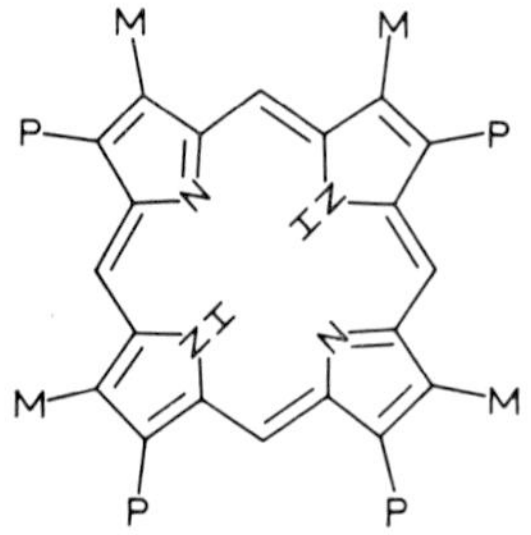

Fig. 6. Coproporphyrin IV.

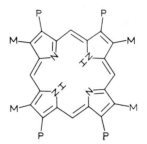

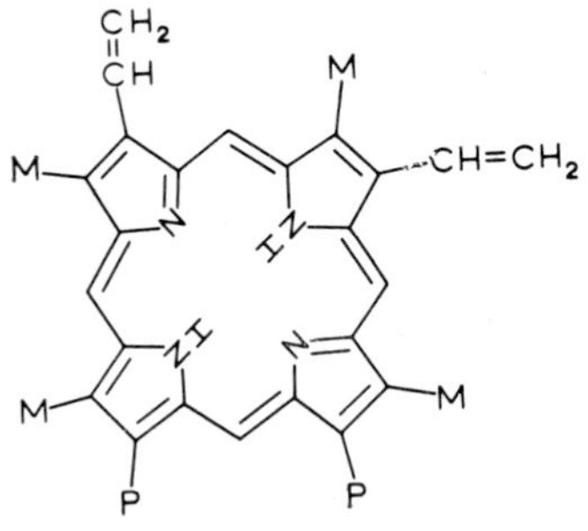

Fig. 7. Protoporphyrin IX.

When there are *three* different substituent groups, fifteen such isomers are possible. Protoporphyrins belong to this series; though others have been synthesized[1], isomer IX (Fig. 7) only is of importance in biology.

It will be seen (Table II) that protoporphyrin IX is formally related to aetio-, copro- and uroporphyrins III. Every porphyrin and metalloporphyrin known to have a biological function is modelled on this pattern. This generalization includes the prosthetic groups of all known haemoproteins, and the chlorophylls (Mg-complexes of substituted chlorins, (Fig. 2), whether there are two, three or even more different substituents. Porphyrins of isomer-series I occur under certain pathological conditions[3] and are formed in experiments on porphyrin biosynthesis *in vitro*, but no haems (iron complexes) or other metal complexes related to them are known to occur naturally, and they have no known biological functions.

Systematically, protoporphyrin IX is: 1,3,5,8-tetramethyl-2,4-divinyl-porphin-6,7-dipropionic acid. It is more convenient to refer to the porphyrins by their trivial names, which are defined in Table II.

TABLE II

THE SIDE CHAINS OF SOME COMMON PORPHYRINS

	Side chains (see Fig. 1)							
	1	*2*	*3*	*4*	*5*	*6*	*7*	*8*
Aetioporphyrin I	M	E	M	E	M	E	M	E
Coproporphyrin I	M	P	M	P	M	P	M	P
Coproporphyrin II	M	P	P	M	M	P	P	M
Coproporphyrin III	M	P	M	P	M	P	P	M
Coproporphyrin IV	P	M	M	P	M	P	P	M
Uroporphyrin I	A	P	A	P	A	P	A	P
Uroporphyrin III	A	P	A	P	A	P	P	A
Protoporphyrin IX	M	V	M	V	M	P	P	M
Deuteroporphyrin IX	M	H	M	H	M	P	P	M
Haematoporphyrin IX	M	B	M	B	M	P	P	M
Mesoporphyrin IX	M	E	M	E	M	P	P	M
Chlorocruoroporphyrin	M	F	M	V	M	P	P	M
Pyrroporphyrin IX	M	E	M	E	M	H	P	M
2-Desethylpyrroporphyrin IX	M	H	M	E	M	H	P	M
Rhodoporphyrin XV	M	E	M	E	M	C	P	M
Oxorhodoporphyrin	M	Ac	M	E	M	C	P	M

Side chain abbreviations: A, —CH₂COOH; B, —CH(OH)CH₃; F, —CHO; H, —H; M, —CH₃; P, —CH₂CH₂COOH; V, —CH=CH₂; Ac, —COCH₃; C, —COOH.   E ? ?

(c) *Crystal structure*

Brief crystal analyses[13,14] were made in 1942, but the first complete X-ray crystallographic analysis of a porphyrin was made by Crute[15], in 1959, using Ni-aetioporphyrin (Fig. 8). The dimensions found are, as expected, slightly different from those of the related molecule phthalocyanin, analysed by Robertson[16] in 1936. The bond lengths and the symmetry of the molecule are in full accord with the aromatic nature of the nucleus, well established by its chemical properties and by the heats of combustion of porphyrins[17]. The porphin nucleus is a plane of about 8.5·8.5 Å with a thickness of approximately 4.7 Å.

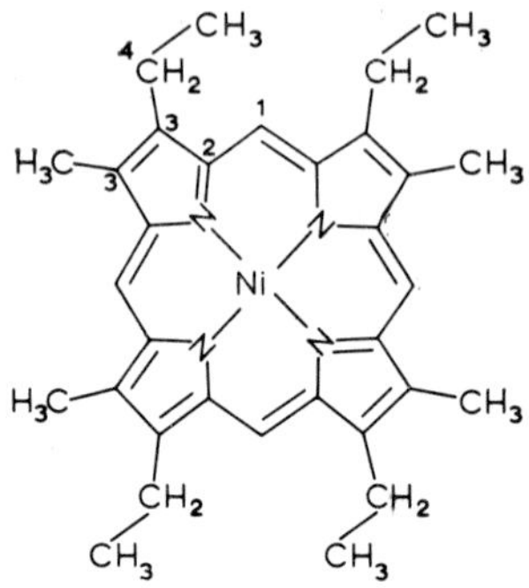

Fig. 8. Ni-aetioporphyrin II. Intramolecular distances[15]: Ni–N 1.84 ± 0.03 Å; N–C$_2$ 1.35 ± 0.05 Å; C$_1$–C$_2$ 1.43 ± 0.05 Å; C$_2$–C$_3$ 1.40 ± 0.05 Å; C$_3$–C$_3$ 1.47 ± 0.08 Å; C$_3$–C$_4$ 1.50 ± 0.05 Å.

(d) Hydrogen bonding

The question of hydrogen bonding between the central nitrogen atoms of porphyrins has long been argued. Robertson found that while in Ni-phthalocyanin the four N-atoms formed the corners of a square, in the metal-free compound one axis was longer than the other. A similar comparison cannot be made for porphyrins, since the data for a metal-free porphyrin are not yet available. Arguing from the similarity of the visible absorption spectra in neutral solvents of porphyrins and N-methyl porphyrins, Erdman and Corwin[18] concluded that hydrogen bonding does not occur in porphyrins. Falk and Willis[19], however, from a study of the infrared spectra of porphyrins and haems, concluded that the —NH groups are occupied in intramolecular hydrogen bonding; further infrared studies[12] have led to the same conclusion. Thus the existence of separate —NH tautomers does not appear possible; much early work seeking to isolate tautomeric forms is summarized by Lemberg and Legge[2].

4. Physical properties

The physical properties of porphyrins and metalloporphyrins are discussed in detail in the following chapter and a brief outline only is given here.

(a) Stability

Free porphyrins are rather unstable to light and to peroxides. The metal complexes are in general more stable but iron complexes (haems) in particular are readily destroyed by peroxides through their own peroxidative properties[2].

(b) Acid–base properties and solubility

(i) Free porphyrins

The naturally occurring porphyrins all possess carboxyl side chains, and are thus ampholytes, soluble in alkali by virtue of the carboxyl groups and in mineral acids by virtue of the ring nitrogens. The isoelectric points of most common porphyrins lie between pH 3 and 4.5; in this pH range they may be precipitated from aqueous solutions. All porphyrins are soluble in glacial acetic acid, strong mineral acids, pyridine and related solvents and in dioxane, and less soluble in methyl and ethyl alcohols, acetone and ether. They are freely soluble in polar organic solvents containing acids — e.g., acetone–HCl, ether–acetic acid or ethyl acetate–acetic acid mixtures, and they are soluble in aqueous solutions of anionic, cationic or neutral detergents (cf. p. 35). Porphyrins do not dissolve readily in ether from the solid state, and transference from aqueous phases to ether depends on vigorous dispersion with the ether immediately after bringing to the isoelectric point, before flocculation occurs. They may be extracted from ether by aqueous alkalies or mineral acids. Of the common porphyrins, uroporphyrins are the most water-soluble, and in fact can be brought into organic solvents under special conditions only. Thus they may be transferred to cyclohexanone from aqueous solutions[119] of pH 1.8.

pH numbers. The "pH number" is defined as the pH of a buffer solution which extracts half of a porphyrin from four volumes of its ether solution[20].

HCl number or "Willstätter number". This is much more commonly used, and Fischer and Orth[1] have recorded HCl numbers for many porphyrins. It is defined as that concentration of HCl (in % w/v) which from an equal volume of an ether solution of a porphyrin extracts two thirds of the porphyrin[21].

The HCl number depends on both the dissociation of the porphyrin as a base, and on the distribution coefficient of the free porphyrin and its hydrochloride between water and the organic solvent[22]. HCl numbers are commonly used to separate mixtures of porphyrins, and some approximate values are given in Table III. The effects of hydrophilic side chains (—COOH; —CHOH—CH₃) on this property diminish from uro- to aetio-porphyrin. The effects of electrophilic side chains are seen in the weakened basicity of proto- and chlorocruoro-porphyrins, which must be at least as hydrophilic as mesoporphyrin, and the effect of additional lipophilic character is seen in the porphyrin esters.

Some studies have been made[23-25] of the behaviour of porphyrins in counter-current distribution between organic solvents and dilute hydrochloric acid solutions. Distribution coefficients have been determined for several porphyrins. These values are more precise than the HCl numbers. Quantitative measurements of basicity and the partition coefficients on which these distributions depend, are discussed later (pp. 35 and 40).

TABLE III

HCl NUMBERS

	Free porphyrin	Methyl ester
Uro		1.5
Copro	0.08	1.5
Haemato	0.1	
Deutero	0.3	2.0
Meso	0.5	2.5
Aetio	3.0	
Proto	2.5	5.5
Chlorocruoro	4.6	

(*ii*) *Porphyrin esters*

Porphyrins with carboxyl side chains are readily esterified, and the esters hydrolysed, without degradation (see p. 24). The esters are more lipophilic than the free porphyrins, as indicated by their HCl numbers (Table III), and are more soluble in organic solvents. Unlike the free porphyrins, they are soluble in $CHCl_3$, CCl_4, C_6H_6, CS_2, etc. Purification of porphyrins is often carried out via the methyl esters, particularly when column chromatography is required. The esters crystallize well, having characteristic, though high, melting-points[1]. Mixed melting-point curves are available for the methyl esters of coproporphyrins[26] I and III and uroporphyrins[27] I and III.

(*iii*) *Metal complexes*

The metal complexes of porphyrins have no basic nitrogen function and are thus insoluble in aqueous acids. They are soluble in alkali, pyridine, dioxane, and less so in alcohol; they can be brought into strong solution in ethyl acetate or ether via their ready solubility in acidified organic solvents (see p. 9). Protohaem and protohaemin (ferro- and ferri-protoporphyrin respectively) dissolve readily in cold concentrated sulphuric acid, which removes the iron. This treatment does not alter the porphyrin nucleus, but causes hydration of the vinyl side chains to hydroxyethyl (see haematoporphyrin, p. 27). Copper is removed from turacin (copper-uroporphyrin) by similar treatment.

Esters of metalloporphyrins may be prepared in two ways; the carboxyl side chains of metalloporphyrins may be esterified, or the metal may be introduced into the esterified porphyrin. The esters have lost their alkali-solubility, have gained solubility in $CHCl_3$, CCl_4, etc., and otherwise have similar solubilities to the unesterified compounds.

(c) Introduction to spectra of porphyrins and metalloporphyrins

The theoretical aspects of porphyrin spectra are discussed in the following chapter (p. 44), and qualitative aspects only of the spectra are described here.

Extinction coefficients for the more common compounds are given in Tables IV, V and VI.

TABLE IV

POSITIONS AND EXTINCTION COEFFICIENTS OF SORET BANDS

	Concn. of HCl (N)	Soret max. (mμ)	$10^{-5} \varepsilon_M$	Mol. wt.
In chloroform				
Porphyrin ester				
Uroporphyrin III octamethyl ester		405–6	2.17	942
Coproporphyrin III tetramethyl ester		399.5	1.80	710
Deuteroporphyrin dimethyl ester		399	1.75	538
Protoporphyrin dimethyl ester		407.5	1.71	590
In aqueous HCl				
Porphyrin				
Uroporphyrin III	0.5	405.5	5.41	830
Coproporphyrin III	0.1	399.5	4.89	654
Deuteroporphyrin	0.1	398	4.33	510
Protoporphyrin	1.37	408	2.75	562

The values of λ and ε for uro- and copro-porphyrins I are identical to those of the corresponding isomers of series III. The data quoted are from Rimington[117], who gives also correction factors for use when porphyrins in tissue extracts are determined by measurement at the Soret band. The position and intensity of the Soret band varies with HCl concentration[28,29].

TABLE V

POSITIONS AND EXTINCTION COEFFICIENTS OF BANDS IN THE VISIBLE REGION (NEUTRAL SPECTRA)

	I		Ia		II		III		IV	
Porphyrin band	λ_{max} (mμ)	$10^{-4} \varepsilon_M$	λ_{max} (mμ)	$10^{-4} \varepsilon_M$	λ_{max} (mμ)	$10^{-4} \varepsilon_M$	λ_{max} (mμ)	$10^{-4} \varepsilon_M$	λ_{max} (mμ)	$10^{-4} \varepsilon_M$
Protoporphyrin	630	0.558	603	0.141	575	0.678	537	1.158	503	1.464
Uroporphyrin	624	0.412	596	0.137	569	0.711	532	0.957	499	1.567
Coproporphyrin	621	0.515	595	0.132	567	0.672	529	0.997	497	1.470
Mesoporphyrin	620	0.541	594	0.133	567	0.659	528	0.982	496	1.424
Deuteroporphyrin	618	0.433	593	0.129	565	0.680	525	0.859	495	1.595

The values given, for the methyl esters in dioxane solution, are from the papers of Stern and Wenderlein cf. ref. 31. For use with porphyrins dioxane must be purified[31].

References p. 31

TABLE VI

ABSORPTION SPECTRA OF PYRIDINE HAEMOCHROMES

Haem	Band: α		β		Soret		Ref.
	λ_{max} (mμ)	$10^{-4}\,\varepsilon_M$	λ_{max} (mμ)	$10^{-4}\,\varepsilon_M$	λ_{max} (mμ)	$10^{-4}\,\varepsilon_M$	
Proto	557	31.5	525		418.5	191.5	2
Meso	547	33.2	517		407	140.4	3
Deutero	545	24.0	515		406		4
Haemato	549		519				4
Chlorocruoro	583		545				1
Haem a	587		*				1
4-Formyldeutero	578		548				1,5
2,4-Diformyldeutero	584		550				1
2-Hydroxymethyldeutero	546		515				4
2-Hydroxyethyl-4-vinyldeutero	552		520				4
4-Acetyldeutero	571		530				1
2,4-Diacetyldeutero	575		540				1
2-Acetylrhodo ("Oxorhodo")	582		*				1

* The β-band is absent in these compounds; 1. Lemberg and Falk[31]; 2. Paul, Theorell and Åkeson[121]; 3. Lemberg and Legge[2]; 4. Porra and Jones[122]; 5. Porra and Jones[122] found α 581, β 532.

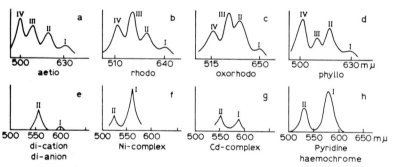

Fig. 9. Visible absorption spectra of some porphyrins and their derivatives. The structures of the parent porphyrins of these spectral types are given in Table II.

The spectrum of most common porphyrins in neutral solvents consists of four relatively sharp bands, increasing stepwise in intensity from band I, in the region of 620 mμ, to band IV, in the region of 500 mμ. Between bands I and II a very small band, Ia, occurs in some porphyrins. This type of spectrum in the visible region is called aetio-type (Fig. 9a). In addition, a band much more intense than band IV is found in the region of 400 mμ; this is the "Soret" band, characteristic of all conjugated tetrapyrroles, but lacking when the conjugation is broken as in the bile pigments.

Solutions of porphyrins in aqueous mineral acids have two bands in the visible region (Fig. 9e), characteristic of the porphyrin di-cation. The Soret band also is present, its maximum being found at longer wave lengths as the proton concentration increases[28,29].

Complexes of porphyrins with metals such as Ni, Cd, Cu, have spectra of the type shown in Fig. 9f, while in complexes such as those with Zn, Co, Mg, the relative intensities of the bands are reversed (Fig. 9g) cf. ref. 30. The coordination chemistry of these complexes is discussed in detail in the following chapter.

(d) Correlations between structure and visible spectrum

The firm correlations[31,32] which exist between the nature of the side chains on different porphyrins, and the positions and order of intensity of their visible bands, are of great value for purposes of identification. Much use has

TABLE VII

EFFECT OF SUBSTITUENTS ON WAVELENGTH AND TYPE OF VISIBLE
SPECTRUM OF PORPHYRINS

Substituent at position			Band I max. ($m\mu$)	Spectral type (cf. Fig. 9, a–d)
Deuteroporphyrin*	2	4		
	—H	—H	618	Aetio
	—C$_2$H$_5$	—C$_2$H$_5$	620	Aetio
	—CH : CH$_2$	—CH : CH$_2$	630	Aetio
	—H	—CHO	640	Rhodo
	—H	—C : NOH	630	Aetio
	—CHO	—CH : CH$_2$	641	Rhodo
	—C : NOH	—CH : CH$_2$	635.5	Aetio
	—CHO	—CHO	650	Aetio
	—C : NOH	—C : NOH	639	Aetio
	—CO·CH$_3$	—CO·CH$_3$	639	Aetio
	—C(:NOH)·CH$_3$	—C(:NOH)·CH$_3$	625	Aetio
Pyrroporphyrin*	6			
	—H		620	Aetio
	—CH : CH$_2$		624	Aetio
	—CHO		635.5	Rhodo
	—CO·CH$_3$		632	Rhodo
	—CO·C$_6$H$_5$		627	Rhodo
	—COOCH$_3$		632	Rhodo
	—CH : CH·COOCH$_3$		624.5	Rhodo
2-Desethylpyrro-porphyrin*	2	6		
	—C$_2$C$_5$	—COOCH$_3$	632	Rhodo
	—CH : CH$_2$	—COOCH$_3$	638.5	Rhodo-oxorhodo
	—CO·CH$_3$	—COOCH$_3$	637	Oxorhodo
	—C(:NOH)CH$_3$	—COOCH$_3$	631	Rhodo
	—COCH$_3$	—COCH$_3$	637	Oxorhodo

* For structures, see Table II. The values given are for the porphyrin esters in dioxane solution; references and further details are given by Lemberg and Falk[31].

been made of these correlations in studies on the structure of haem a (p. 19 ff.). While substituents such as

$$—CH_3, —CH_2CH_3, —CH_2CH_2COOH, —CH(OH)CH_3,$$

have little effect upon the spectrum, electron-attracting side chains such as

$$—CH=CH_2, —COOH, —CHO, —COCH_3, —CH=CH—COOH,$$

which extend the conjugation of the nucleus, have important effects on the wave length and on the relative intensities of the bands in the visible region. Such side chains are called "rhodofying"[31], and result in the absorption maxima appearing at longer wave lengths; the effects on wave length of several such substituents are additive. While all porphyrins fully substituted with non-rhodofying side chains have aetio-type spectra (IV, III, II, I) (Fig. 9a), one conjugated side chain causes a change to rhodo-type (III, IV, II, I) (Fig. 9b), and the absorption maxima are at longer wave length (Table VII). When two rhodofying side chains are on diagonally opposite pyrrole rings a further change to oxorhodo-type (III, II, IV, I) (Fig. 9c) occurs. When two rhodofying groups are on neighbouring pyrrole rings, however, the change in wave length persists but the spectrum reverts to aetio-type. Some examples of the use of these correlations are given on p. 19 ff.

The phyllo-type (IV, II, III, I) spectrum shown in Fig. 9d is typical of porphyrins with a substituent on the carbon atom of one of the methene bridges.

(e) Fluorescence

On irradiation with light at about 400 mμ (e.g. ultraviolet light filtered through Wood's glass) porphyrins have a characteristic, very intense orange to red fluorescence. The fluorescence is quenched by some organic solvents, and by a variety of biological compounds, and thus for quantitative determinations strict control of the conditions is necessary. The fluorescence is best observed in aqueous HCl solutions, in which less than 0.1 μg/ml is quite visible to the eye; very much lower concentrations are detectable by fluorimetry[33]. Metal complexes such as those with Cd, Zn, Mg fluoresce in some solvents, but the Co, Ni, Fe, Cu complexes, for example, do not[30] (cf. p. 48).

5. The iron complexes of porphyrins and their derivatives

(a) Introduction and definitions

The coordination chemistry of porphyrins is described fully in the following chapter (p. 52); here a brief description only is given.

When a metal cation coordinates with a porphyrin, two protons are lost from the pyrrole nitrogen atoms leaving two formal negative charges on the nucleus. Thus, apart from the charge on the carboxylic acid side chains, with a divalent metal ion the complex has a residual charge of zero.

(Proto-)*haem* = ferroprotoporphyrin, is usually written as in Fig. 10.

When the metal is trivalent (*e.g.* Fe^{3+}) the complex has a formal positive charge.

(Proto-)*haemin* (chlorhaemin) = ferriprotoporphyrin chloride (Fig. 11).

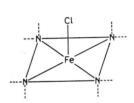

Fig. 10. Protohaem.   Fig. 11. Chlorhaemin.

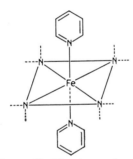

Fig. 12. Pyridine haemochrome.

Though haemin is often written as a dissociable salt, the chloride ion appears to be coordinated to the metal, at least in some solvents; thus no conductivity was found for haemin in nitrobenzene solution[34].

In alkaline solution the residual charge is satisfied by an hydroxyl ion: (Proto-)*haematin* = hydroxyferriprotoporphyrin.

Metalloporphyrins are essentially square-planar tetracoordinate complexes; further ligands can be added, one on each side of the plane, to form essentially octahedral complexes. When, with the Fe^{2+}-complexes, these extra ligands are nitrogenous bases, the products are known as haemochromes.

Pyridine(proto-)*haemochrome* = 5,6-bispyridylferroprotoporphyrin (Fig.

12). The haemochromes may be oxidized to their ferric forms, and the oxidation is reversible.

Pyridine(proto-)*haemichrome* = 5,6-bispyridylferriprotoporphyrin.   The haemochromes are also called haemochromogens, and the haemichromes, parahaematins.

(b) The prosthetic groups of haemoproteins

(i) Protohaem

Protohaem (Fig. 10) has been specifically identified as the prosthetic group in haemoglobins, erythrocruorins[35,36] (the haemoglobin analogue of many invertebrates[2]), myoglobins[37], some peroxidases[38], catalases[39,40] and cytochromes b[2,41]. Like mammalian haemoglobin, blood catalase has four molecules of protohaem per molecule of apoprotein. In liver catalase, as isolated, one of the protohaem molecules may be replaced by a molecule of the iron complex of the bile pigment biliverdin, though it is not yet clear whether this is either present or functional in intact tissues[2].

In 1871 Hoppe-Seyler[42] obtained, on treatment of haemoglobin with concentrated sulphuric acid, a purple pigment which he called haematoporphyrin (Fig. 14) (Gk. porphyros=purple). By 1901, Nencki and coworkers[43] had prepared pure haematoporphyrin hydrochloride following treatment of haemin with HBr in glacial acetic acid, and mesoporphyrin by treatment of haemin with HI. We now know that haemato- and meso-porphyrins are derivatives of protohaem, but this was not clearly understood until about 1925.

The chemical studies, largely by Hans Fischer's school, which established the structure of protoporphyrin and many other porphyrins and culminated in the total synthesis of protohaem have been reviewed fully by Corwin[44].

(ii) Chlorocruorohaem

Chlorocruorohaem is the prosthetic group of chlorocruorin, the oxygen-carrying pigment of certain polychaete worms. It was formerly known as

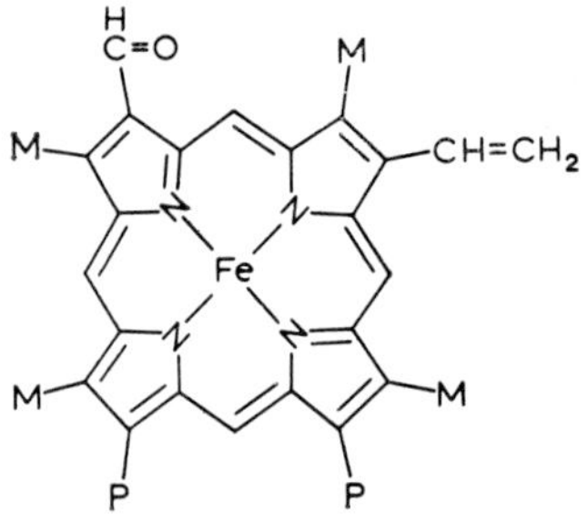

Fig. 13. Chlorocruorohaem.

spirographis haem. Its structure (Fig.13) has been established for some time, cf. ref. 1, and it has been prepared from protohaem[45,46], from which it differs only in that the vinyl group on position 2 is replaced by a formyl group. This haem has played an important role as a model compound in studies of haem a (see below) which also has a formyl side chain.

(iii) Haem c

Haem c, the prosthetic group of the cytochromes c of mammalian and other tissues[41], unlike most other haem prosthetic groups, is not easily split from the protein of the cytochrome to which it is covalently bound. Our knowledge of its structure began with the isolation by Hill and Keilin[47] in 1930 of a water-soluble, ether-insoluble porphyrin after treatment of cytochrome c with SO_2. Theorell found that this porphyrin contained peptide groups, which could be removed by hydrolysis, and sulphur, which could not. The early investigations are described by Lemberg and Legge[2].

In retrospect, the attack on this problem has involved a series of degradations of the cytochrome which have gradually become more sophisticated as suitable techniques have been developed. The final elucidation of the structure owes much to the persistence and inspiration of Theorell.

Hill and Keilin[47] had found also that digestion of cytochrome c with HBr in acetic acid led to haematoporphyrin (Fig. 14); reduction of this with HI ($-CH(OH)CH_3 \rightarrow -CH_2CH_3$) yielded mesoporphyrin, which gave no depression of melting point with mesoporphyrin IX obtained by reduction of protoporphyrin IX. Like haematoporphyrin prepared chemically from protoporphyrin, the haematoporphyrin obtained was optically inactive, though there are two centres of asymmetry in the molecule. In 1950 Paul[48] discovered a method for splitting the prosthetic group from the protein by mild treatment with silver sulphate and acetic acid; optically active "haematoporphyrin c" was obtained[49], with a specific rotation of $-97°$. This material gave a melting point depression with synthetic (optically inactive) haematoporphyrin, and had a slightly different infrared spectrum; the rates of dehydration to protoporphyrin were, however, identical for the two porphyrins. The product of the silver sulphate treatment was thus an optically active isomer of haematoporphyrin.

Meanwhile Theorell[50] reinvestigated Hill and Keilin's water-soluble, peptide-containing porphyrin c; by an improved method he prepared a porphyrin c which upon re-introduction of iron was found to contain total N : amino N : S : COOH : Fe in the ratios 6 : 2 : 2 : 4 : 1. Four haem-nitrogen atoms and two ninhydrin-reacting amino-groups accounted for all the nitrogen, so that the amino acid could not be bound to the haem by a nitrogen atom. No free sulphide groups could be detected, but on melting with solid potassium hydroxide a sulphide was formed. Potentiometric titration gave pK values consistent with two of the carboxyl groups being those of propionic acid side chains of haem; the other two pK values were typical of α-amino carboxyl groups. Later[51], on further hydrolysis of this porphyrin, l-cysteine was isolated.

The above evidence suggested a structure in which two cysteine residues were bound, by their sulphur atoms, to the α-carbon atoms of side chains in positions 2 and 4 of a porphyrin otherwise identical to haematoporphyrin. Such a molecule has been synthesized[118].

In recent years this structure for haem c has been amply justified. By pepsin digestion of cytochrome c "haemopeptide c" (Fig. 15) was obtained. After splitting off the attached haem by Paul's silver sulphate method, a peptide was obtained[52] in which the sequence of amino acids shown in Fig. 15 was found[54]. Studies[53] of haemopeptides c from a variety of species (Table VIII) have revealed a great deal of constancy in the location of the two cysteine residues which bind the haem side chains, and of the histidine residue which is thought to coordinate to the haem iron.

TABLE VIII

COMPARISON OF A HOMOLOGOUS REGION IN CYTOCHROMES c FROM VARIOUS SOURCES[53]

Ox	...-Val-Glu(NH_2)-Lys-Cys-Ala-Glu(NH_2)-Cys-His-Thr-Val-Glu-Lys-...
Horse	..................-Lys-Cys-Ala-Glu(NH_2)-Cys-His-Thr-Val-Glu-Lys-...
Pig	..................-Lys-Cys-Ala-Glu(NH_2)-Cys-His-Thr-Val-Glu-Lys-...
Salmon	...-Val-Glu(NH_2)-Lys-Cys-Ala-Glu(NH_2)-Cys-His-Thr-Val-Glu-........
Fowl	...-Val-Glu(NH_2)-Lys-Cys-*Ser*-Glu(NH_2)-Cys-His-Thr-Val-Glu-........
Silkworm	...-Val-Glu(NH_2)-*Arg*-Cys-Ala-Glu(NH_2)-Cys-His-Thr-Val-Glu-........
Yeast	...-*Phe-Lys-Thr*------*Arg*-Cys-*Glu-Leu*-------Cys-His-Thr-Val-Glu-........

Ehrenberg and Theorell[54] have made careful models of haemopeptide c. They have shown that a left-handed α-helical structure allows the two cysteine residues of the peptide to bond without strain to the side chains of the haem as well as strain-free coordination of the haem iron by the nearby histidine residue. It is thought that a second histidine residue binds the haem iron on the opposite side of the flat haem molecule to the first; the position of this second residue in the protein is not certain, and indeed its identity has been questioned. That the second coordinating group may be a primary amino-group has been suggested recently by Margoliash[55].

Just what is to be called the prosthetic group of cytochrome c is to some extent an arbitrary matter — a decision has to be made as to where the prosthetic group finishes and the apoprotein begins. The structure in Fig. 16 is perhaps the most convenient abbreviated form, and the haem should be quoted in preference to its iron-free derivative porphyrin c, which in much of the literature is referred to as the prosthetic group.

Though the biosynthetic route to haem c is not known, it will be observed that it may be regarded as a bis-cysteine adduct of protohaem.

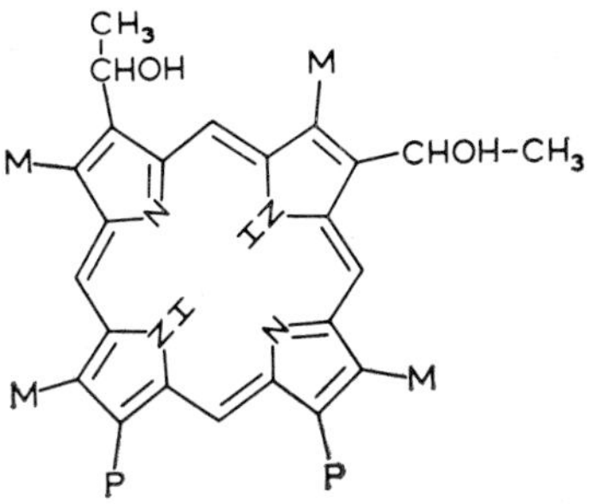

Fig. 14. Haematoporphyrin.

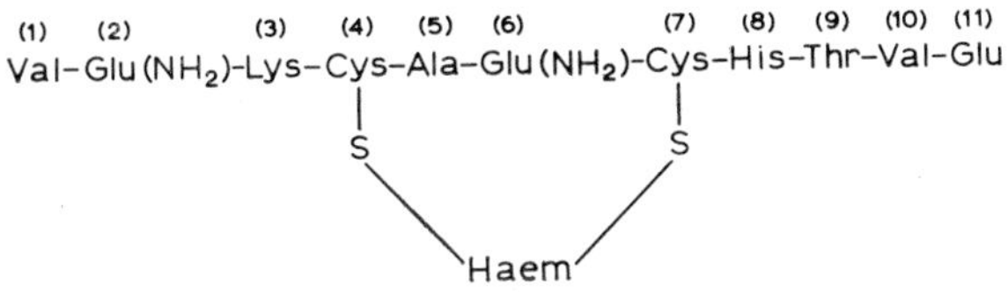

Fig. 15. Haemopeptide c.

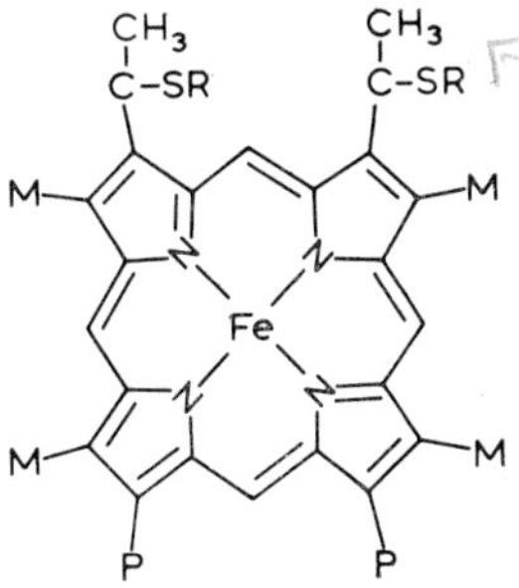

Fig. 16. Haem c (R = —CH₂CH(NH₂)COOH).

(iv) Haem a

Haem a is the prosthetic group of the cytochromes a and a_3 of mammalian tissues, and of the cytochrome a_1 of certain bacteria[56-58]. Investigations of the structure have been long and tedious. Though easily split from its apoprotein, the haem is relatively unstable. In addition it possesses a lipid side chain and is associated in tissue extracts with other lipids of similar physico-chemical properties. Its purification is thus very difficult.

The structure in Fig. 17 was announced, and the evidence for it fully reviewed, by Morell, Barrett, Clezy and Lemberg[56], Lemberg, Clezy and Barrett[57] and Morrison and Stotz[58] at the International Symposium on Haematin Enzymes in Canberra in 1959. Except for the details relating to

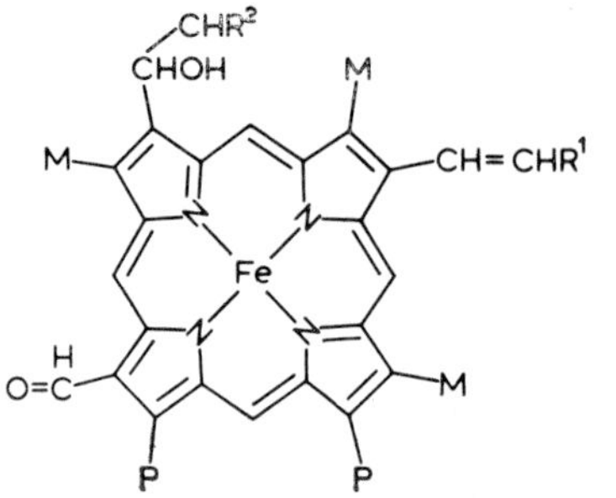

Fig. 17. Haem *a*.

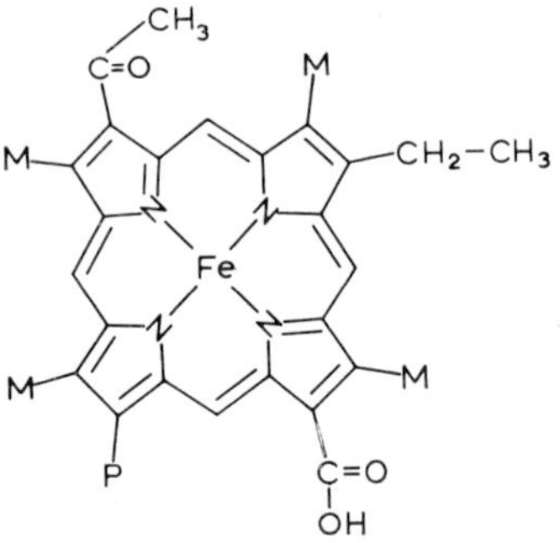

Fig. 18. Oxorhodohaem.

the alkyl chain(s) (R^1, R^2) this structure is fairly well established, though Morrison and Stotz[58] believe that the side chain in position 2 is —CHOH· CO·R^2. The final evidence for the relative positions of the side chains in positions 2, 4 and 8 came from synthetic proof, by MacDonald in Montreal, of the structure of the cytodeuteroporphyrin of Warburg, from the identification of a further degradation product by Nicolaus in Naples and from spectroscopic evidence from Lemberg's school in Sydney.

The formyl group. In his classical studies of cytochrome oxidase (Atmungsferment) by photochemical action spectra, Warburg[59] had postulated the presence of a formyl group from analogy with the spectrum of chlorocruorohaem (Fig. 13). A variety of reactions subsequently found confirm this. The rapid rate of formation of the oxime[31], the formation of a bisulphite complex[60] and the dehydration of the oxime to a nitrile[61], prove that the group is not a ketonic side chain. A ketonic group in an isocyclic ring (as in chlorophyll) is excluded by the reversibility of methyl acetal formation[57] which does not occur in the chlorophyll series, and by infrared spectra[62]. Recently, the formyl group has been oxidized to —COOH, reduced to hydroxymethyl and a condensation product with acetone–HCl has been made[57].

That only one carbonyl group is present on the porphyrin ring has long been evident from the magnitude of the changes in position of the visible absorption maxima on treatment with reagents for such groups. With haem *a* and a number of model porphyrins with single carbonyl side chains, after oxime formation the maxima are found at approximately 8 mμ to shorter wavelengths. The change with model porphyrins with two such groups[31,57] is about 12 mμ.

The unsaturated side chain. The presence of an unsaturated side chain conjugated to the nucleus was indicated by changes in spectrum found when the porphyrin was treated with HI or with diazoacetic ester[60,63], and more recently[64] catalytic hydrogenation has shown an uptake of two hydrogen atoms only per molecule.

The relative positions of the formyl and the unsaturated side chains. The evidence rests largely on the correlations (p. 13) between the nature and relative positions of side chains and the character of the visible absorption spectra.

Porphyrin *a* has an oxorhodo-type spectrum, and the pyridine haemochrome of haem *a*, unlike all other naturally occurring haems, has one band only in the visible region (587 mμ). The model compound acetylrhodoporphyrin (Fig. 18) called by Fischer oxorhodoporphyrin, has a III, II, IV, I spectrum not unlike that of porphyrin *a*, and the pyridine haemochrome of its haem, like that of haem *a*, has[31] a single visible band (582 mμ; pyridine protohaemochrome 558 mμ). Oxorhodoporphyrin and chlorocruoroporphyrin (Fig. 13) and their haems have been important model compounds throughout the studies on haem *a*. While chlorocruoroporphyrin has a rather weak rhodo-type spectrum (ratio III/IV = 1.3–1.4) porphyrin *a* has a very strong oxorhodo spectrum (III/IV = 2.4). The order of strength of the rhodofying influence of side chains is[57]

$$—CHO = —ring\ CO > —CH=CH—COOCH_3 > —COOCH_3 = —COR$$
$$> —CH=NOH = —CH=CH_2$$

A vinyl group alone increases the intensity of band III, but not sufficiently to make it more intense than band IV and so cause a rhodo-type spectrum. An acrylic acid side chain in haem *a* was postulated as a similar but stronger rhodofying group[31], but infrared evidence[62] has disproved this.

It has now been shown[57] with model compounds that formyl and vinyl side chains on diagonally opposite pyrrole rings may cause oxorhodo-type spectra, while on neighbouring rings, as in Fig. 13, they do not. This suggests strongly that in porphyrin *a* the formyl and the unsaturated side chains are on opposite pyrrole rings, and this conclusion is confirmed by the synthetic and degradative evidence described below.

The α-hydroxylalkyl side chain. Evidence from chemical degradation (see below) had shown that porphyrin *a* contained a third labile substituent group. Barrett[65] found that the paper chromatographic behaviour of porphyrin *a* was consistent with the presence of an α-hydroxylalkyl group (like the α-hydroxyethyl groups of haematoporphyrin (Fig. 14)), and was able to acetylate this group. Clezy and Barrett[66] obtained a new ketonyl group on oxidation (after protection of the formyl group by oxidation of it to —COOH) and in addition were able to dehydrate with formation of a new double bond, which had effects upon spectra typical of a vinyl or substituted vinyl group.

The degradative and synthetic evidence. Warburg and Gewitz[64] had obtained crystalline haem *a*, and had found on analysis 6 oxygen atoms. Of these, 5 only are accounted for by two propionic acid side chains (see below) and the formyl group. An hydroxyalkyl group makes up this deficiency. It was also found[64] that porphyrin *a* contains about 16 more C atoms than proto-porphyrin.

In 1953, Warburg and Gewitz[67] subjected haem *a* to the resorcinol melt treatment of Schumm[68] (see p. 28); this treatment is known to remove side chains such as $-CH=CH_2$, $-CH(OH)CH_3$, $-COOH$, and $-CHO$ from haems. After removal of iron, they obtained a crystalline porphyrin ester which they called cytodeuteroporphyrin ester. It differed from deuteropor-phyrin ester (obtained by treatment in the resorcinol melt of proto-, haem-ato-, 2,4-diformyl-, 2,4-diacetyldeuteroporphyrins, for example). Though bromination indicated the presence of three unsubstituted β-positions, for-mula 19a was suggested. In 1959, MacDonald and collaborators[69] succeeded in synthesizing cytodeuteroporphyrin (Fig. 19b).

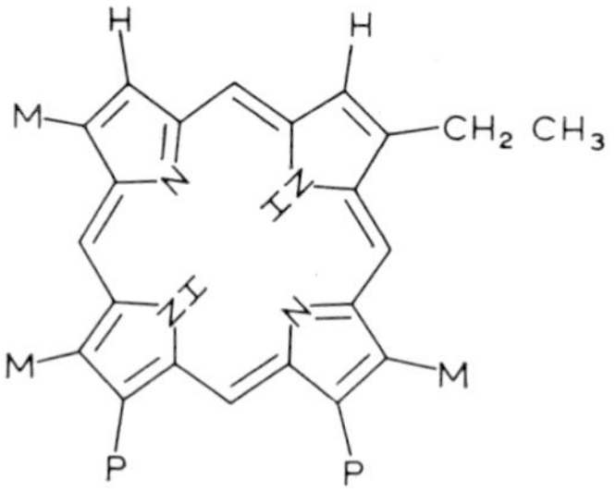

Fig. 19a. 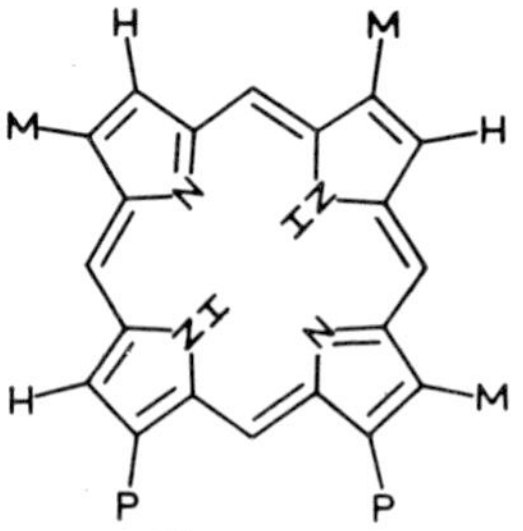   Fig. 19b.

This synthesis proved the presence of three unsubstituted β-carbon atoms and showed their positions; in addition it proved the presence of two pro-pionic acid side chains, and that the extra 16 carbons of haem *a*, since they are not contained in cytodeuteroporphyrin, must be associated with either the α-hydroxyalkyl or the vinyl group. There is evidence[57] which suggests that part of this alkyl side chain is associated with the vinyl group.

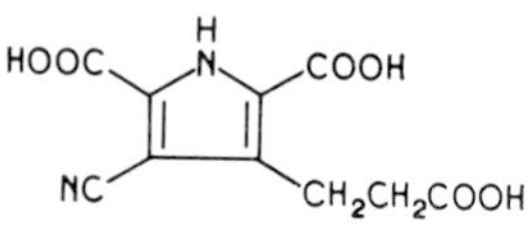

Fig. 20.

The position of the three groups relative to each other was not yet quite certain, though (see above) spectroscopic evidence showed that the vinyl and formyl groups must be on diagonally opposite pyrrole rings. The final evidence was furnished by Nicolaus[70], who after conversion of porphyrin a to its nitrile (—CHO → —CN), and oxidation of this with chromic acid, isolated the substituted pyrrole shown in Fig. 20.

This could only have been derived from ring IV (cf. Fig. 19b) locating the formyl group definitively in position 8. The vinyl group, to be on an opposite pyrrole ring, must then be on position 4, leaving position 2 for the α-hydroxy-alkyl group (Fig. 17).

(v) Haem a_2

Haem a_2 is the prosthetic group of cytochrome a_2, which occurs in certain bacteria[41]. The spectroscopic and other properties of cytochromes a_2 speak strongly against a simple haem as the prosthetic group, and Barrett[71] has now shown that this is an iron-chlorin, in which ring IV is hydrogenated. Barrett has isolated the iron-chlorin, and has purified chlorin a_2, obtained by removal of iron; its properties are consistent with the possible structures[71] shown in Fig. 21. The prosthetic group is thus an iron-chlorin corresponding to protohaem, but probably having an hydroxyalkyl side chain[85] in place of one of the vinyl groups.

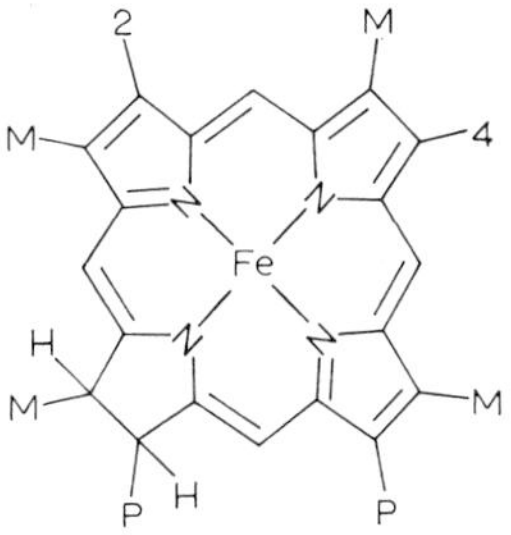

Fig. 21. Haem a_2. Postulated[71] substituents in positions:

	2	4
	V	B
or	B	V
or	V	E
or	E	V
or	V	V

For abbreviations, see Table II.

6. Haemins and porphyrins of importance in the laboratory and their preparation

Both haemin (from blood) and chlorophyll may be obtained conveniently in quantity, and serve as starting products for a large number of compounds which are used in the laboratory for various purposes. Before treating individual compounds, some general procedures are described.

References p. 31

(a) Removal of iron from haemins and its insertion into porphyrins

A variety of methods[1,2] is available for the removal of iron; they all depend upon the fact that in these complexes, ferrous iron is more readily replaced by protons than is ferric iron. Most iron-porphyrin complexes and their derivatives are readily autoxidized, so that most processes for the removal of iron feature a reducing agent (e.g. iron powder, stannous chloride, sodium amalgam) and a proton-source (formic, oxalic, acetic, hydrochloric acids[2]). On the small scale, a convenient and widely-used method is that of Warburg and Negelein[72]; to the haem refluxing in glacial acetic acid are added ferrous acetate (prepared by refluxing iron powder with glacial acetic acid under CO_2 or N_2) and concentrated HCl. Care must of course be taken that iron particles are not transferred with the ferrous acetate, otherwise hydrogenation may occur. The reaction is virtually instantaneous and is quantitative. Vinyl and other unsaturated side chains are relatively unstable to strong acids; the process has been modified and much improved by making use of ferrous sulphate in place of ferrous acetate[73].

For the introduction of iron into porphyrins, the reverse of this process is used: ferrous acetate prepared as above is added to the porphyrin refluxing in glacial acetic acid, and refluxing is continued in air until the ferrous haem has autoxidized to the more stable ferric state (haemin). The methods for the insertion of metals other than iron have been summarized by Lemberg and Legge[2].

(b) Esterification and saponification

Porphyrins readily form esters with alcohols; of these, methanol is most commonly used. The porphyrin is dissolved in anhydrous methanol saturated with gaseous HCl or, much more conveniently, in anhydrous methanol to which 5% (v/v) concentrated sulphuric acid has been added. The solution is allowed to stand in the dark for about 24 h at room temperature. This time and temperature are required for full esterification of, e.g. uro- and coproporphyrins, but protoporphyrin in particular is fully esterified in 24 h, and suffers less decomposition, at 0°. To the solution an equal volume of crushed ice is added, and as quickly as possible the ester is extracted into chloroform and the chloroform solution washed with water, with 2 N-ammonia and finally with water until the washings are neutral. The chloroform is removed in vacuo and the porphyrin ester crystallized from a methanol–chloroform mixture. Traces of unesterified porphyrin, though they should be extracted by ammonia, sometimes persist. Free porphyrins do not move from the origin in paper chromatography by the method of Falk and Benson[74] and may thus be detected, as may also partly esterified porphyrins, which are sometimes soluble in chloroform. The methyl esters may be prepared also, very conveniently, by reaction with diazomethane in ethereal solution.

Porphyrin esters, unlike the free acids, have high but characteristic meltting points; the esters are much more soluble in organic solvents than the acids, and are conveniently purified on column chromatograms.

The esters are saponified by standing at room temperature for about 40 h in 7 N HCl, or by treatment with methanolic KOH at room temperature.

(c) Chromatography

Methods for the chromatography of porphyrins on columns and on paper were reviewed in 1954 (ref. 75) and in 1961 (ref. 75a).

For preparative purposes it is most convenient to chromatograph the porphyrin esters on columns of Al_2O_3 or MgO, developing with organic solvents[76]; the free acids may be chromatographed on talc[77] or celite columns, development being with aqueous HCl. Hyflo columns have given part separation[78] of uroporphyrins I and III.

The paper chromatographic methods available allow considerable choice for specific purposes. For the identification of free porphyrins the basic method is that of Nicholas and Rimington[79]; it has been modified[75,80,81], and in addition to giving a separation in which R_F is inversely related to the number of carboxyl side chains[79], it has been found to allow separation of some isomers[75,83] e.g. the tetracarboxylic coproporphyrins I, II and III. Unfortunately, isomers III and IV have identical R_F values, and the separation of these isomers has not yet been achieved. Coproporphyrins I and III in the form of their tetramethyl esters are separated by the method of Chu, Green and Chu[82], and Falk and Benson[74] have modified this procedure to obtain the separation of the esters of uroporphyrins I and III. The latter method[74] helped to reveal the presence in certain mixtures of a new porphyrin which has been called *pseudo*uroporphyrin[83,25] (see p. 29), and in addition is useful as a test for the presence in preparations of porphyrin esters of traces of unesterified or incompletely esterified porphyrins, which do not move from the origin. Methods have been described for the separation of porphyrins with hydroxyethyl side chains[84,85], and for the separation of the iron-complexes of porphyrins[86,87].

(d) Individual compounds
(i) Haemin

Haemin (chlorhaemin: $C_{34}H_{32}O_4N_4FeCl$, Fig. 11) crystallizes in typical rhombic ("Teichmann") crystals when haemoglobin is heated with acetic acid containing sodium chloride. The reaction may be carried out on the microscope slide for the detection of traces of blood, and is used also for bulk preparations[88], in which yields of the order of 80% are commonly obtained. An improved method has been described recently[89]. Trace impurities only are usually present, but these can be important; thus in experiments on porphyrin and haem biosynthesis *in vitro*, where the blood contains considerable amounts of free porphyrins, these may adsorb on the haemin crystals and are not easily removed by recrystallization. Other means, however, are available[90] (see also p. 30). Haemin is usually recrystallized from a chloroform–pyridine mixture[88]. It does not have a melting point.

(ii) Protoporphyrin

Protoporphyrin ($C_{34}H_{34}O_4N_4$, Fig. 7) is most commonly prepared from haemin by the ferrous acetate–HCl method described above or by heating the haemin in formic acid with iron powder[91]; the crude protoporphyrin is recrystallized from pyridine, chloroform being added to facilitate filtering and then removed *in vacuo* for crystallization. Yields of 80–90% of theory are readily obtained, but examination by paper chromatography and countercurrent distribution shows[25] that the product is grossly impure.

It may be purified by countercurrent distribution[25], and rather less efficiently by fractional extraction in bulk from ether by aqueous HCl solutions. The vinyl side chains render protoporphyrin particularly sensitive to light, and there is a known hydration of proto- to haematoporphyrin in aqueous mineral acid solutions[25]. It is often more convenient to use the ester, which may be purified by chromatography (see *c*) without exposure to mineral acids, and for other purposes the more stable derivative of haemin, mesoporphyrin (see below) is useful.

The potassium salt of protoporphyrin is insoluble, and may be crystallized; the sodium salt also is only slightly soluble. The hydrochloride of protoporphyrin is fairly soluble in chloroform and may be extracted into this solvent from dilute (1.5 N) hydrochloric acid solution[2].

(iii) Protoporphyrin dimethyl ester

Protoporphyrin dimethyl ester ($C_{36}H_{38}O_4N_4$) may be prepared from free protoporphyrin by the method described above. It is much more conveniently prepared in quantity by the method of Grinstein[92]; as described, the raw material is defibrinated blood. Heparinized and citrated blood are equally suitable, and the method may be adapted to any form of haem or haemin. The process involves essentially the removal of iron from the ferrous complex by proton competition, followed by proton-catalysed esterification of the propionic acid side chains. Some precautions have been found essential by the writer; the HCl gas must be passed into the solution very vigorously; all chloroform must, as in all porphyrin manipulations, have been washed well with water on the day of use to free it from phosgene; to avoid saponification the reaction mixture must be kept cold while diluting with water and transferring the ester to chloroform, and the latter solution must be washed free of HCl as quickly as possible.

The reaction may be followed by the hand spectroscope; when it is complete, the haemin band at about 630 mμ has disappeared entirely, and is replaced by the sharp bands at 557 > 602 mμ of protoporphyrin ester hydrochloride. A band at approximately 670 mμ, due to a decomposition product, appears also.

The ester crystallizes well from chloroform–methanol; it is dissolved in chloroform, and to the solution while refluxing gently about 0.25 vol. of dry, distilled methanol is added. If crystals are not obtained on cooling, some chloroform is removed by distillation. The impurity absorbing at 670 mμ is not easily removed by repeated recrystallizations, but is separated by chromatography on Al_2O_3 columns[90]. The melting point of the pure ester is 231°.

Derivatives of protohaem and protoporphyrin

(iv) Haematoporphyrin

Haematoporphyrin ($C_{34}H_{38}O_6N_4$, Fig. 14) is obtained, as mentioned above, on treatment of blood or of protohaem with concentrated sulphuric acid; the latter both removes the iron from protohaem and causes the hydration of its vinyl side chains to α-hydroxyethyl. It may be prepared from haemin by the action of HBr in acetic acid, and arises in a certain proportion whenever protoporphyrin is exposed to mineral acids (see $(d)(ii)$). Haematoporphyrin has two asymmetric atoms (the —CH(OH)-carbons) but the product prepared from protohaem is optically inactive (see p. 17). The dimethyl ether dimethyl ester ("tetramethyl-haematoporphyrin") crystallizes well, but four modifications with different melting points have been found[1]; it is not yet clear whether these are due to polymorphism or diastereoisomerism, or both. The sodium salt of haematoporphyrin is relatively soluble. The dimethyl ester melts at 212°.

(v) Mesoporphyrin

Mesoporphyrin ($C_{34}H_{38}O_4N_4$, see Table II) is obtained from protohaem or protoporphyrin by reduction of the vinyl side chains to ethyl. Yields of 60% or higher have been obtained by reduction with hydrazine hydrate, formic acid and colloidal palladium or HI in acetic acid containing ascorbic acid[2]; a convenient modification of the Pd-catalyst method has been introduced[93].

The sodium salt of mesoporphyrin is insoluble in aqueous alkali. Mesoporphyrin dimethyl ester melts at 216°. Since it lacks unsaturated side chains, mesoporphyrin is more stable than protoporphyrin and is a useful derivative of protohaem for chemical and biochemical purposes.

(vi) *Deuteroporphyrin*

Deuteroporphyrin ($C_{30}H_{30}O_4N_4$, see Table II) and deuterohaemin are very easily prepared from protohaemin, from which they differ in that positions 2 and 4 are substituted by H atoms instead of vinyl groups. A variety of groups may be introduced into these positions by aromatic substitution reactions — for example the 2,4-dibromo, -dicyano, -diacetyl, -diformyl and other derivatives are described by Fischer and Orth[1]. Deuteroporphyrin occupied a key position as the first porphyrin formed in the total synthesis of protohaemin. On heating to 200° for 45 min in resorcinol (the "resorcinol melt" method of Schumm[68]), protohaemin is converted in good yield to deuterohaemin. The process has been modified by Chu and Chu[120]. For most substitution reactions the haemin is more suitable than the porphyrin. Deuteroporphyrin forms an insoluble sodium salt. It is extracted by chloroform from 0.05 N HCl solutions. Its dimethyl ester melts at 224°.

(vii) *Coproporphyrins* ($C_{36}H_{38}O_8N_4$).

As described above (p. 3), isomers I and III only of the coproporphyrins are of biological importance. All four isomers (Figs. 3–6) have been synthesized[1,94]. The best source of isomer I is meconium, and isomer III is best obtained from bacterial cultures; the classical source is *C. diphtheriae* cultured in a medium low in iron.

The coproporphyrins are extracted readily from biological materials by treatment with glacial acetic acid followed by addition of ether. They are extracted from ether by very weak aqueous acid (see Table III), and the aqueous phase must be kept above a pH of about 4.5 while washing the ether free of acetic acid. Their alkali salts also are readily soluble in water.

In some materials, such as certain pathological urines and the products of some *in vitro* porphyrin syntheses, isomers I and III occur together. Their identification, separation and quantitative analysis in such mixtures have been the subject of much study. The melting points of the tetramethyl esters of the coproporphyrins are discussed by Lemberg and Legge[2], who point out that identification of isomer I or III on a basis of melting point of the ester only is inadequate, and suggest that the copper complexes of the esters may be more useful for this purpose. The legends at the top and bottom of the melting point–composition curves of Jope and O'Brien[26], as reproduced in Fig. 10 of Lemberg and Legge[2], should be reversed. A method[95] depending upon the quenching of the fluorescence of isomer I but not of isomer III is useful, and paper-chromatographic methods (see p. 25) are available for the identification of the isomers.

(viii) *Uroporphyrins* ($C_{40}H_{38}O_{16}N_4$)

While Fischer[1] had isolated uroporphyrins I and III, and had assigned to them, on the basis of much indirect evidence, the structures given in Table II, it was not until recently[94] that isomers II and IV were obtained by synthesis and the structure of all four isomers proved. The acetic-acid side chains of uroporphyrins may be decarboxylated, leaving the propionic acid side chains intact; the products are thus the related coproporphyrins. The method of decarboxylation has been greatly improved by Schwartz[96]. Uroporphyrins I and III only are known to occur in nature, and their separation from mixtures is very difficult. Melting point–composition curves are available[27].

The best natural source of pure uroporphyrin I is the urine of human subjects or cattle suffering from congenital porphyria (see Table I); it may be prepared also from porphobilinogen (Fig. 23) by treatment in alkali[97] or enzymically[98]. Pure uroporphyrin III has been obtained from Turaco feathers[7], but in other samples[8], isomers I and III have both been found. Porphobilinogen may be converted to uroporphyrin III by reaction in acid conditions[97,99–100] or enzymically[100–102]. Uroporphyrin III occurs in considerable quantity in the urine of patients suffering from acute porphyria (see Table I), accompanied by varying amounts of uroporphyrin I; both porphyrins arise here largely from self-condensation of porphobilinogen, which is the main excretory product[3].

(ix) Pseudouroporphyrin

In experiments on porphyrin biosynthesis *in vitro* it has been found[25,83,100] that a porphyrin with solubility and spectroscopic properties very like those of a uroporphyrin is formed. Paper chromatography shows[83] that it is not one of the uroporphyrin isomers I, II, III or IV. On decarboxylation it yields coproporphyrin III only. The structure of this porphyrin is not yet known but it may have significance in relation to the biosynthetic pathway[100].

(x) Porphyrinogens

Classically, the porphyrinogens are hexahydroporphyrins, in which four pyrrole rings are joined by methylene ($—CH_2—$) bridges. The porphyrin conjugation is lacking and the compounds are colourless. They are usually prepared from porphyrins by reduction with sodium amalgam[103]. More recently, reduction by sodium or potassium borohydride has been used[104].

Leucoporphyrins which may be converted to porphyrins by autoxidation, or by treatment with I_2 or with ultraviolet light, have been found in pathological urines[3]. Strong suggestive evidence[105–107] that the intermediate tetrapyrroles in the biosynthesis of haem are not fully oxidized porphyrins, but leuco-compounds of some kind, has been confirmed amply by the use of porphyrinogens in biosynthetic experiments[102,109–111]. The various possible stages of reduction have been discussed fully by Granick[111], who has studied the enzymic conversion of porphobilinogen to uroporphyrinogen[110], and of the latter to coproporphyrinogen[111], and has found also that the autoxidation of uroporphyrinogen to uroporphyrin is photocatalytic and is sensitized by the reaction product, uroporphyrin. Pending knowledge of the exact nature of the reduced compound in any particular biochemical situation, the term "pro-porphyrins" has been suggested[105]. Chemical studies of the incorporation of iron into porphyrins have shown much faster incorporation after the porphyrin had been treated for short periods with sodium amalgam[112], though the enzymic incorporation[108] of iron into the porphyrin appears to be more rapid than into the porphyrinogen[104,113,122].

(xi) Isotopically labelled porphyrins

Protohaem, and thus protoporphyrin and all porphyrins derivable from it (see above) can be prepared labelled with either ^{15}N or ^{14}C by incubation of the blood or the washed erythrocytes of duck or chicken with [^{15}N]- or [2-^{14}C]-glycine. For labelling with ^{59}Fe, it is more convenient to inject the isotope into an experimental animal[114].

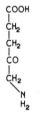

Fig. 22. δ-Aminolaevulic acid.

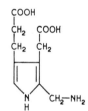

Fig. 23. Porphobilinogen.

On incubation of avian blood with labelled glycine, both the haemin and the free protoporphyrin are labelled. If the radioactivity of the haemin and the free protoporphyrin are both to be measured, it is necessary to purify the haemin carefully[90] to ensure the removal of traces of free porphyrin. The latter is much more radioactive than the haemin, since it is nearly all newly formed from labelled glycine, while the smaller amount of newly synthesized, labelled haemin is greatly diluted by preformed haemin.

Labelled copro- and uroporphyrins are formed, and little or no protoporphyrin or protohaem, when the above incubation is carried out under anaerobic conditions[101], or when mammalian erythrocytes[100] or the supernatant from haemolysed chicken erythrocytes[25] are used. Incubation of [2-^{14}C]-δ-aminolaevulic acid[115,116] (Fig. 22) or porphobilinogen (Fig. 23) with certain chicken erythrocyte preparations gives better yields of labelled uro- and coproporphyrins.

REFERENCES

1 H. FISCHER AND H. ORTH, *Die Chemie des Pyrrols*, Vol. 2, Part 1, Akademische Verlagsgesellschaft, Leipzig, 1937, pp. 398, 480.
2 R. LEMBERG AND J. W. LEGGE, *Haematin Compounds and Bile Pigments*, Interscience, New York, 1949.
3 J. E. FALK, *Biochem. Soc. Symposia (Cambridge, Engl.)*, 12 (1954) 17.
4 H. KLÜVER, *J. Psychol.*, 25 (1948) 331.
5 J. E. FALK, C. A. APPLEBY AND R. J. PORRA, *Soc. Exptl. Biol. Symposia*, 13 (1959) 73.
6 R. H. GOODWIN, V. M. KOSKI AND O. V. H. OWENS, *Am. J. Botany*, 38 (1951) 629.
7 R. E. H. NICHOLAS AND C. RIMINGTON, *Biochem. J.*, 50 (1951) 194.
8 C. J. WATSON AND M. BERG, *J. Biol. Chem.*, 214 (1955) 537.
9 D. C. BORG AND G. C. COTZIAS, *Nature*, 182 (1958) 1677.
10 S. KROL, *J. Org. Chem.*, 24 (1959) 2065.
11 U. EISNER AND R. P. LINSTEAD, *J. Chem. Soc.*, (1955) 3749.
12 S. F. MASON, *J. Chem. Soc.*, (1958) 976; C. RIMINGTON, S. F. MASON AND O. KENNARD, *Spectrochim. Acta*, 12 (1958) 65.
13 H. O'DANIEL AND A. DAMASCHKE, *Z. Krist.*, 104 (1942) 114.
14 C. L. CHRIST AND D. HARKER, *Amer. Mineralogist*, 27 (1942) 219.
15 M. B. CRUTE, *Acta Cryst.*, 12 (1959) 24.
16 J. M. ROBERTSON, *J. Chem. Soc.*, (1936) 1195.
17 A. STERN AND G. KLEBS, *Ann.*, 505 (1933) 295.
18 J. G. ERDMAN AND A. H. CORWIN, *J. Am. Chem. Soc.*, 68 (1946) 1885.
19 J. E. FALK AND J. B. WILLIS, *Australian J. Sci. Research, Ser. A*, 4 (1951) 579.
20 A. TREIBS AND E. WIEDEMANN, *Ann.*, 471 (1929) 150.
21 R. WILLSTÄTTER AND W. MIEG, *Ann.*, 350 (1906) 1.
22 K. ZEILE AND B. RAU, *Z. physiol. Chem.*, 250 (1937) 197.
23 S. GRANICK AND L. BOGORAD, *J. Biol. Chem.*, 202 (1953) 781.
24 K. G. PAUL, *Scand. J. Clin. & Lab. Invest.*, 5 (1953) 212.
25 J. E. FALK, E. I. B. DRESEL, A. BENSON AND B. C. KNIGHT, *Biochem. J.*, 63 (1956) 87.
26 E. M. JOPE AND R. J. P. O'BRIEN, *Biochem. J.*, 39 (1945) 239.
27 R. E. H. NICHOLAS AND C. RIMINGTON, *Biochem. J.*, 55 (1953) 109.
28 M. GRINSTEIN AND M. M. WINTROBE, *J. Biol. Chem.*, 172 (1948) 459.
29 J. BRUGSCH AND F. KUBOWITZ, *Biochem. Z.*, 324 (1953) 244.
30 J. E. FALK AND R. NYHOLM in A. ALBERT, G. M. BADGER AND C. W. SHOPPEE (Eds.), *Current Trends in Heterocyclic Chemistry*, Butterworth, London, 1958, p. 130.
31 R. LEMBERG AND J. E. FALK, *Biochem. J.*, 49 (1951) 674.
32 R. LEMBERG, *Nature*, 172 (1953) 619.
33 S. SCHWARTZ, L. ZIEVE AND C. J. WATSON, *J. Lab. Clin. Med.*, 37 (1951) 843.
34 J. E. FALK AND R. S. NYHOLM, quoted by J. E. FALK AND D. PERRIN in J. E. FALK, R. LEMBERG AND R. K. MORTON (Eds.), *Haematin Enzymes*, Pergamon, London, 1961.
35 K. SALOMON, *J. Gen. Physiol.*, 24 (1941) 367.
36 A. KIRRMANN, *Bull. soc. chim. biol.*, 12 (1930) 1146.
37 R. SCHÖNHEIMER, *Z. physiol. Chem.*, 180 (1929) 144.
38 D. KEILIN AND T. MANN, *Proc. Roy. Soc. (London)*, B,122 (1937) 119.
39 K. ZEILE AND H. HELLSTRÖM, *Z. physiol. Chem.*, 192 (1930) 171.
40 K. G. STERN, *J. Biol. Chem.*, 112 (1936) 661.
41 R. K. MORTON, *Revs. Pure Appl. Chem.*, 8 (1958) 161.
42 F. HOPPE-SEYLER, *Medizin.-chem. Untersuchungen*, 1–4 (1871).
43 M. NENCKI AND J. ZALESKI, *Z. physiol. Chem.*, 34 (1901) 997.
44 A. H. CORWIN in H. GILMAN (Ed.), *Organic Chemistry*, Vol. 2, 2nd ed., Wiley, New York, 1943.
45 H. FISCHER AND K. DEILMANN, *Z. physiol. Chem.*, 280 (1944) 186.
46 R. LEMBERG AND J. PARKER, *Australian J. Exptl. Biol. Med. Sci.*, 30 (1952) 163.
47 R. HILL AND D. KEILIN, *Proc. Roy. Soc. (London), B*, 107 (1930) 286.

[48] K. G. Paul, *Acta Chem. Scand.*, 4 (1950) 239.
[49] K. G. Paul, *Acta Chem. Scand.*, 5 (1951) 389.
[50] H. Theorell, *Biochem. Z.*, 298 (1938) 242.
[51] H. Theorell, *Enzymologia*, 6 (1939) 88.
[52] H. Tuppy and S. Paleus, *Acta Chem. Scand.*, 9 (1955) 353.
[53] H. Tuppy in A. Neuberger (Ed.), *Symposium on Protein Structure*, Methuen, London, 1958, p. 66.
[54] A. Ehrenberg and H. Theorell, *Acta Chem. Scand.*, 9 (1955) 1193; *Nature*, 176 (1955) 158.
[55] E. Margoliash, N. Frohwirt and E. Wiener, *Biochem. J.*, 71 (1959) 559.
[56] D. B. Morell, J. Barrett, P. Clezy and R. Lemberg in J. E. Falk, R. Lemberg and R. K. Morton (Eds.), *Haematin Enzymes*, Pergamon, London, 1961.
[57] R. Lemberg, P. Clezy and J. Barrett in J. E. Falk, R. Lemberg and R. K. Morton (Eds.), *Haematin Enzymes*, Pergamon, London, 1961.
[58] M. Morrison and E. Stotz in J. E. Falk, R. Lemberg and R. K. Morton (Eds.), *Haematin Enzymes*, Pergamon, London, 1961.
[59] O. Warburg, *Heavy Metal Prosthetic Groups and Enzyme Action*, Trans. A. Lawson, Clarendon Press, Oxford, 1949.
[60] J. Parker, *Biochim. et Biophys. Acta*, 35 (1959) 496.
[61] H. Dannenberg and M. Kiese, *Biochem. Z.*, 322 (1952) 395.
[62] R. Lemberg and J. B. Willis, unpublished.
[63] C. Rimington, J. H. Hale, W. A. Rawlinson, R. Lemberg and J. E. Falk, *1st Int. Congr. Biochem. Abstr.*, 1949, pp. 351, 378, 379.
[64] O. Warburg and H. S. Gewitz, *Z. physiol. Chem.*, 288 (1951) 1.
[65] J. Barrett, *Nature*, 183 (1959) 1185.
[66] P. Clezy and J. Barrett, *Biochim. et Biophys. Acta*, 33 (1959) 584.
[67] O. Warburg and H. S. Gewitz, *Z. physiol. Chem.*, 292 (1953) 174.
[68] O. Schumm, *Z. physiol. Chem.*, 178 (1928) 1.
[69] G. S. Marks, D. K. Dougall, E. Bullock and S. F. MacDonald, *J. Am. Chem. Soc.*, 82 (1960) 3183.
[70] R. A. Nicolaus, *Rass. med. sperimentale*, suppl. 2 (1960) 1.
[71] J. Barrett, *Biochem. J.*, 64 (1956) 626.
[72] O. Warburg and E. Negelein, *Biochem. Z.*, 244 (1932) 9.
[73] D. B. Morell and M. Stewart, *Australian J. Exptl. Biol. Med. Sci.*, 34 (1956) 211.
[74] J. E. Falk and A. Benson, *Biochem. J.*, 55 (1953) 101.
[75] J. E. Falk, *Brit. Med. Bull.*, 10 (1954) 211.
[75a] J. E. Falk, *J. Chromatog.*, 5 (1961) 277.
[76] R. E. H. Nicholas, *Biochem. J.*, 48 (1951) 309.
[77] A. Comfort, *Biochem. J.*, 44 (1949) 111.
[78] T. C. Chu and E. J. Chu, *J. Biol. Chem.*, 227 (1957) 505.
[79] R. E. H. Nicholas and C. Rimington, *Scand. J. Clin. & Lab. Invest.*, 1 (1949) 12.
[80] R. Kehl and W. Stich, *Z. physiol. Chem.*, 289 (1951) 6.
[81] L. Eriksen, *Scand. J. Clin. & Lab. Invest.*, 5 (1953) 155.
[82] T. C. Chu, A. A. Green and E. J. Chu, *J. Biol. Chem.*, 190 (1951) 643.
[83] J. E. Falk in *The Biosynthesis of Porphyrins and Porphyrin Metabolism*, Ciba Foundation Conf., Churchill, London, 1955, p. 63.
[84] T. C. Chu and E. J. Chu, *J. Biol. Chem.*, 208 (1954) 537.
[85] J. Barrett, *Nature*, 183 (1959) 1185.
[86] T. C. Chu and E. J. Chu, *J. Biol. Chem.*, 212 (1955) 1.
[87] J. L. Connelly, M. Morrison and E. Stotz, *J. Biol. Chem.*, 233 (1958) 743.
[88] H. Fischer, *Org. Syntheses*, 3 (1955) 442.
[89] R. F. Labbe and G. Nishida, *Biochim. et Biophys. Acta*, 26 (1957) 437.
[90] E. I. B. Dresel and J. E. Falk, *Biochem. J.*, 63 (1956) 72.
[91] V. G. Ramsey, *Biochem. Preparations*, 3 (1953) 39.
[92] M. Grinstein, *J. Biol. Chem.*, 167 (1947) 515.

93 H. M. Muir and A. Neuberger, *Biochem. J.*, 45 (1949) 163.
94 S. F. MacDonald and K. H. Michl, *Canad. J. Chem.*, 34 (1956) 1768.
95 S. Schwartz, V. E. Hawkinson, S. Cohen and C. J. Watson, *J. Biol. Chem.*, 168 (1947) 133.
96 P. R. Edmondson and S. Schwartz, *J. Biol. Chem.*, 205 (1953) 605.
97 G. H. Cookson and C. Rimington, *Biochem. J.*, 57 (1954) 476.
98 L. Bogorad, *J. Biol. Chem.*, 233 (1958) 501.
99 R. G. Westall, *Nature*, 170 (1952) 614.
100 E. I. B. Dresel and J. E. Falk, *Biochim. et Biophys. Acta*, 39 (1960) 458.
101 J. E. Falk, E. I. B. Dresel and C. Rimington, *Nature*, 172 (1953) 292.
102 L. Bogorad, *J. Biol. Chem.*, 233 (1958) 510.
103 H. Fisher, F. Röse and E. Bartholomäus, *Z. physiol. Chem.*, 84 (1913) 262.
104 G. Nishida and R. F. Labbe, *Biochim. et Biophys. Acta*, 31 (1959) 519.
105 S. Schwartz and K. Ikeda in *The Biosynthesis of Porphyrins and Porphyrin Metabolism*, Ciba Foundation Conf., Churchill, London, 1955, p. 209.
106 E. I. B. Dresel in *The Biosynthesis of Porphyrins and Porphyrin Metabolism*, Ciba Foundation Conf., Churchill, London, 1955, p. 72.
107 E. I. B. Dresel and J. E. Falk, *Biochem. J.*, 63 (1956) 388.
108 R. A. Neve, R. F. Labbe and A. Aldrich, *J. Am. Chem. Soc.*, 78 (1956) 691.
109 L. Bogorad, *J. Biol. Chem.*, 233 (1958) 516.
110 S. Granick and D. Mauzerall, *J. Biol. Chem.*, 232 (1958) 1119.
111 D. Mauzerall and S. Granick, *J. Biol. Chem.*, 232 (1958) 1141.
112 J. Orlando, *Dissertation*, University of California, Berkeley, 1958.
113 R. F. Labbe, *Biochim. et Biophys. Acta*, 31 (1959) 589.
114 C. Rimington, *Revs. Pure Appl. Chem.*, 8 (1958) 129.
115 E. I. B. Dresel and J. E. Falk, *Nature*, 172 (1953) 1185.
116 A. Neuberger and J. J. Scott, *J. Chem. Soc.*, (1954) 1820.
117 C. Rimington, *Biochem. J.*, 75 (1960) 622.
118 J. B. Neilands and H. Tuppy, *Biochim. et Biophys. Acta*, 38 (1960) 351.
119 E. I. B. Dresel, C. Rimington and B. Tooth, *Scand. J. Clin. & Lab. Invest.*, 8 (1956) 73.
120 T. C. Chu and E. J. Chu, *J. Am. Chem. Soc.*, 74 (1952) 6276.
121 K. G. Paul, H. Theorell and Å. Åkeson, *Acta Chem. Scand.*, 7 (1953) 1284.
122 R. J. Porra and O. T. G. Jones, *Biochem. J.*, (1962) in the press.

Chapter II

Physico-Chemical Properties of Porphyrins

J. N. PHILLIPS

Division of Plant Industry, C.S.I.R.O., Canberra, A.C.T. (Australia)

1. Introduction

The tetrapyrrole pigments in the form of their magnesium or iron complexes play many roles in nature; they are involved in such diverse phenomena as photosynthesis and nitrogen fixation in plants and oxygen transport in the blood, as well as forming the prosthetic groups of the haem enzymes which include the cytochromes, peroxidases and catalases. The specific biological activities of these compounds are associated with different physico-chemical properties of the metalloporphyrins. Thus the photosynthetic action spectrum of plants and the photocatalysed greening step are related to the absorption spectra of chlorophyll and protochlorophyll respectively. The electron transferring properties of the cytochrome chain can be related to the redox behaviour of the haem prosthetic groups and to extensive electron delocalization that is characteristic of the porphyrin nucleus. The formation of protein–pigment complexes can be associated with the tendency of the iron and magnesium tetrapyrroles for further coordination — a tendency which is also responsible for the oxygen carrying capacity of haemoglobin.

An understanding of the physico-chemical behaviour of the porphyrins is clearly pertinent to a detailed understanding of their biological functions. This chapter is primarily concerned with the physico-chemical properties of the fully unsaturated porphyrins (*i.e.* porphins), their salts and metal complexes. Occasional reference has been made to the comparative behaviour of porphins and chlorins (dihydroporphins). Chlorophyll and related chlorins are discussed in detail in Chapter III.

Review type references have been cited in the text, wherever possible, and the reader is referred to these review articles (refs. 1–15) for a more detailed coverage of the literature.

2. Acid–base behaviour[15]

(a) Ionization of the ring nitrogens

Structurally the tetrapyrrole nucleus may be regarded as a potential tetra-valent ampholyte with the two imino type ($-N=$) nitrogen atoms capable of accepting protons and therefore of acting as basic centres and the two pyrrole type ($-NH-$) nitrogen atoms capable of either losing or accepting protons and therefore of acting as acidic or basic centres. The seven possible species are shown in Fig. 1. Four of these species, PH_4^{2+}, PH_3^+, PH_2 and P^{2-}

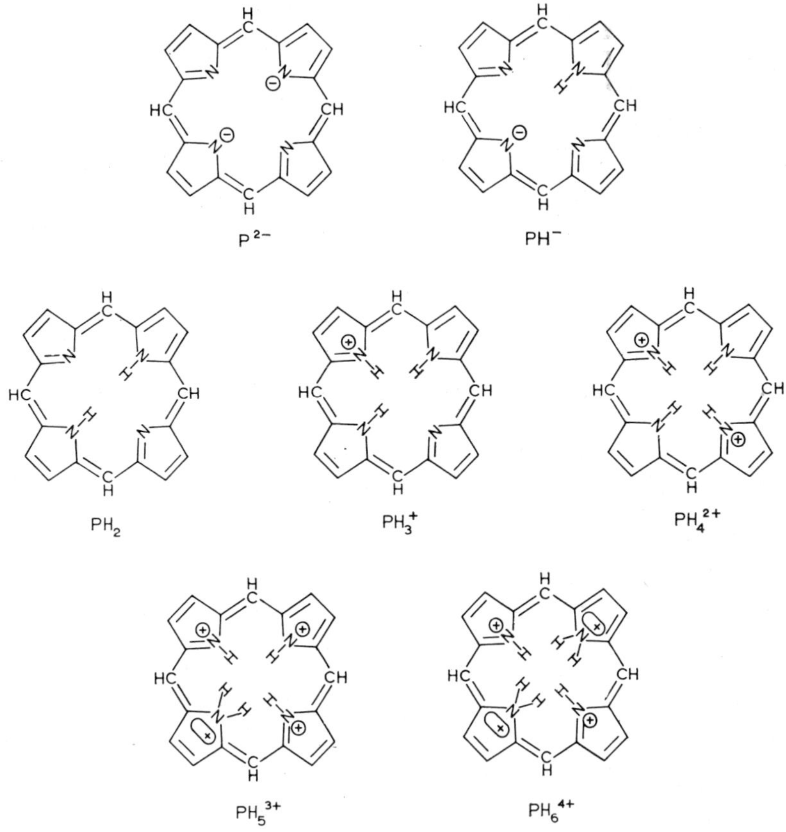

Fig. 1. Possible acidic, basic and neutral porphyrin species.

have been observed spectroscopically and the free base (PH_2), the dicationic salt ($PH_4^{2+}Cl_2^{2-}$) and the dianionic salt ($Na_2^+P^{2-}$) have been chemically isolated.

Different conventions have been used in assigning pK values to the porphyrin nucleus but the most convenient is to express both acidity and basicity equilibria in terms of the negative logarithm of the acid dissociation constant and to number such pK's in order of decreasing positive value. This means that pK_1 and pK_2 refer to the acidic equilibria involved in the dissociation of protons from the pyrrole type nitrogens and pK_3 and pK_4 to the basic equilibria associated with the addition of protons to the imino type nitrogens. The pK values are defined by

$$pK_1 = pH - \log [P^{2-}]/[PH^-]$$
$$pK_2 = pH - \log [PH^-]/[PH_2]$$
$$pK_3 = pH - \log [PH_2]/[PH_3^+]$$
$$pK_4 = pH - \log [PH_3^+]/[PH_4^{2+}]$$

Porphyrins generally behave as extremely weak acids. The neutral species (PH$_2$) is stable in concentrated sodium hydroxide and one must resort to the more alkaline sodium alkoxide solutions to observe the dianion (P^{2-}) spectroscopically. Both pK_1 and pK_2 have been estimated[16] to be of the order of $+16$ in the case of aetioporphyrin. On the other hand the basicity of

TABLE I

THE BASICITY OF SUBSTITUTED DEUTEROPORPHYRIN ESTERS IN 2.5 % SODIUM DODECYL SULPHATE[15] AT 20°

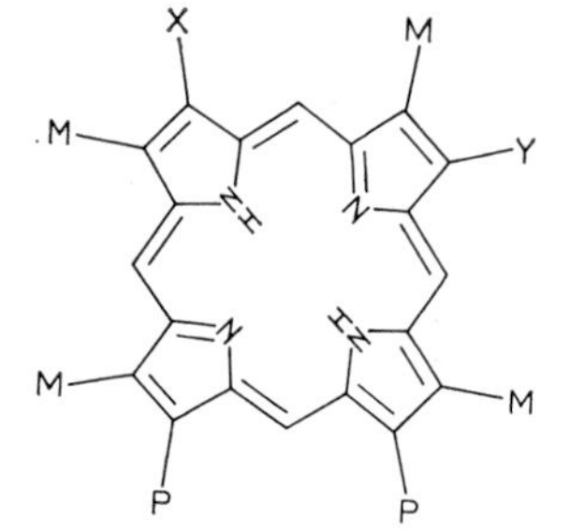

Porphyrin	X	Y	p$K_3 (\pm 0.05)$
Meso-	—CH$_2$CH$_3$	—CH$_2$CH$_3$	5.94
Deutero-	—H	—H	5.63
Copro-	—P**	—P**	5.58
Proto-	—CH=CH$_2$	—CH=CH$_2$	4.89
4-Formyldeutero-	—H	—CHO	3.90
2,4-Diacetyldeutero-	—COCH$_3$	—COCH$_3$	3.50
2,4-Diformyldeutero-	—CHO	—CHO	2.90

* M = —CH$_3$
** P = —CH$_2$CH$_2$COOCH$_3$

porphyrins can be demonstrated readily by their solubility in dilute ($\sim$ 0.1 N) mineral acids where the dicationic species is usually observed, and in fact most studies on ionization have been concerned with the basicity of the nucleus. Measurements in aqueous solution are limited by solubility considerations and this has led to the use of such techniques as potentiometric titration in glacial acetic acid[17] and spectroscopic titration in nitrobenzene[18] and in aqueous detergent solutions[19] for determining the relative basicity of different porphyrins. Table I summarizes pK_3 values for a number of related porphyrin esters as determined in 2.5% sodium dodecyl sulphate (S.D.S.).

An estimate of the overall basicity ($pK_3 + pK_4$) of a porphyrin containing n carboxylic acid groups can be obtained from the acid number and the pH number (pH_n) which have been defined elsewhere (see p. 9). It can be shown[15] that

$$pK_3 + pK_4 = npH_n + 2pH_A - npK_{COOH} - 0.3$$

where pH_A is the pH corresponding to the hydrochloric acid concentration expressed by the acid number and pK_{COOH} is the mean pK of the carboxylic acid groups at pH_n (see section 1b). Table II summarizes $pK_3 + pK_4$ values determined in this way for several porphyrins.

TABLE II

$pK_3 + pK_4$ VALUES FROM PHASE DISTRIBUTION STUDIES[15]

Porphyrin	Number of carboxyl groups (n)	pH_A	pH_n	pK^*_{COOH}	$pK_3 + pK_4$
Phylloporphyrin	1	+1.1	10.4	4.8	7.5
Pyrroporphyrin	1	+0.65	10.4	4.8	6.4
Rhodoporphyrin	2	—0.25	8.25	5.7	4.3
Phyllochlorin	1	—0.40	12.2	4.8	6.7
Pyrrochlorin	1	—0.40	12.0	4.8	6.5

* pK_{COOH} is the mean pK of the carboxylic acid group at pH_n. For porphyrin monocarboxylic acids pK_{COOH} is assumed to equal the intrinsic value for propionic acid (*i.e.* 4.8) at all pH's. For polycarboxylic acids see section 1b.

In general pK_3 and pK_4 are not widely separated, differing by only 2–3 pK units. This can be attributed to the increased resonance stabilization of the symmetrical dication over the unsymmetrical monocation and it is this relatively small difference between pK_3 and pK_4 that makes the detection of the monocationic species so difficult in practice (see section 2a).

Structural effects play an important part in determining the proton affinity, *i.e.* the basicity, of porphyrins. Some of the factors are summarized below:

(i) Electron attracting power of β-substituents

In general the more electron attracting the substituent the weaker the basicity of the porphyrin. It will be observed from Table I that the relative proton affinity for a series of substituted deuteroporphyrin esters varies progressively over a thousand-fold range between the diethyl and diformyl derivatives. A similar effect is observed in the chlorophyll series, the greater electronegativity of the formyl as compared with the methyl group being responsible for the weaker basicity of the chlorophyll b compared with the chlorophyll a derivatives.

(ii) Dihydro derivatives

Reduction of the porphin to the dihydro compound, i.e. the chlorin, leads to a weakening of the basicity of the ring nitrogens. However the high acid numbers associated with the chlorins as compared with the porphins are a reflection not only of the weakened basicity but also of the greater lipoid-solubility of the dihydro derivatives.

(iii) The isocyclic ring

The base-weakening effect of the isocyclic ring associated with chlorophyll and its derivatives is greater than would be predicted solely on the basis of electron-attracting character. This extra effect has been ascribed to enolization of the ketonic group resulting in the isocyclic ring being more effectively conjugated to the porphyrin nucleus[20].

(iv) The electrostatic field effect

All naturally occurring porphyrins contain carboxylic acid side chains which ionize simultaneously with the porphyrin ring nitrogens. The electrostatic field set up around the ionized carboxyl group attracts hydrogen ions and leads to an apparent enhancement of porphyrin basicity. The magnitude of the effect in the case of N-methyl coproporphyrin I is reflected in the difference in aqueous pK value between the free acid ($+11.3$) and the ester[21] ($+8.3$). The electrostatic effect can be avoided experimentally by studying the ionization behaviour of porphyrin esters in non-aqueous or detergent solutions. However, the effect is likely to be important in determining the ionization state of a porphyrin in vivo where, in addition to the electrostatic effect of the side chains there will be superimposed an electrostatic contribution from the surrounding macro-ion environment. Thus the intrinsic pK_3 for coproporphyrin in water can be estimated to be ~ 5 but the effective pK_3 in aqueous solution[21] is 7.2 due to the ionized carboxyl groups. In the biological environment one would expect about 50% of this porphyrin to be in the monocationic form.

(b) Ionization of the acid side chains

Most naturally occurring porphyrins have β-substituted carboxylic acid side chains, usually acetic or propionic acid groups, which greatly influence their solubilities and partition coefficients. The pK values of analogous pyrrole carboxylic acids are of the order of $+4.8$ and these are likely to correspond to the intrinsic pK values of similarly substituted porphyrin monocarboxylic acids. In polycarboxylic acid porphyrins, however, such intrinsic pK values will be modified by the electrostatic effect arising from the other ionized carboxylate groups and from the ionized ring nitrogens. Since the magnitude of this effect depends on the charge density of the nucleus the apparent pK will vary with pH. However the mean pK values for polycarboxylic acid porphyrins approach a limiting value in the alkaline pH region where the carboxylic acid groups are effectively all ionized. Assuming the pK for a monocarboxylic acid ($n = 1$) porphyrin to be 4.8, the mean limiting pK where $n = 2$ would be approximately 5.7, where $n = 4$, approximately 6.5, and where $n = 8$ approximately 7.3. These would represent reasonable values for pK_{COOH} which could be used to determine (pK_3 + pK_4) values from the acid and alkali numbers (see section 1a).

3. Phase distribution phenomena[5]

(a) Solubility in aqueous solution

The solubility of porphyrins in various media has been discussed qualitatively in Chapter I (p. 9), and here it is proposed to consider some quantitative aspects of porphyrin solubility in aqueous solution, which is the environment of biological interest.

Free porphyrins and their esters are sparingly soluble in aqueous solution at near neutral pH values. Thus for example the solubility of protoporphyrin dimethyl ester in water has been estimated to be of the order of 10^{-10} M. Relatively stable dispersions can be obtained at higher porphyrin concentrations but these can be distinguished from true porphyrin solutions by their diffuse absorption bands in the visible and near ultraviolet regions of the spectrum and by their lack of fluorescence. Porphyrins and their esters can however be dispersed molecularly in dilute aqueous detergent solutions at concentrations up to 10^{-5} M. Such solutions are stable and fluorescent and have absorption spectra similar to those observed in organic solvents[22].

Porphyrins and their esters are soluble in dilute (~ 0.1 N) mineral acids, usually as the dication (PH_4^{2+}). The relatively small difference between pK_3 and pK_4 of about 2 pK units coupled with the very low solubility of the free porphyrin in water makes it extremely difficult to detect the monocation experimentally. Fig. 2 illustrates the calculated effect of pH on

References p. 72

the concentrations of the different ionic species in a saturated aqueous solution of a porphyrin ester assuming the solubility of the free base (PH_2) to be 10^{-10} M and pK_3 and pK_4 to be 4 and 2 respectively. It will be noted that at pH values at which the porphyrin concentration is spectroscopically detectable (*i.e.* $> 10^{-7}$ M) the dication is the predominant species. Monocations can generally be observed in anionic detergent solutions where they are stabilized by interaction with the oppositely charged micelles.

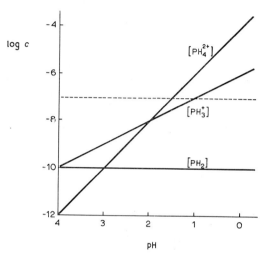

Fig. 2. The effect of pH on the concentration (c) of free base (PH_2), monocation (PH_3^+) and dication (PH_4^{2+}) in a saturated solution of a porphyrin ester calculated by assuming the solubility of the free base to be 10^{-10} M and pK_3 and pK_4 to be 4 and 2 respectively. The dotted line represents the minimum porphyrin concentration that is spectroscopically detectable.

Porphyrins with carboxylic acid side chains dissolve in aqueous alkali by forming the alkali carboxylate salt; the greater the number of carboxylic acid groups the less alkaline the pH required to dissolve the porphyrin.

Metalloporphyrin esters are generally insoluble in aqueous solution though metalloporphyrins with carboxyl side chains will dissolve in aqueous alkali. Such solutions are sometimes polymeric in nature, however; for example iron (Fe^{2+} and Fe^{3+}) protoporphyrin is colloidally dispersed in aqueous alkali in the form of loosely bound aggregates which are in turn made up of strongly bound dimeric units[2].

(b) Ether—water partition coefficients

The partition of porphyrins between ether and hydrochloric acid solutions forms the basis of an extraction and purification technique commonly used in porphyrin chemistry (see Chapter I, p. 9). The ether–water partition coefficients (K_p) for a number of porphyrins are summarized in Table III. It will be noted that K_p is of the order 10^4 to 10^7 and that chlorins have higher partition coefficients than the corresponding porphins.

TABLE III

ETHER – WATER PARTITION COEFFICIENTS[15]

Porphyrin	$K_p(Et_2O/H_2O) \cdot 10^{-5}$
Rhodoporphyrin	0.3
Pyrroporphyrin	1
Phylloporphyrin	1
Pyrrochlorin	400
Phyllochlorin	625

The effect of varying acid strength on the effective ether–water partition coefficient (K'_p), under conditions where the dication only can be detected in the aqueous phase, can be calculated to be given by

$$K'_p = \frac{K_p K_3 K_4}{[H^+]^2}$$

i.e. K'_p varies inversely as the square of the hydrogen ion activity. This calculated relationship is in fact observed experimentally and can be used for example to calculate the most suitable acid concentration to separate porphyrins by countercurrent distribution[23].

(c) Surface activity

The flat porphin nucleus is essentially hydrophobic in character. The introduction, however, of two hydrophilic carboxyl groups on adjacent positions as in protoporphyrin makes the molecule surface-active at the air–water interface.

Protoporphyrin forms an unstable condensed film with the carboxyl groups in the aqueous phase and the porphyrin nucleus vertically oriented with respect to the interface[24]. The condensed nature of the monolayer is indicative of the high degree of van der Waal's attraction between the aromatic porphyrin nuclei. Haematoporphyrin, in which two hydrophilic ($-CHOH-CH_3$) groups are introduced opposite to the carboxyl groups, tends to form vapour expanded films with the porphyrin lying flat on the water surface. When more carboxyl groups are introduced symmetrically as in copro-(4COOH) and uro-(8COOH) porphyrins, the hydrophilic–hydrophobic balance is upset and the surface activity lowered.

4. Spectroscopic behaviour[3,5,8-14]

(a) *Visible and near ultraviolet absorption spectra*

The tetrapyrrole pigments are characterized by a four-banded spectrum in the visible region (4,500–7,000Å) and a single absorption maximum (the

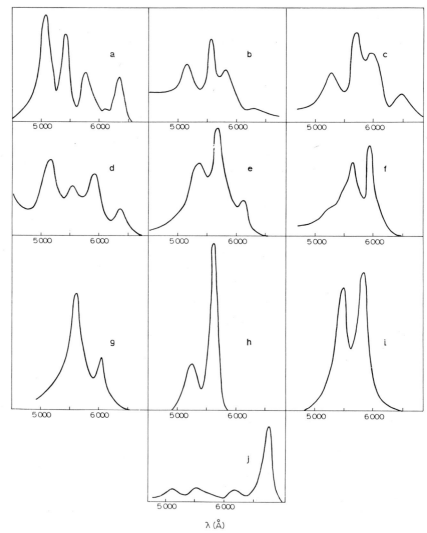

λ (Å)

Fig. 3. Typical visible porphyrin spectra: (*a*) aetio free base; (*b*) rhodo free base; (*c*) oxorhodo free base; (*d*) phyllo free base; (*e*) aetio monocation; (*f*) oxorhodo monocation; (*g*) dication; (*h*) Ni(II) complex; (*i*) Zn(II) complex; (*j*) chlorin free base.

Soret band) in the near ultraviolet (~4,000 Å), the visible bands being numbered sequentially I to IV from the red end of the spectrum. In some porphyrins a fifth band (Ia) or low intensity and lying between bands I and II is observed.

The intensity of the Soret band in most porphyrins is approximately twenty-fold the intensity of the strongest visible band and is such that porphyrins can be readily characterized in cells of 1 cm path length in the Soret and visible band regions at concentrations of the order of 10^{-5} and 10^{-6} M, respectively. Porphyrins and their metal complexes show no characteristic ultraviolet absorption bands but it should be noted that this region of the spectrum has not been greatly studied.

Porphyrins can be typed according to the relative intensity of their four main visible bands. There are twenty-four possible arrangements but in practice only four are observed, the most common being the so called "aetio" type in which the relative intensity of the bands fall in the order IV > III > II > I (see Fig. 3a). Aetio-type spectra are characteristic of porphyrins in which the substituents are attached to the nucleus through saturated carbon atoms and also of porphyrins in which two unsaturated groups are attached directly to the nucleus in adjacent (*i.e.* vicinal) pyrrole rings. This group includes the naturally occurring proto-, copro-, uro-, and deutero-porphyrins, and also haemato- and pyrro-porphyrins (for structures see Chapter I, pp. 6, 7). The other spectral types *viz.* "rhodo", "oxorhodo" and "phyllo" are shown in Figs. 3b, c and d respectively. The rhodo-type spectrum (III > IV > II > I) is associated with those porphyrins in which one unsaturated group is attached directly to the nucleus and the oxorhodo-type spectrum (III > II > IV > I) with those porphyrins in which two unsaturated groups are attached directly to the nucleus on opposite pyrrole rings. The phyllo-type spectrum (IV > II > III > I) is associated with mono-substituted methene bridge derivatives.

The spectra of porphyrin monocations (PH$_3^+$) usually consist of a Soret band and three visible absorption bands. The relative intensities of the visible bands are sensitive to the position of substituents on the nucleus. Figs. 3e and f illustrate the visible spectra of the aetio-(II > III > I), and oxo-rhodo-(I > II > III) type monocations[25]. Porphyrin dication (PH$_4^{2+}$) and dianion (P^{2-}) spectra are generally identical and consist of a Soret and two visible bands (Fig. 3g). The intensity ratio of bands I/II is usually ≪ 1 and is relatively unaffected by substituent position. The effect of ionization on the Soret band is to displace the Soret peak of the monocation to the blue and that of the dication and dianion to the red of the corresponding free base.

The metal porphyrin complexes generally show two absorption maxima (termed α-(nearest the red) and β-bands) in the visible region of the spectrum and a Soret absorption maximum (γ-band) around 4,000 Å. The ratio of the

α/β band intensities may vary from $\gg 1$ as in the thermodynamically stable complexes as for example Ni(II) (Fig. 3h) to ~ 1 as in the less stable complexes such as Zn(II) (Fig. 3i). The spectra of the iron porphyrin complexes which are of considerable biological interest are discussed in section 3c.

Reduction of a porphin to a chlorin has a marked effect on the visible spectrum corresponding to the observed colour change from red to green. Chlorin spectra although still four-banded in the visible region have a very predominant I or α-band (Fig. 3j). The ratio of Soret to α-band intensity in a chlorin is of the order of 5 as compared with the corresponding porphin ratio of approximately 20. The spectra of the dianionic and the mono- and dicationic chlorin salts are similar to those of the corresponding free chlorins, with both the α- and the Soret band displaced to the blue in the monocation and to the red in the dianion and dication. Metallochlorins have four-banded visible spectra (I $\gg$ II $>$ III $>$ IV) with the α-(I) band displaced to the blue of the α-band of the corresponding chlorins.

Spectroscopic changes are also associated with the further coordination of such metalloporphyrins as the cobalt, iron, manganese, magnesium, zinc and cadmium complexes, whereby ligand molecules become attached to the metal ion above and below the plane of the porphyrin ring. In such cases there is, in general, a spectroscopic shift to the red, irrespective of whether one (as with zinc porphyrin complexes) or two (as with cobalt porphyrin complexes) ligand molecules are coordinated (see section 5).

(b) Theoretical interpretation of the visible absorption spectra

The tetrapyrrole nucleus because of its symmetry, planarity and high degree of conjugation is particularly amenable to theoretical treatment and in recent years several theoretical interpretations of the absorption spectra of porphyrins have been proposed (cf. refs. 3, 10, 26, 27). The porphyrin molecule can be regarded as a framework of atoms held together by two-electron single (σ) bonds, the remainder of the valence electrons occupying molecular orbitals extending throughout the whole of the assembly. This strong delocalization of the mobile (π) electrons results in the highest of the occupied molecular orbitals and the lowest of the vacant orbitals differing in energy by an amount small enough for transitions between them to correspond to absorption bands in the visible and near ultraviolet regions of the spectrum. It has been suggested that the four visible bands associated with the neutral porphyrins are really two pairs of bands (I and II, and III and IV), which would be superimposed if the porphyrin nucleus were strictly square but arise because the structure is slightly distorted by hydrogen bonding between adjacent nitrogen atoms. This distortion is eliminated in the dianion, the dication and the metal complexes and in these cases two main bands are observed. Molecular orbital calculations indicate that the visible bands are all associated with one electronic transition and the Soret band with a second electronic transition. It has been suggested that the visible bands arise from transitions between orbitals of A_{2u}-type symmetry and vacant E_g type orbitals, as illustrated in Fig. 4.

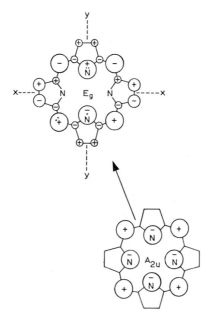

Fig. 4. The suggested nature of the electronic transition giving rise to the visible bands in porphyrin spectra.

The visible band transitions are associated with an electronic displacement towards the periphery which may be either along (bands III and IV) or perpendicular to (bands I and II) the axis through the two hydrogens on the opposite nitrogens. Since bands I and III are interpreted as 0–0 vibrational transitions, their intensities will be more sensitive to electronic symmetry in the molecule than will bands II and IV which are interpreted as 0–1 vibrational transitions. Such symmetry will be little affected by alkyl substituents but would be disturbed for example by formyl and acetyl substituents, the effect depending on their positions relative to each other. Since two adjacently substituted unsaturated groups would be similar to each other in their influence on electronic displacement in the x and y directions (see Fig. 4) it is not surprising that such derivatives show the aetio-type spectrum characteristic of alkyl substituted porphyrins. On the other hand monosubstituted or oppositely substituted unsaturated derivatives would greatly disturb the electronic symmetry and it is with such porphyrins that rhodo- and oxorhodo-type spectra are observed.

The α-bands of the metal porphyrin spectra seem to be related to bands I and III in the free porphyrin, *i.e.* to an o–o vibrational electronic transition, and the β-bands to bands II and IV, *i.e.* to an o–i vibrational electronic transition; bands II, IV, and β are little affected by substituents whilst bands I, III and α vary considerably. It is interesting to note that in the stable complexes (Cu, Co and Ni) the α-band is dominant whilst in the weaker complexes (Mg and Ba) the β-band is stronger, suggesting that the more thermodynamically stable the complex the more rigid its structure. This seems likely to be related to the observation that the more stable metal complexes do not fluoresce.

The theoretical approach has also been applied to the dihydro porphins (*i.e.* the chlorins) with some success. In the case of the chlorins it is clear that the symmetry-disturbing influence of the dihydro structure is dominant since intense α-bands are associated with the free chlorins, their mono- and di-basic salts and their metal complexes.

(c) *Iron porphyrin (haem) spectra*

The iron porphyrins differ from the other metalloporphyrins in being octahedral complexes in which two extra ligands are attached to the iron atom above and below the plane of the porphyrin ring. This further coordination of the iron porphyrins which may take place with ligand molecules such as water, pyridine, carbon monoxide, or oxygen, or ligand ions such as hydroxide or cyanide and the biochemical nomenclature associated with such complexes is discussed in section 5b. The iron porphyrin ligand complexes show characteristic visible absorption spectra, a number of which are illustrated in Fig. 5.

The rather diffuse nature of ferri-porphyrin spectra (Figs. 5a and 5b) can be attributed to the effect of charge transfer from the ligand to the ferric ion interacting with the electronic transitions normally associated with the porphyrin nucleus.

The dipyridine ferro-porphyrin complex (Fig. 5c) represents the classical haemochrome spectrum and in general both saturated (*e.g.* methylamine) and unsaturated (*e.g.* pyridine) nitrogen donor ligands show virtually identical spectra. The sharpening of the haem spectrum in detergent solution as compared with aqueous alkali (see Figs. 5d and 5e) can be ascribed to a change from the dimeric to the monomeric species (see section 5b). The haem spectrum in detergent solution (Fig. 5e) is similar to a normal pyridine haemochrome spectrum (Fig. 5c) with the bands displaced 16–17 mμ to the

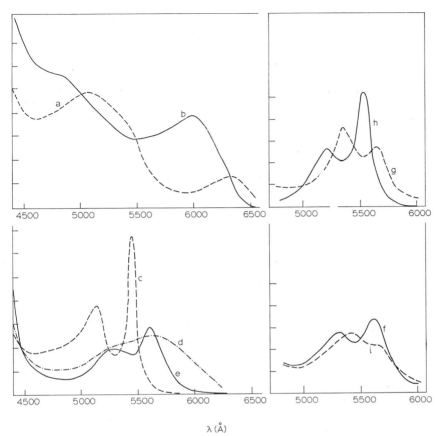

Fig. 5. Typical visible haem spectra: (a) ferri-porphyrin (haemin) chloride; (b) ferri-porphyrin hydroxide (haematin); (c) dipyridine ferro-porphyrin (pyridine haemochrome); (d) ferro-porphyrin in aqueous alkali (dimeric haem); (e) ferro-porphyrin in aqueous detergent solution (water haemochrome); (f) carbon monoxide–water ferro-porphyrin; (g) carbon monoxide–cyanide ferro-porphyrin; (h) cyanide–water ferro-porphyrin; (i) dicyanide ferro-porphyrin.

red. The species in the detergent solution is believed to be the monomeric water haemochrome complex with two water molecules in place of the two pyridine molecules.

Mixed ligand complexes such as the carbon monoxide–pyridine, carbon monoxide–water (Fig. 5f) and cyanide–water (Fig. 5h) complexes also show typical haemochrome spectra with a slight displacement of the bands relative to the pyridine haemochrome. However the carbon monoxide–cyanide (Fig. 5g) and dicyanide complexes (Fig. 5i) in which both ligands are coordinated through their carbon atoms do not show characteristic haemochrome spectra — rather the bands are displaced to the red and the relative intensities of the α- and β-bands reversed.

The spectra of haemochrome-type complexes of both ferro- and ferriporphyrins are sensitive to the electronic configuration of the metal ion, and in particular to whether the iron atom is in the high- or low-spin state (see section 7). Fig. 6 illustrates typical visible spectra for high- and low-spin ferri-haem complexes. Spectroscopic measurements have been used to determine the equilibrium between high- and low-spin forms in certain haemoprotein complexes (see Table XII, section 7).

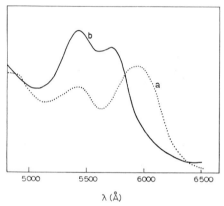

Fig. 6. Effect of spin type on visible haem spectra: (*a*) high-spin ferri-porphyrin hydroxide; (*b*) low-spin ferri-porphyrin hydroxide.

(*d*) *Fluorescence spectra*

Solutions of porphyrins or their salts when irradiated with ultraviolet light (mercury lamp — Wood's glass filter) exhibit a red fluorescence which can be detected by eye at concentrations of the order of 10^{-8} M and photoelectrically down to 10^{-10} M. The fluorescence can be used to estimate quantitatively porphyrin concentrations in this region, and as an analytical technique is complementary to absorption spectroscopy, which is applicable at higher porphyrin concentrations. Porphyrins do not usually fluoresce in the solid state or when colloidally dispersed in aqueous solution. Moreover the fluorescence in true solution can be partly or completely quenched by the presence of other solutes. High concentrations of sodium chloride or hydrochloric acid, for example, quench partly the fluorescence of porphyrin dications. It is clear that when fluorescence is used for quantitative analytical purposes great care must be taken to standardize the experimental procedure.

Fluorescent excitation spectra for porphyrins and their salts correspond to the absorption spectra in the Soret and visible regions. Usually one fluorescent emission band only is observed in the visible region and this occurs slightly to the red of the absorption band of longest wavelength. Table IV compares the absorption maxima with the fluorescent excitation and fluorescent emission maxima for various species derived from protoporphyrin-dimethyl ester in 2.5% sodium dodecyl sulphate.

TABLE IV

SPECTROSCOPIC PROPERTIES OF SOME PROTOPORPHYRIN DERIVATIVES IN
2.5% SODIUM DODECYL SULPHATE[19]

Species	Absorption maxima ± 5 Å	Fluorescence excitation maxima ± 20 Å	Fluorescence emission maxima ± 10 Å
PH_2	4080 5050 5405 5780 6330	4150 5080 5420 5820 6340	6340
PH_3^+	3985 5350 5680 6095	4080 5370 5660 6100	6125
PH_4^{2+}	4120 5570 6020	4130 5580 6020	6060
ZnP	4120 5425 5790	4150 5440 5780	5890

Solutions of metalloporphyrins in non-coordinating solvents (*e.g.* carbon tetrachloride, cyclohexane) do not fluoresce when irradiated with ultraviolet light. The Zn-, Cd- and Mg-porphyrin complexes do, however, fluoresce in coordinating solvents (pyridine, dioxane, water) or in non-coordinating solvents containing a polar ligand, for example an alcohol or an amine. It has been suggested[28] that the metalloporphyrin ligand complex is the active fluorescent species (see section 5). In general, it would appear that the less thermodynamically stable metalloporphyrins are fluorescent in polar solvents whilst the more stable complexes are non-fluorescent under all conditions.

(e) Infrared spectra

The infrared spectra of a number of natural and synthetic porphyrins have been reported[11,29-31]. The N–H stretching and bending frequencies have been determined by comparing the infrared spectra of deuterated and non-deuterated porphyrins. The N–H stretching frequency is found at approximately 3300 cm^{-1} and is virtually unaffected by a change from the solid state to carbon tetrachloride solution. This indicates that there is a high degree of intramolecular hydrogen bonding within the porphyrin nucleus. Bands in the region of 980 cm^{-1} and 720 cm^{-1} have been assigned as in plane and out of plane N–H bending frequencies. The infrared spectra are found to be consistent with a porphyrin model in which the hydrogen atoms are attached to opposite nitrogen atoms and each is hydrogen bonded to an adjacent nitrogen atom.

Infrared spectra can be used to characterize substituents on the porphyrin nucleus. Table V summarizes mean values of the absorption bands for differently substituted carbonyl groups.

TABLE V

CHARACTERISTIC INFRARED FREQUENCIES OF CARBONYL SUBSTITUTED PORPHYRINS[30]

Substituent group*	Mean absorption frequency (cm^{-1}) ($\pm$ 5 cm^{-1})
—CH$_2$COOR	1735–1740
—CH$_2$COOH	1705–1710
—COOR	~1700
—COOH	1665–1670
—CHO	1670
—COCH$_3$	1660
—CH$_2$—CO— (isocyclic ring)	1695–1710

* Substituents attached to β-pyrrole positions (1 → 8) except for the isocyclic ring, which bridges the γ- and 6-positions.

It has been suggested[11] that the position of a strong infrared absorption band in the region of 1,000 cm^{-1} can be correlated with the thermodynamic stability of metal porphyrin complexes in a closely related series. In general the more the band is displaced towards higher wave numbers (greater energy) the more stable the complex.

(f) Spectroscopic correlations with basicity and metal complex stability

The spectroscopic behaviour of the porphyrins may be correlated with other physico-chemical properties, including their basicity and the thermodynamic stability of their metal complexes. The electronic transitions giving rise to the visible absorption bands are associated with a movement of electrons towards the periphery of the nucleus (see section 3*b*) and the same is believed to be true of the electronic transitions giving rise to the Soret band. It would be expected that the greater the electron density on the ring nitrogens the more difficult it would be to displace the electrons to the periphery and hence the shorter the wave length of the transition, *i.e.* the stronger the basicity of the porphyrin the more the absorption bands should be shifted to the blue. Experimentally it is observed that electron-attracting substituents exert a bathochromic effect on porphyrin spectra. Fig. 7 illustrates the relationship between pK_3 and the wave number of the Soret transition of the monocation for the deuteroporphyrin ester series shown in Table I.

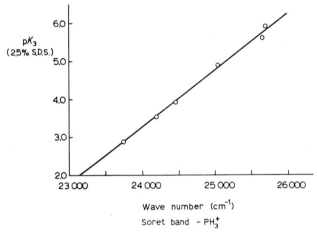

Fig. 7. The relationship between pK_3 and the wave number of the Soret transition of the monocation for the deuteroporphyrin series of Table I.

Similarly a correlation can be predicted for the relative stability of complexes formed by the one metal with different porphyrins — the more the absorption bands are shifted to shorter wave lengths the more stable the complex. Another correlation has been noted among complexes formed from the same porphyrin with different divalent metal ions. Again the more the absorption maxima are displaced to the blue the more stable the complex. This effect, which is discussed further in section 4*b*, can be interpreted simply, since the stronger the metal–porphyrin bond the more difficult it will be to displace electrons from the centre to the periphery of the nucleus. Other correlations, between the thermodynamic stability of metalloporphyrins and their fluorescence (section 3*d*) and infrared spectra (section 3*e*) have already been noted.

5. Metal ion chelation[9,15]

(*a*) *Introduction*

The chelation of metal ions by porphyrins is one of their most characteristic and biologically important properties. Divalent metal ions react by replacing the two dissociable hydrogens attached to the porphyrin nucleus. According to the classical picture, the metal ion is held in the plane of the porphyrin

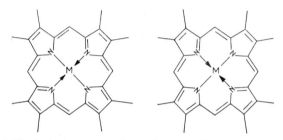

Fig. 8. Equivalent resonance forms for a metalloporphyrin complex.

ring by two coordinate and two ionic bonds from the four nitrogen atoms, two of the equivalent resonance forms being as shown in Fig. 8. Certain divalent metal complexes *e.g.* Fe(II), Co(II) and Mn(II) may be oxidized to the trivalent state, the excess positive charge being neutralized by an anion such as chloride or hydroxide. Complexes in which the dissociable hydrogens have been replaced by two monovalent metal ions, *e.g.* Na^+, K^+, Li^+ or Ag^+ are also known but are of low thermodynamic stability.

Porphyrins differ from most common chelating agents in that there is an appreciable activation energy associated with the incorporation of the metal ion, the reaction rate being dependent upon the nature of the porphyrin, the nature of the metal ion and the solvent medium. It is therefore necessary in discussing metalloporphyrin complexes to distinguish between the thermodynamic stability *i.e.* the equilibrium affinity of a porphyrin for a metal ion and the kinetic stability (or lability) *i.e.* the ease with which a complex may be formed or dissociated. Although chemically the former may be the more interesting property the latter is likely to be important from the biological point of view.

(b) Thermodynamic stability of metalloporphyrin complexes

The stability constant (K_s) for a metalloporphyrin complex can be represented by the general expression

$$K_s = \frac{[MP]}{[M^{2+}][P^{2-}]}$$

where $[MP]$ is the activity of the metalloporphyrin complex, $[M^{2+}]$ is the activity of the metal ions, and $[P^{2-}]$ is the activity of the dianionic porphyrin species.

The only reported stability constant[19] for a metalloporphyrin complex is a value for log K_s of $+29$, estimated for the zinc mesoporphyrin ester complex in 0.25% cetyltrimethylammonium bromide solutions at room temperature. This value when compared with the corresponding log K_s values for the zinc chelates of 8-hydroxyquinoline-5-sulphonic acid $(+16)$, ethylene diamine $(+11)$ and glycine $(+9.5)$ illustrates the stabilizing influence of the quadradentate porphyrin ligand.

The relative stability of metalloporphyrin complexes can be determined qualitatively in a number of ways. One method involves heating an equimolar mixture of a metalloporphyrin (M*P*) and either a metal ion (M²⁺) or free porphyrin (PH₂) in a suitable solvent and observing whether replacement occurs. Such reactions may be represented generally by:

$$M^*P^* + M^{2+} \rightleftharpoons MP^* + M^{*2+}$$

and:

$$M^*P^* + PH_2 \rightleftharpoons M^*P + P^*H_2$$

If replacement occurs, then the complex formed is more stable, thermodynamically, than the original complex. No conclusion can be drawn, however, from a negative result, since the reaction may not have proceeded to equilibrium. Experiments of this type with *meso*-tetraphenylporphin as the ligand have indicated the following order of decreasing stability of the metal complex.

$$Cu(II) > Zn(II) \gg Hg(II) > Pb(II) \gg Li(I) > Na(I) > K(I)$$

Replacement reaction studies have also indicated that metalloporphins are more stable than the corresponding metallochlorins.

A dissociation reaction represents a special type of replacement reaction in which the metal is displaced from the complex by hydrogen ions. It may be represented thus:

$$MP + 2H^+ \rightleftharpoons PH_2 + M^{2+}$$

Many qualitative observations have been made on the stability of metallo-

References p. 72

porphyrins towards acids, and three types of complexes have been distinguished: (*i*) those dissociated in water, *e.g.* Na, K, Li, Pb(II) and Hg(II), (*ii*) those dissociated in dilute mineral acid, *e.g.* Zn, Cd, Fe(II) and Mg, and (*iii*) those dissociated in concentrated acid solutions, *e.g.* Co(II), Ni(II), Cu(II), Ag(II) and Fe(III).

The thermodynamic stability of metalloporphyrin complexes has been correlated also with the position of the absorption band maxima in the ultraviolet, visible and infrared regions of the spectrum. In general for a given porphyrin in a non-coordinating solvent (cyclohexane, carbon tetrachloride) the more a band is displaced towards shorter wavelengths the more stable the metal complex (see section 3*f*). The relative stability of the metalloporphyrin complexes is reflected also in the ratio of the intensities of the α- and β-visible absorption bands, α/β varying from $\gg 1$ for highly stable complexes such as Co, Ni and Cu to $\ll 1$ for weakly stable complexes such as Na, Li, K and Ag.

The order of stability of the metal complexes deduced from spectroscopic data and from replacement and dissociation reactions is given by:

$$\text{Pt(II)} > \text{Pd(II)} > \text{Ni(II)} > \text{Co(II)} > \text{Ag(II)} > \text{Cu(II)} > \text{Fe(II)} > \text{Zn(II)} > \text{Mg(II)} >$$
$$\text{Cd(II)} > \text{Sn(II)} > \text{Li} > \text{Na} > \text{Ba} > \text{K} > \text{Ag}$$

The anomalous spectroscopic behaviour of Pb(II) and Hg(II) complexes makes it impossible to place those ions accurately in the above series, although replacement studies suggest that Zn(II) > Hg(II) > Pb(II) > Li.

This stability order differs from the normal series[32], *i.e.* Pd(II) > Cu(II) > Ni(II) > Pb(II) > Co(II) > Zn(II) > Cd(II) > Fe(II) > Mn(II) > Mg(II) > Ba(II) > Li > Na, in a number of respects. The relatively low stability of the Pb(II), Cd(II) and Ba(II) porphyrin complexes compared with their position in the standard series can be attributed to the large size of these ions preventing them from sitting in the plane of the porphyrin ring.

Despite the lack of quantitative data available, it is clear that the tetrapyrrole nucleus confers an extraordinarily high thermodynamic stability on its metal complexes. Although this may be attributed partly to the quadradentate nature of the ligand, with its consequent statistical advantage over the more common bidentate ligands, much of its stabilizing influence is associated with other factors such as the stereochemistry and aromaticity of the system.

The rigid stereochemical arrangement of the ligand allows some metal ions to be accommodated so that there is a considerable overlap between the bonding orbitals of the metal ion and of all four nitrogen atoms. The near planar configuration of the highly stable nickel aetioporphyrin complex, deduced from X-ray studies[33] (see p. 8) indicates a very small degree of orbital distortion and a similar situation is likely to apply to the stable cobalt and copper complexes. On the other hand large ions such as lead, cadmium, mercury and barium have difficulty in fitting in the plane of the porphyrin ring and in consequence form relatively unstable complexes. In general it would appear that throughout any group in the periodic table the smaller the ion the more stable the complex, thus Zn(II) > Cd(II) and Li > Na > K.

Another factor favouring the high stability of metalloporphyrin complexes is that the metal ion is coordinated to atoms which are mesomerically linked to each other. Thus the metal ion becomes an integral part of the aromatic system by providing alternative electron pathways between the nitrogen atoms. The pronounced influence of substituents in the peripheral (β) positions of the porphyrin ring both on the stability of the complex and on the further coordination of certain metalloporphyrins (see section 5) indicates the high degree of conjugation between the metal ion and the porphyrin nucleus. The more electron-attracting the substituent in the β-positions of the pyrrole rings the less the electron density on the ring nitrogens and the lower the thermodynamic stability of the complex.

(c) Kinetics of metal ion–porphyrin interactions

The incorporation of metal ions into porphyrins is a problem of particular interest to the biochemist concerned with haem and chlorophyll biosynthesis. Synthetic methods for preparing metalloporphyrins have been discussed elsewhere (see Chapter I, p. 24) but from the physico-chemical point of view it is interesting to note that many complexes can be obtained simply by treating a porphyrin and metal salt in an organic solvent. The choice of solvent can, however, be quite critical for optimum reaction conditions. Thus Co^{2+}-ions react rapidly with porphyrins in anhydrous acetone at room temperature, but the addition of as little as 2% water greatly inhibits the reaction. Ni^{2+} on the other hand reacts very slowly in acetone, pyridine or methanol, moderately in ethanol and quite rapidly in propyl or longer-chain alcohols or in phenol. The reactivity of all metal ions is greatly diminished in aqueous solution where only Cu^{2+} and to a lesser extent Zn^{2+} show appreciable incorporation rates. It is of interest that the biologically important ions Co^{2+}, Fe^{2+} and Mg^{2+} react extremely slowly in the aqueous environment.

Recent experiments[34] on metal ion incorporation in aqueous detergent solutions have shown that the incorporation rate of Cu^{2+} into protoporphyrin-dimethyl ester is some 20,000 times faster in the presence of an anionic detergent than in the presence of a cationic or non-ionic detergent. This has been attributed to an electrostatic effect attracting Cu^{2+}-ions to the anionic micelle–water interface. Moreover the reaction rate can be markedly influenced by the presence of certain chelating agents, for example 8-hydroxy-quinoline (oxine). The 1 : 1 copper–oxine complex is catalytically active in incorporating Cu^{2+} from the aqueous detergent solution into the porphyrin nucleus, whereas the 1 : 2 copper–oxine complex is inhibitory to the reaction (see Fig. 9). The coordination effect has been estimated to increase the incorporation rate several hundred-fold not by influencing the activation energy of the reaction but rather by increasing the probability of an effective collision, *i.e.* by affecting the entropy of activation.

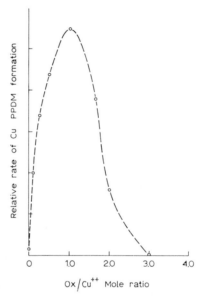

Fig. 9. The effect of 8-hydroxyquinoline (Ox) concentration on the rate of reaction between cupric ions (Cu^{2+}) and protoporphyrindimethyl ester in 2.5% sodium dodecyl sulphate[34] at 20°.

In the particular case of coproporphyrin an almost instantaneous incorporation of ferrous ions has been observed[35] in the presence of sodium amalgam in aqueous solution at pH 7. It has been suggested that this is due to the formation of a porphyrin in which the methene bridges are reduced and the coplanarity of the pyrrole groups destroyed. The rapid incorporation was ascribed to the nitrogen atoms being more accessible to attack by metal ions under these conditions. Such a mechanism does not seem highly probable however, since a metal ion would have to displace four hydrogens, one from each of the pyrrole nitrogens, in order to form the complex. An alternative explanation is that after the addition of 6 hydrogen atoms to the

porphyrin, the hydrogens originally present on the ring nitrogens tauto-
merize to the β-positions of one of the pyrrole rings in order to preserve maximum conjugation throughout the system (see Fig. 10). This leaves the four
nitrogen atoms unsubstituted and exposed to ready attack by metal ions.

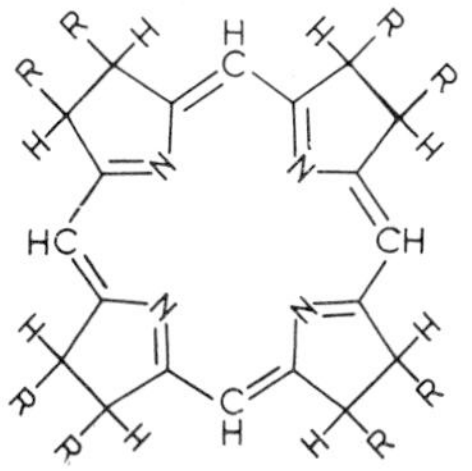

Fig. 10. The hexahydroporphin structure of maximum conjugation.

In the normal case of metal ion incorporation into a porphyrin there are
two possible reaction mechanisms:

(*a*) a dissociation mechanism in which the hydrogen ions are first dissociated from the pyrrole-type nitrogen atoms, followed by reaction between
the metal ion and the porphyrin dianion and

(*b*) a substitution mechanism in which the metal ion first forms a transient
complex with the porphyrin and subsequently displaces the hydrogen ions
from the nitrogen atoms. A clue to the actual mechanism is provided by the
effect of substituents in the β-position on the incorporation rate. According
to the dissociation mechanism electronegative substituents will increase the
reaction rate by increasing the acid strength of the pyrrole-type nitrogens,
whereas according to the substitution mechanism electronegative substituents will depress the reaction rate by reducing the electron availability
on the nitrogen atoms and hence lessen the tendency to form the transient
complex. In fact it is found that the more electronegative the substituent the
less the rate of metal ion incorporation. This supports the substitution mechanism. It seems likely that the transient complex involves coordination
between the metal ion and the electron pair on the pyrrole-type nitrogens.
The orbital associated with this electron pair is directed outwards from the
plane of the porphyrin ring and is therefore capable of interacting with a
metal ion in close proximity to the porphyrin nucleus.

6. Further coordination of metalloporphyrin complexes[2,12,15]

(a) *Introduction*

The ability of many metalloporphyrins to coordinate with other ligands has
long been recognized as forming the primary basis for the attachment be-

tween proteins and the iron and magnesium tetrapyrroles found in nature. Metalloporphyrins in so far as further coordination is concerned fall into three classes:

(*i*) Those such as the iron, cobalt and manganese complexes, which readily add two ligand molecules to form an octahedral structure in which the metal ion is hexacoordinated.

(*ii*) Complexes such as those with magnesium, zinc and cadmium, which readily add one ligand molecule to form a square pyramidal structure in which the metal ion is pentacoordinated.

(*iii*) Those such as the copper and nickel complexes, which show a very low affinity for further coordination and tend to retain the square planar configuration in which the metal ion is tetracoordinated.

Further coordination is generally associated with significant changes in the spectroscopic properties of the molecules. Thus zinc, cadmium and magnesium porphyrin complexes are non-fluorescent in pure non-polar solvents, but fluoresce in polar solvents or in non-polar solvents containing a polar ligand. Moreover, metal complexes capable of further coordination show large spectral shifts to longer wavelengths when the solvent medium is varied from a non-polar to a polar type (see Table VI).

TABLE VI

λ_{max} (SORET) FOR METALLO-PROTOPORPHYRIN COMPLEXES IN VARIOUS SOL-VENTS[36] AT 20°

Porphyrin	Carbon tetrachloride Å	Benzene Å	Dioxane Å	Pyridine Å
Protoporphyrin	4115	4095	4060	4100
Zn(II)	4115	4140	4175	4225
Cd(II)	4140	4240	4225	4325
Cu(II)	4090	4085	4080	4110
Ag(II)	4175	4175	4145	4175
Co(II)	4030	4035	4145	*
Ni(II)	4030	4025	4000	4050

* Very poorly soluble — exceptionally broad band.

(b) Iron porphyrin (haem) complexes

Because of their biological interest it is convenient to treat the iron porphyrin complexes separately from the otherwise similar cobalt and manganese complexes. The specialized biochemical terminology associated with these complexes has already been discussed briefly (see Chapter I, p. 15). Thus a ferrous (ferro-) (Fe^{2+}) porphyrin is termed a haem, a ferric (ferri-) (Fe^{3+})

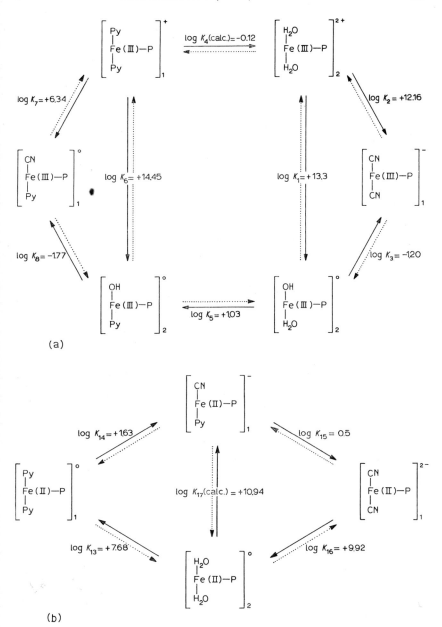

Fig. 11. (a) Ferri-protoporphyrin equilibria with pyridine (Py), cyanide ions (CN⁻) and hydroxide ions (OH⁻) in aqueous solution at 30°. (b) Ferro-protoporphyrin equilibria with pyridine (Py) and cyanide ions (CN⁻) in aqueous solution at room temperature.

porphyrin chloride a haemin chloride, a ferric porphyrin hydroxide a haematin, and the nitrogenous base complexes of the ferro- and ferri-porphyrins, haemochromes and haemichromes respectively. The corresponding complexes of mesoporphyrin for example, would be mesohaem, mesohaemin chloride and mesohaematin, the dipyridine complexes of mesohaem and mesohaemin chloride being termed the pyridine mesohaemochrome and the pyridine mesohaemichrome respectively. It is proposed to represent haemo(i)chrome structures thus:

$$\begin{pmatrix} \begin{array}{c} L_1 \\ | \\ Fe(II) \\ | \\ L_2 \end{array} \end{pmatrix}^p_q \qquad \begin{pmatrix} \begin{array}{c} L_1 \\ | \\ Fe(III) \\ | \\ L_2 \end{array} \end{pmatrix}^p_q$$

Haemochrome   Haemichrome

Where L_1 and L_2 refer to the ligands, p to the net charge on the complex and q to the degree of polymerization ($q = 1$ for a monomer, $q = 2$ for a dimer).

In general, the coordination of ferro- and ferri-porphyrins has been studied in aqueous alkali, where the porphyrin is maintained in solution by means of its ionized carboxylic acid groups. At best this restricts measurements to the alkaline region and even under these conditions it has been shown that neither ferro- nor ferri-porphyrins are molecularly dispersed in the solution. Rather they form strongly associated dimeric units which are loosely bound together as colloidal aggregates[2]. This greatly complicates quantitative studies of ligand binding because the dimerization energy is unknown. The complication may be avoided by the use of aqueous detergent systems in which all the species appear to be monomeric.

The ligands studied most extensively comprise pyridine, the classical haemochrome ligand, cyanide ions and hydroxide ions[2]. Fig. 11 summarizes the quantitative data available on the interaction of these three ligands with ferro- and ferri-protoporphyrin in aqueous alkaline solution.

A large number of other haemochrome-forming ligands have also been studied. These include simple aliphatic amines, isocyanides, peptides, amino acids, amino acid esters and various substituted pyridines and imidazoles, as well as gaseous ligands such as carbon monoxide and oxygen.

The stability of the iron porphyrin-ligand complex is affected by a number of factors:

(i) The electronegativity of the porphyrin

The greater the electron-attracting power of the porphyrin substituent groups the more stable the haemo(i)chrome complex, although the metal complex itself is less stable (see section 4b). This is due to the electron-at-tracting substituent inducing a partial electron deficiency both on the nitro-gen atoms and on the central iron atom, so that the nitrogen atoms have less tendency to donate electrons to the metal ion (hence a less stable metal complex) but the metal ion has a greater tendency to accept electrons from a ligand donor atom (hence a more stable haemo(i)chrome complex).

Thus for the haemin–haematin reaction in 2.5% CTAB, $i.e.$:

$$
\left(
\begin{array}{c}
H_2O \\
| \\
Fe(III) \\
| \\
H_2O
\end{array}
\right)^{+}_{1}
\quad \rightleftharpoons \quad
\left(
\begin{array}{c}
OH \\
| \\
Fe(III) \\
| \\
H_2O
\end{array}
\right)^{0}_{1}
+ H^{+}
$$

the pH for 50% transformation of mesohaemin is 6.6 whilst for protohaemin it is 5.9. Similarly in 2.5% CTAB the pyridine protohaemochrome is half-formed at a concentration of $2 \cdot 10^{-3}$ M pyridine whilst half-formation of the corresponding mesohaemochrome requires $5 \cdot 10^{-3}$ M pyridine[36].

(ii) The chemical nature of the coordinating atom

The order of stability of the haemochrome-like complexes appears to be: carbon-donor ligands ($e.g.$ cyanide) > nitrogen-donor ligands ($e.g.$ pyridine) > oxygen-donor ligands ($e.g.$ water).

(iii) Charge neutralization

The stability of the complex is increased if charge neutralization is in-volved in the reaction, $i.e.$ negatively charged ligands form more stable com-plexes with the positively charged haemins than with the neutral haems.

(iv) Ligand basicity

There is little correlation between ligand basicity and haemochrome stability. It can be predicted that the stronger the base the more stable the complex, but as Table VII shows this does not hold even for a closely related series of substituted pyridine mesohaemochromes, presumably due to the interplay of other factors (see particularly (v), (vi) and (vii) below).

(v) Back double bonding capacity of the ligand

The greater the capacity of a ligand to accept electrons back from the 3d orbitals of the metal ion ($i.e.$ to back double bond) the greater the stability of the complex. In order to back double bond the ligand must have vacant π

TABLE VII

LIGAND EFFECTS ON THE STABILITY OF MESOHAEMOCHROMES[36] AT 20°

Ligand (L)	pKs* (2.5% CTAB)	pKa (H₂O)
Pyridine	4.6	5.2
2-Methylpyridine	< 1	6.1
3-Methylpyridine	5.25	5.5
4-Methylpyridine	5.5	6.1
2-Aminopyridine	< 1	6.7
3-Aminopyridine	4.2	6.0
4-Aminopyridine	4.0	9.2
3-Cyanopyridine	5.1	—
2,6-Dimethylpyridine	2.8	7.0

* $pKs = -2 \log [L50\%]$, where $[L50\%]$ is the ligand concentration for half haemo-chrome formation.

orbitals in which to accept metal electrons, *i.e.* the ligand must be unsaturated. Pyridine, cyanide, azide, carbon monoxide and oxygen are examples of back double bonding, haemochrome-forming ligands.

(vi) Homopolar charge resonance

Certain ligands (such as imidazole and its derivatives and 4-aminopyridine), in which a positive charge can resonate between two nitrogen atoms, show an unusually high affinity for ferri-porphyrins and a relatively low affinity for ferro-porphyrins as judged from their basicity. Haemichrome stabilization can be attributed to the resonance of the excess positive charge associated with the ferric ion between the nitrogen atoms on the ligand (see Fig. 12). Because of the dipolar character of the ligands, the coordinating

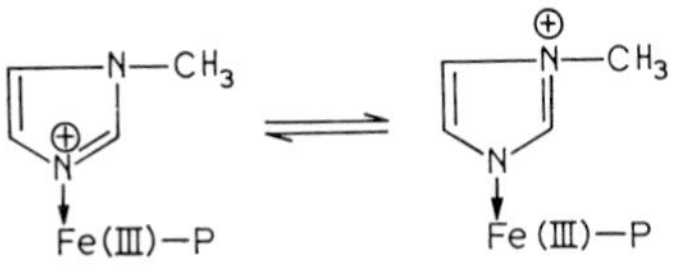

Fig. 12. Homopolar charge resonance forms in an imidazole-ferriporphyrin complex.

nitrogen atom will tend to acquire a partial negative charge which will inhibit back-double bonding; this could account for the relatively low haemochrome stability of, for example, 4-aminopyridine (see Table VII).

(vii) Ligand stereochemistry

Steric factors are important in determining haemo(i)chrome stability. Thus imidazoles substituted in the 2 or 4,5 positions[2], or pyridines substituted in position 2 have a much lower affinity for both ferri- and ferro-porphyrins than other isomers. Surprisingly, 2,6-dimethylpyridine forms a more stable haemochrome than the 2-methyl derivative, although its stability is still much less than that of the pyridine haemochrome itself (see Table VII).

(viii) Mixed complexes

In general, mixed complexes, i.e. complexes with two different ligands such as cyanide–pyridine, hydroxide–pyridine or carbon monoxide–pyridine are more stable, in both the ferrous and the ferric state, than the corresponding pure complexes.

(c) Oxy-haem complexes

It is relatively simple to obtain solutions of carbon monoxide-haem complexes[37] which are analogous to carboxyhaemoglobin, but extremely difficult to obtain the corresponding oxygen-haem complexes analogous to oxy-haemoglobin since in the presence of oxygen the iron is oxidized from the ferrous to the ferric state. Recently however a synthetic haem complex has been reported[38] which reacts reversibly with oxygen and carbon monoxide even in the presence of water. This complex, formed by dispersing a carbon monoxide-1-(2-phenylethyl)-imidazole haemochrome in a polystyrene matrix, is of interest in that it appears to confirm a suggestion that the unusual stability of oxyhaemoglobin is due to the haem group being embedded in a region of low dielectric constant.

(d) Manganese and cobalt porphyrin complexes

Manganese and cobalt porphyrin complexes behave like the iron porphyrins

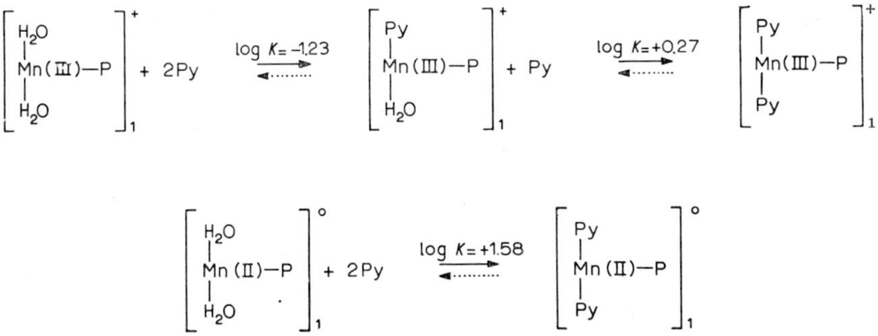

Fig. 13. Equilibrium constants for the Mn(II) and Mn(III) mesoporphyrin–pyridine reaction in aqueous solution at room temperature.

References p. 72

in undergoing oxidation–reduction reactions and in coordinating with two ligand molecules to form octahedral complexes.

Their relative affinity for further coordination, however, is probably less than that of the iron porphyrins, since whilst the latter are invariably octahedral complexes the former may be either square planar or octahedral according to the solvent medium.

The only quantitative data available refer to the Mn(II) and Mn(III)-mesoporphyrin–pyridine reaction in aqueous solution[2]. The reaction scheme and equilibrium constants are set out in Fig. 13. It is clear that, as in the iron series, pyridine has a greater affinity for the manganese porphyrin complex in which the metal ion has the lower valency.

(e) Zinc, cadmium and magnesium porphyrin complexes

Mention has already been made of the affinity of the zinc, cadmium and magnesium porphyrin complexes for further ligands and of the accompanying spectroscopic changes (see sections 3a and 3d). The effect is observed with both metalloporphins and metallochlorins, and Table VIII summarizes sta-

TABLE VIII

STABILITY CONSTANT VALUES FOR CHLOROPHYLL a-LIGAND COMPLEXES IN BENZENE[28,39]

Ligand	log K_s*
Dimethylaniline	+1.02
Phenol	+1.19
Aniline	+1.66
Benzyl alcohol	+3.46
Octyl alcohol	+3.66
Quinoline	+4.12
Benzylamine	+4.43
Water	+4.47
n-Heptylamine	+5.19

* Calculated on the assumption that 1 ligand molecule (L) combines with 1 chlorophyll molecule (MP).
i.e.

$$K_s = \left(\begin{matrix} L \\ | \\ MP \end{matrix} \right) / (MP)(L)$$

bility values for the further coordination of chlorophyll a (magnesium phaeophytin a) with different ligands in benzene solution. It would appear that the electronegativity of the coordinating atom is the important factor in determining stability.

The affinities of different metal complexes of tetraphenyl-porphin and

-chlorin for further coordination with pyridine in benzene solution are summarized in Table IX. It will be noted that whereas the Zn, Cd and Mg complexes are half-coordinated at pyridine concentrations of the order of $3 \cdot 10^{-4}$ M pyridine, and the Hg complex at about 10^{-1} M pyridine, the Cu and Ni complexes would be less than 50% coordinated even in pure pyridine.

TABLE IX

THE STABILITY OF SOME PYRIDINATE COMPLEXES OF METALLOTETRAPHENYL PORPHINS AND CHLORINS[40]

Porphyrin	Metal	log K_s*
Tetraphenylporphin	Mg(II)	+3.3
	Zn(II)	+3.57
	Cd(II)	+3.43
	Hg(II)	+1.08
	Cu(II)	—1.3
	Ni(II)	—1.3
Tetraphenylchlorin	Mg(II)	+3.6
	Zn(II)	+3.72

* K_s is defined in Table VIII.

7. Redox equilibria[2,12]

Certain metalloporphyrins, notably the iron, cobalt and manganese complexes, readily undergo reversible oxidation–reduction (redox) reactions. Redox equilibria play an important role in a number of biochemical processes and are of particular importance in the haem-containing enzymes (the cytochromes) whose function it is to catalyse electron transfer from a substrate to the terminal acceptor, oxygen.

The oxidation–reduction potential (E) for the thermodynamically reversible reaction

$$M^{3+} + e \rightleftharpoons M^{2+}$$

is given by

$$E = E_0 + \frac{RT}{F} \log \frac{[M^{3+}]}{[M^{2+}]}$$

where E_0 is the standard oxidation–reduction potential and is normally expressed with reference to the standard hydrogen electrode, [X] is the activity of species X, R is the universal gas constant, T is the absolute temperature and F is the Faraday constant.

The standard oxidation–reduction potential (E_0) is a measure of the relative stability of the reduced and oxidized states. According to the standard

British convention the more stable the reduced state the more positive the E_0 value. On this scale the E_0 value for the Fe^{2+}/Fe^{3+} couple in aqueous solution is $+77$ mV.

The E_0 values for the iron, cobalt and manganese porphyrin complexes are considerably less than the corresponding metal ion couples in water (see Table X), indicating that in each case the porphyrin has stabilized the oxidized state. This effect can be predicted from simple electrostatic considerations since in general the greater the charge density on the metal ion the more stable the complex. That the effect is more pronounced with the cobalt and manganese porphyrins than with the iron porphyrins can probably be attributed to the stabilizing influence of particular electronic configurations. For example the isoelectronic Co^{3+} and Fe^{2+} ions each with 6 electrons in the 3d shell require just 12 electrons to reach the inert gas configuration, and thus tend to form low-spin octahedral complexes with strong-field ligands, each of the six coordinating atoms donating two electrons to the metal orbitals (d^2sp^3 complexes in valence bond terminology). Such considerations tend to favour the Co^{3+} over the Co^{2+} and the Fe^{2+} over the Fe^{3+} porphyrin species, and in comparing such a strong-field (porphyrin) complex with a weak-field (aqua) complex it follows that the electrostatic effect, which invariably favours the higher valency state, will be enhanced in the case of cobalt and reduced in the case of iron as is found to be the case (see Table X).

TABLE X

REDOX POTENTIALS OF SOME AQUEOUS METAL ION COUPLES AND OF THE CORRESPONDING DIPYRIDINE METALLOMESOPORPHYRIN COMPLEXES[7] AT 25°

| Metal | E_0 (mV) | | ΔE_0 (mV) |
	Aqua complex	Dipyridine metallomesoporphyrin complex	
Mn	$+151$	-387	538
Fe	$+ 77$	$- 63$	140
Co	$+184$	-265	449

The effect of substituents in the porphyrin nucleus on the redox potential follows the simple rule that the more electron-attracting the substituent the more stabilized is the reduced form, i.e., the more positive the E_0 value. This is illustrated in Table XI for the dicyanide derivatives of a series of substituted deutero-haems.

The influence on the redox potential of ligands in the 5th and 6th coordination positions can be predicted with less certainty. It is known that an anionic ligand such as a cyanide ion favours the higher valency state more

TABLE XI

REDOX POTENTIALS OF DICYANIDE DERIVATIVES OF SUBSTITUTED DEUTERO-HAEMS[7]

| Haem | Substituents* in position | | E_0 (mV) |
	2	4	
Coprohaem	—CH₂CH₂COOH	—CH₂CH₂COOH	—247
Mesohaem	—C₂H₅	—C₂H₅	—229
Haematohaem	—CHOH—CH₃	—CHOH—CH₃	—200
Protohaem	—CH=CH₂	—CH=CH₂	—183
Monoformyldeuterohaem	—CHO	—H	—113

* All other positions are identically substituted.

than a neutral ligand such as pyridine, an effect which can be accounted for electrostatically. Amongst neutral ligands with the same donor atom no simple correlations can be made since a number of factors such as ligand basicity, back double bonding and homopolar charge resonance are involved. In general, however, the ferric state will be stabilized (*i.e.* E_0 lowered) the greater the basicity, the greater the homopolar charge resonance and the less the back double bonding capacity of the ligand.

8. The metal–porphyrin bond[13,14]

(a) Introduction

Metal ligand bonds may be classified in one of a number of ways according to the theoretical or experimental basis involved. Thus for example they may be described as ionic or covalent "high" or "low" spin, "outer" or "inner" d bonded (valence bond terminology) "weak" or "strong" field type (ligand field terminology). Such classifications though conceptionally different are essentially equivalent in practice thus:

Ionic = high-spin type = "outer" d bonded = weak-field type

and

Covalent = low-spin type = "inner" d bonded = strong-field type

For purely descriptive purposes it is convenient to retain the ionic–covalent classification though in discussing the iron porphyrins (below) the experimentally based high-spin–low-spin classification has been used.

The covalent type metalloporphyrins include the Pt(II), Pd(II), Ni(II), Co(II), Cu(II) and Ag(II) complexes. Such complexes are characterized by a high thermodynamic stability, and have α/β intensity ratios $\gg 1$. Magnetic moment evidence in benzene indicates that the Ni(II) complex has no unpaired electrons and the Co(II) complex one unpaired electron[41].

The ionic metalloporphyrins include the alkali, alkaline earth, Ag(I), Mg(II), Sn(II), Pb(II) and Hg(II) complexes. These have a low thermodynamic stability, and, like the dicationic salt, have α/β band ratios $\ll 1$. In general the ionic type complexes are the more kinetically labile.

The Zn(II) and Cd(II) complexes are intermediate in type. They are dissociated in dilute mineral acid, and have α/β intensity ratios of approximately unity.

(b) Haem complexes

It is not possible to classify the octahedral iron porphyrin complexes by the same criteria which have been applied to other square planar metalloporphyrins although it may be noted that whereas the Fe(II) complexes are dissociated in dilute mineral acid, the Fe(III) complexes are stable except in concentrated sulphuric acid. The α/β intensity ratio would place the Fe(II) complex as more covalent than the Zn(II) complex but less covalent than the Cu(II) or Ag(II) complex.

Conventionally iron complexes can be typed by their magnetic moment which is related to the number of unpaired electrons associated with the metal ion. Thus with the ferri-complexes there is the possibility of 5, 3 or 1 unpaired electrons in the 3d shell of the iron atom and with the Fe(II) porphyrins the possibility of 4, 2 or 0 unpaired electrons (see Fig. 14). Although recently it has been shown[42] that in a regular octahedral complex the Fe^{2+} ion can have either 0 or 4 but not 2 unpaired spins and the Fe^{3+} ion either 1 or 5 but not 3 unpaired spins, magnetic moment measurements indicate that iron porphyrin-ligand complexes, like other iron complexes, can

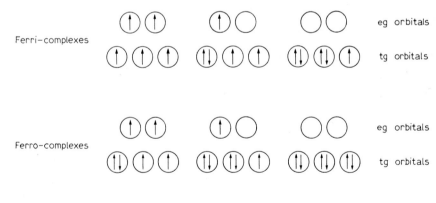

Fig. 14. Electronic configurations in the 3d shell of octahedral ferro- and ferri-complexes of high-, low- and intermediate-spin type.

be classified as of high-spin, low-spin or intermediate-spin type. It must be concluded therefore either that such complexes are greatly distorted from a regular octahedral structure or that they are a mixture of a high- and low-spin form. This latter could arise either through a thermal equilibrium between distinct chemical complexes of different spin type or by resonance between different electronic states in the one chemical complex. In the case of a number of ferri-haemoprotein hydroxides the evidence points to a thermal mixture of a high- and low-spin component. Table XII shows the

TABLE XII

THE % LOW-SPIN COMPONENT IN VARIOUS FERRI-HAEMOPROTEIN LIGAND COMPLEXES[13]

Haemoprotein	Ligand	% Low-spin form
Ferrileghaemoglobin	Hydroxide	100
Ferrihaemoglobin	Hydroxide	50
Ferrimyoglobin	Hydroxide	30
Ferrimyoglobin	Cyanide	0
Ferrimyoglobin	Fluoride	100

TABLE XIII

SORET ABSORPTION MAXIMA FOR FERRO- AND FERRI-HAEMOPROTEINS WITH DIFFERENT LIGANDS[14]

Haemoprotein	Ferro-coordinating ligand			Ferri-coordinating ligand		
	Water	Carbon monoxide	Pyridine	Water	Hydroxide	Cyanide
Peroxidase	438	425	420	404	418	425
Myoglobin	435	424	420	405	414	425
Haemoglobin	430	418	420	404	409	419
Cytochrome b*	425	425	425	416	416	416
Cytochrome c*	415	415	415	410	410	410
Bond type	Ionic → Covalent			Ionic → Covalent		

* Covalent under all conditions.

calculated % of high- and low-spin forms for some ferri-haemoprotein ligand complexes at room temperature. It will be noted that the resultant spin type depends both on the nature of the porphyrin and of the extra ligand groups present. The high- and low-spin type complexes are associated with characteristic spectra as was shown in Fig. 6.

The spectroscopic changes which occur when one ligand is replaced by another can be correlated with changes in spin type. This is particularly so in the Soret region where, as the complex becomes more covalent, ferro absorption maxima are displaced to shorter wavelengths and ferri absorption maxima to longer wavelengths (see Table XIII).

9. Correlations of structure and physico-chemical behaviour[15]

Various examples of structural influences on the physico-chemical behaviour of the porphyrins will be found throughout the preceding sections and it is proposed to summarize here some of the more general correlations.

(a) Substituent effects

Increasing electron-attracting character of substituents in the β-positions of the porphyrin nucleus is associated with: (i) A shift to the red of the Soret and visible absorption bands and of the visible fluorescence band (where present). This effect is observed with free porphyrins, their esters, salts and metal complexes and haemochromes. (ii) A weaker basicity of the imino type (—N=) nitrogens and presumably an enhanced acidity of the pyrrole type (—NH—) nitrogens. (iii) A slower rate of metal ion incorporation. (iv) A thermodynamically less stable metalloporphyrin complex. (v) An enhanced affinity for further coordination of the Co, Mn, Fe, Zn, Cd and Mg porphyrin complexes with other ligands. (vi) A stabilization of the lower valency species in the transition metal (Co, Mn, Fe) complexes, i.e. an increase in the positive value of $E°$.

(b) Metal ion effects

The order of decreasing covalent character of the metal–porphyrin bond in the square planar metal porphyrin complexes would appear to be:

$$Pt(II) > Pd(II) > Ni(II) > Co(II) > Ag(II) > Cu(II) > Zn(II) > Mg(II) > Cd(II) > Sn(II) > Li > Na > Ba > K > Ag.$$

This order is associated with:

(i) A shift in the Soret and visible absorption bands to the red; (ii) An increase in the α/β band intensity ratio, and (iii) A decrease in the thermodynamic stability of the metal porphyrin complex.

(c) Extra ligand effects

The greater the electron-donating capacity of the ligand the greater the stability of the Zn, Cd, and Mg porphyrin ligand complexes. In the transition metal (Mn, Fe, Co) porphyrin complexes thermodynamic stability is associated both with the electron-donating and back double bonding capacity of the ligand as well as with steric factors. Thus in the case of the haemochromes the stronger the electron-donating and back double bonding capacity of the ligand the greater the stability of both the oxidized and reduced metal ion species. Since the former is the more stabilized, $E°$ becomes more negative. The nature of the extra ligands may also influence the bond type in the transition metal–porphyrin complexes — saturated ligands favouring high-spin complexes and unsaturated ligands favouring low-spin complexes.

REFERENCES

1 H. FISCHER AND H. ORTH, *Die Chemie des Pyrrols*, Vol. II, part I, Leipzig Akad. Verlagsges., 1937; H. FISCHER AND A. STERN, *Die Chemie des Pyrrols*, Vol. II, part II, Leipzig Akad. Verlagsges., 1940.

2 W. M. CLARK et al., *J. Biol. Chem.*, 135 (1940) 543; 171 (1947) 143; 198 (1952) 33; 205 (1953) 617.

3 E. RABINOWITCH, *Revs. Modern Phys.*, 16 (1944) 226.

4 S. GRANICK AND H. GILDER, *Advances in Enzymol.*, 7 (1947) 305.

5 R. LEMBERG AND J. W. LEGGE, *Hematin Compounds and Bile Pigments*, Interscience, New York, 1949.

6 R. LEMBERG AND J. W. LEGGE, *Ann. Rev. Biochem.*, 19 (1950) 431.

7 A. E. MARTELL AND M. CALVIN, *The Chemistry of the Metal Chelate Compounds*, Prentice Hall, New York, 1953, p. 192.

8 R. LEMBERG, *Fortschr. Chem. org. Naturstoffe*, 11 (1954) 300.

9 R. J. P. WILLIAMS, *Chem. Revs.*, 56 (1956) 299.

10 J. R. PLATT, *Radiation Biology*, Vol. III, McGraw-Hill, New York, 1956.

11 S. F. MASON, *J. Chem. Soc.*, (1958) 976.

12 J. E. FALK AND D. D. PERRIN in J. E. FALK, R. LEMBERG AND R. K. MORTON (Eds.), *Haematin Enzymes*, Pergamon, London, 1961.

13 P. GEORGE, in J. E. FALK, R. LEMBERG AND R. K. MORTON (Eds.), *Haematin Enzymes*, Pergamon, London, 1961.

14 R. J. P. WILLIAMS, in J. E. FALK, R. LEMBERG AND R. K. MORTON (Eds.), *Haematin Enzymes*, Pergamon, London, 1961.

15 J. N. PHILLIPS, *Revs. Pure Appl. Chem.*, 10 (1960) 35.

16 W. K. McEWEN, *J. Am. Chem. Soc.*, 58 (1936) 1124.

17 J. B. CONANT, B. F. CHOW AND E. M. DIETZ, *J. Am. Chem. Soc.*, 56 (1934) 2185.

18 S. ARONOFF, *J. Phys. Chem.*, 62 (1958) 428.

19 B. DEMPSEY, M. B. LOWE AND J. N. PHILLIPS in J. E. FALK, R. LEMBERG AND R. K. MORTON, *Haematin Enzymes*, Pergamon, London, 1961.

20 R. LEMBERG AND J. E. FALK, *Biochem. J.*, 49 (1951) 674.

21 A. NEUBERGER AND J. J. SCOTT, *Proc. Roy. Soc. (London)*, A, 213 (1952) 307.

22 J. N. PHILLIPS, *Current Trends in Heterocyclic Chemistry*, Butterworths, London, 1958, p. 30.

23 S. GRANICK AND L. BOGORAD, *J. Biol. Chem.*, 202 (1953) 781.

24 A. E. ALEXANDER, *J. Chem. Soc.*, (1937) 1813.

25 B. DEMPSEY AND J. N. PHILLIPS, Unpublished observations.

26 H. KUHN, *Helv. Chim. Acta*, 42 (1959) 363.

27 M. GOUTERMAN, *J. Chem. Phys.*, 30 (1959) 1139.

28 R. LIVINGSTONE AND S. WEIL, *Nature*, 170 (1952) 750.

29 C. W. CRAVEN, K. R. REISSMAN AND H. I. CHINN, *Anal. Chem.*, 24 (1952) 1214.

30 J. E. FALK AND J. B. WILLIS, *Australian J. Sci. Research*, 4 (1951) 579.

31 D. W. THOMAS AND A. E. MARTELL, *Arch. Biochem. Biophys.*, 76 (1958) 286.

32 D. P. MELLOR AND L. E. MALEY, *Nature*, 159 (1947) 370; 161 (1948) 436.

33 M. B. CRUTE, *Acta Cryst.*, 12 (1959) 24.

34 M. B. LOWE AND J. N. PHILLIPS, *Nature*, 190 (1961) 262.

35 J. ORLANDO, Dissertation, Univ. of California, Berkeley, 1958.

36 J. N. PHILLIPS, Unpublished observations.

37 J. KEILIN, *Biochem. J.*, 45 (1949) 440.

38 J. H. WANG, *J. Am. Chem. Soc.*, 80 (1959) 3168.

39 R. LIVINGSTONE, et al., *J. Am. Chem. Soc.*, 71 (1949) 1542.

40 J. R. MILLER AND G. D. DOROUGH, *J. Am. Chem. Soc.*, 74 (1952) 3977.

41 J. E. FALK AND R. S. NYHOLM, *Current Trends in Heterocyclic Chemistry*, Butterworths, London, 1958, p. 130.

42 J. S. GRIFFITH, *Proc. Roy. Soc. (London) A*, 235 (1956) 23.

Chapter III

Chlorophyll

ROBERT HILL

Department of Biochemistry, University of Cambridge (Great Britain)

1. Chlorophyll *a* and *b*

(a) General

The chlorophylls *a* and *b* are regarded now as being completely defined in the chemical sense. A total synthesis of chlorophyll *a* has now become possible; the methods used are of great interest from a chemical standpoint and are described by Woodward *et al.*[1] and by Strell *et al.*[2]. The study of the green leaf pigment in relation to the process of photosynthesis in plants has lead to an extremely wide range of investigations; these are dealt with in a

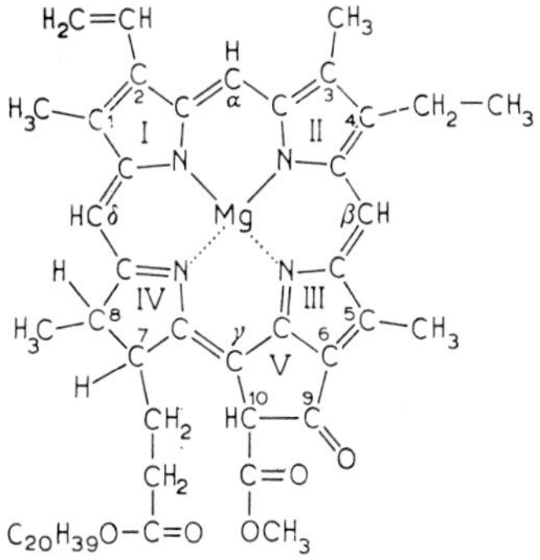

(i)

Chlorophyll a

$C_{55}H_{72}O_5N_4Mg$

masterly fashion by Rabinowitch[3]. Willstätter and Stoll[4] had made detailed chemical studies of the degradation products of chlorophyll and haemin; this work emphasised the close relationship between the two pigments. The

References p. 96

final elucidation of the structures of both by Fischer *et al.*[5,6] resulted from his extensive study of the porphyrins and their synthesis.

Chlorophyll (i) may be considered to be derived from an unsubstituted parent tetrapyrrolic ring structure. This macrocyclic compound is termed "chlorin" and corresponds to a dihydro "porphin". A synthetic method of preparation of these two parent substances is described by Krol[7]. The four pyrrole rings are numbered I to IV, the four methene carbon bridges are referred to by Greek letters and the eight positions of the macrocyclic structure are numbered in the usual way. In chlorophyll the isocyclic ring V is present and the two additional carbon atoms concerned are numbered 9 and 10.

Chlorophyll *b* is represented by the structure given for chlorophyll *a* with the exception of position 3 where $-CH_3$ has to be replaced by $-CHO$. The studies concerning the physiological function of chlorophyll are mainly connected with the photochemical properties. This also includes similar studies regarding the porphyrins because protochlorophyll (ii) which belongs

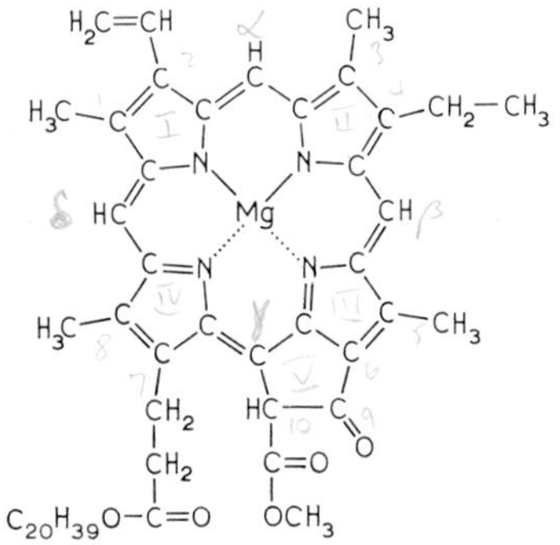

(ii)

Protochlorophyll

$C_{55}H_{70}O_5N_4Mg$

to the class of porphyrin-metal compounds is found as a precursor of chlorophyll *a* in green plants (including *Euglena*). Chlorophyll *a* is derived from protochlorophyll by the addition of two hydrogen atoms at positions 7 and 8. Johns and Linstead[8] have shown these hydrogen atoms to be in the *trans*-orientation. This reduction of the pyrrole residue IV accounts for the main difference in light absorption between the porphin and the chlorin series of compounds. The porphyrins with ring V are termed phaeoporphyrins. In the blood pigment haemin the ring V is absent, there being a three-carbon chain in position 6 and a simple methene bridge C_γ. Chlorophyll and the compounds derived from it which have preserved the asymmetric configuration at

positions 7 and 8 show optical activity (Stoll and Wiedermann[9]). Protochlorophyll and porphyrins in general are not optically active. The grouping
$C_{20}H_{39}O$ refers to the alcohol phytol (iii) in the form of the carboxylic ester.
The carboxyl at C-10 is esterified with methanol. Thus chlorophyll, as distinct
from haem, is a neutral substance.

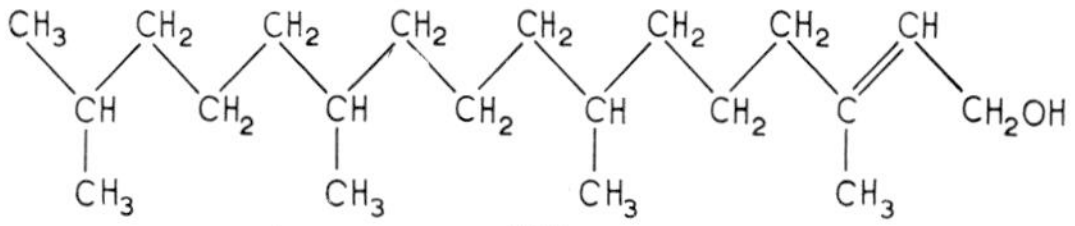

(iii)
Phytol
$C_{20}H_{39}OH$

For the isolation of chlorophyll, involving extraction from leaves, a
variety of conditions determine the choice of suitable plant material. These
are related both to the chemical properties of chlorophyll and to the biochemical differences inherent in plant species. For the accurate determination of the quantity of chlorophyll in a plant material these considerations
are important.

(b) Phaeophytin a and b

If the cell sap of a plant has a low pH there is the possibility that during the
extraction of the chlorophyll the magnesium atom will be removed. The
resulting compounds, analogous to the free porphyrins, are termed phaeophytins, because of their brownish-green colour. The reaction

$$\text{Chlorophyll} + 2H^+ \rightarrow \text{phaeophytin} + Mg^{2+}$$

is irreversible in aqueous media but only occurs rapidly in the presence of
an organic solvent at about pH 3.0 at ordinary temperatures. In less acid
solutions the removal of the magnesium is accelerated by exposure to light.
In the presence of water, chlorophyll has to be regarded as being metastable
with reference to the magnesium. With cupric ions, on the other hand,
the situation is reversed, a stable green Cu-phaeophytin being formed,
from which it is virtually impossible to remove the metal. The magnesium
can be introduced into phaeophytin to give chlorophyll under anhydrous
conditions using a modified Grignard reagent or magnesium methoxide with
magnesium in the presence of pyridine. The reaction requires about one hour
at 90°.

References p. 96

(c) Chlorophyllides a and b

The green plants contain an enzyme, chlorophyllase, a type of esterase (Willstätter and Stoll[4]). Very great differences are shown in the activity due to this enzyme when different plant species are compared. When leaves are treated with acetone containing 20% water, to dissolve the chlorophylls, the enzyme will catalyse the following reaction:

$$\text{Chlorophyll} + H_2O \rightleftharpoons \text{chlorophyllide} + \text{phytol}$$

The methyl ester group on C-10 does not appear to be attacked. The whole of the enzymic activity is removed when the solution of chlorophyll obtained from the leaves is filtered from the leaf residue. The enzyme is not extracted from the leaf residue by water or by aqueous organic solvents. When alcohol containing water is used instead of acetone for extraction of the leaf the alcohol replaces the phytol group in the presence of chlorophyllase:

$$\text{Chlorophyll} + C_2H_5OH \rightleftharpoons \text{ethyl chlorophyllide} + \text{phytol}$$

These reactions are reversible and have been used to accomplish the partial synthesis of chlorophyll involving chlorophyllide. The chlorophyllides are readily crystallisable and have long been known in this form; crystals of chlorophyllide often appear in specimens of plants preserved in 70% ethanol.

Phaeophorbides

The chlorophyllides under acid conditions readily lose the magnesium and the products are termed phaeophorbides. They are also derived from phaeophytin by the loss of phytol. Both the free chlorophyllides and phaeophorbides have a free carboxyl group. They can be extracted from their solutions in ethyl ether by 0.01 N sodium hydroxide. This property gives a method of measuring the activity of a chlorophyllase preparation when aqueous acetone is used as a solvent for the chlorophyll. The pigments are passed into ether, washed free of acetone and the ether layer extracted with the dilute alkali. Unaltered chlorophyll will remain in the ether layer.

(d) Allomerised chlorophyll

When chlorophyll, dissolved in inorganic solvents containing oxygen, is allowed to stand in the dark irreversible changes occur. The process was called allomerisation by Willstätter because the properties of the chlorophyll were altered while the appearance and chemical composition seemed to undergo no change. Subsequently it was found that allomerisation was due to a slow process of oxidation involving the removal of the H at C-10 and its replacement by —OH or by an alkyloxy group when alcohols were used as solvents. The reactivity of the —H at C-10 is increased on the alkaline side of neutrality, indicating the dependence on enol formation at C-9. The presence of the magnesium in the molecule seems to favour formation of the enol; phaeophytin is less susceptible to allomerisation.

(e) Chlorins and the phase test

The phase test depends on the colour reaction which occurs when chlorophyll dissolved in ether is shaken with methyl-alcoholic potassium hydroxide. The colour changes at once to a bright yellow with chlorophyll a, to a carmine red with chlorophyll b or to a bright yellowish brown with the natural mixture of the two chlorophylls. After a few moments the green colour begins to reappear and very soon the whole of the green colour is in the lower layer, leaving the ether colourless. With a crude extract of the leaf pigments the ethereal layer is coloured permanently yellow owing to the carotenoid pigments which are unattacked by the alkali. The phase test is positive with phaeophytin, chlorophyllides and phaeophorbides and is completely negative with allomerised chlorophylls and their derivatives. The change in colour depends on the presence of the mobile H atom at C-10, giving the possibility of forming a double bond conjugated with those in the pyrrolic rings. When the phase test is carried out in complete absence of oxygen, ring V is opened and the product is chlorin e_6 which is a tricarboxylic acid. There are now two hydrogen atoms at C-10 and the tri-esters of chlorin e_6 (iv) also give the phase test during their saponification. In the presence of

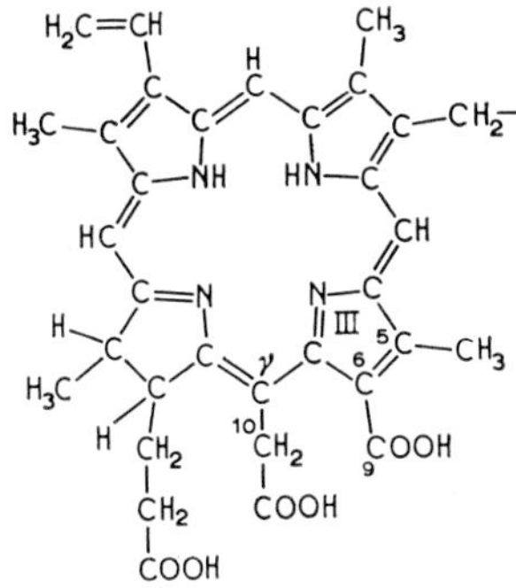

(iv)

Chlorin e_6

oxygen unstable chlorins are formed owing to oxidation at C-10; these, when taken into ether, give a series of compounds called purpurins. The products of the phase test from chlorophyll b are called rhodins because of the colour of their ethereal solutions. During the phase test with chlorophyll the magnesium is not removed so that the magnesium chlorins result; these are sometimes referred to as chlorophyllins. The chemistry of the phase test has recently been examined in detail by Holt[10].

(f) Phyllo- and pyrro-porphyrins

When the chlorophyllides or phaeophorbides are subjected to high temperatures in the presence of alkali and organic solvents the side chains become modified and ring V is destroyed while the tetrapyrrolic nucleus remains intact. Chlorophyll *a* will yield phylloporphyrin (v) in this way and allo-

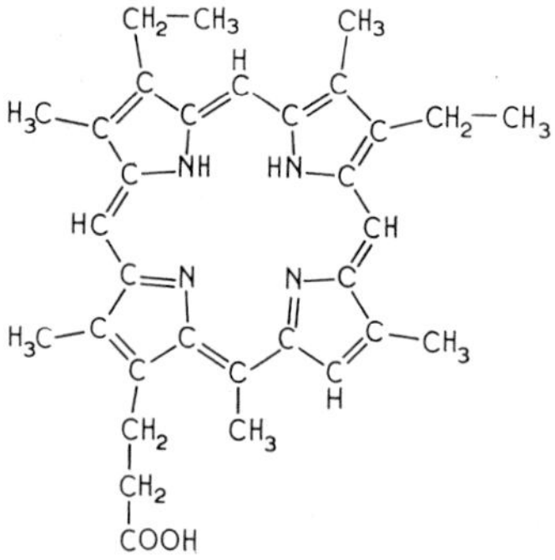

(v)

Phylloporphyrin

merised chlorophyll *a* yields pyrroporphyrin (vi). These compounds were isolated by Willstätter. While phylloporphyrin has C-10 at the γ-position,

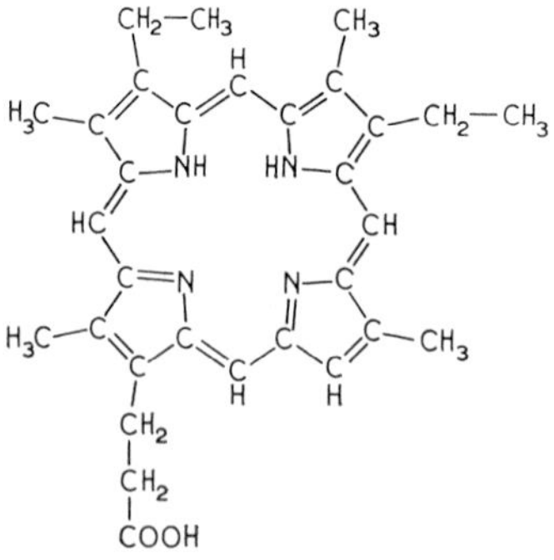

(vi)

Pyrroporphyrin

this position is unsubstituted in pyrroporphyrin. Fischer showed that replacement of the H at C-6 by a propionic side chain gave mesoporphyrin IX;
this established that chlorophyll and haem belong essentially to the same
series of tetrapyrrole isomers. It gave the initial support for the view that
biosynthesis of chlorophyll would follow an initial path similar to biosynthesis of haem.

2. Preparation of the chlorophylls: isolation from plants

The final stage in the preparation of a single chlorophyll component is based
on the original method of Tswett[11] who used column chromatography. The
initial stages in preparation are usually based on the methods developed by
Willstätter and Stoll[4]. When petroleum ether is added to an acetone extract
of leaves in the presence of a little water to give a two-phase system, the
chlorophylls and yellow plastid pigments pass into the petroleum ether
layer. Excess of acetone is removed from the petrol layer by repeated washings with small volumes of water. The yellow xanthophylls can then be
removed by repeated washings of the petroleum ether layer with 90%
methanol. If then the petroleum ether solution is washed with water to
remove the methanol the chlorophylls form a colloidal precipitate which can
be filtered off on talc. The carotene together with small quantities of chlorophyll remain in the filtrate. The chlorophylls on the talc are removed by
dissolving in a small volume of ether. The ether is then evaporated and the
chlorophylls dissolved in a minimal amount of pyridine, which then may be
diluted with the solvent mixture used for the chromatographic separation;
n-octane and butanol has been recommended by Jacobs, Vatter and Holt[12].
The column material can be either sucrose or cellulose powder. The chlorophyll a appears as a green-blue zone in front of the green chlorophyll b zone.
There is usually a grey zone in advance of the chlorophyll a due to phaeophytin. Also a varying amount of green material may be left at and towards
the top of the column. This consists partly of allomerised chlorophyll. The
zone corresponding to chlorophyll a is usually free from chlorophyll b and
can be cut out and the chlorophyll dissolved in ether. The zone of chlorophyll b requires to be extracted and re-chromatographed in order to remove
the remaining chlorophyll a. Jacobs et al.[12] showed that if the ether solution
is evaporated on a water surface the chlorophyll (if it is pure) is deposited in
a crystalline form. The preparations show a dark steel-blue reflexion. The
formation of the crystalline state was found to be accelerated by the presence of divalent cations, for example by quantities of calcium salts in the
water. When the chlorophylls are obtained in a pure crystalline form they
keep relatively well; this does not apply to impure or amorphous preparations. Preparations of chlorophyll, as distinct from those of phaeophytin,

retain from one or two molecules of water which is very firmly bound; this is referred to again in a later section. The solution of chlorophyll *a* in ether is a very bluish-green, almost a pure blue, while that of chlorophyll *b* is a yellowish-green. In concentrated solution the chlorophylls appear red by transmitted light because of the appreciable absorption in the green region of the spectrum, which is not the case with dilute solutions. The chlorophyll components from other photosynthetic organisms may be obtained by a similar method. The preparation of bacteriochlorophyll is described by Holt and Jacobs[13].

(a) Absorption spectra of chlorophylls a and b and protochlorophyll

In the chlorophylls and phaeophytins the absorption towards the longer wavelength is greatly increased as compared with the porphyrins. At the same time the absorption in the violet corresponding to the Soret band of the blood pigment is comparatively less, being of the same order as that in the longer wave-band region. A comparison of the absorption spectrum of chlorophyll *a* with that of protochlorophyll shows this; the extinction coefficients for the absorption maxima are high and the relative positions of the bands clearly defined. Thus it is possible to use a spectrophotometric method for the estimation of the chlorophylls *a* and *b* in a mixture of the pigments which is applicable to very dilute solutions.

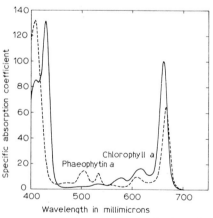

Fig. 1. Absorption spectra of chlorophyll *a* and phaeophytin *a* in ether[14].

The position of the absorption bands and the magnitude of the extinction coefficients vary according to the nature of the solvent. The addition of small quantities of water to the solution of chlorophyll in acetone produces considerable changes in the absorption spectrum; in all cases, however, the main "pattern" of the absorption bands remains unchanged. For spectroscopic estimation of chlorophyll 80% acetone (acetone: water, 4:1 by volume) is generally the most convenient solvent. The concentration of water in this case can vary by 2 or 3% without causing serious errors. The positions of the maxima

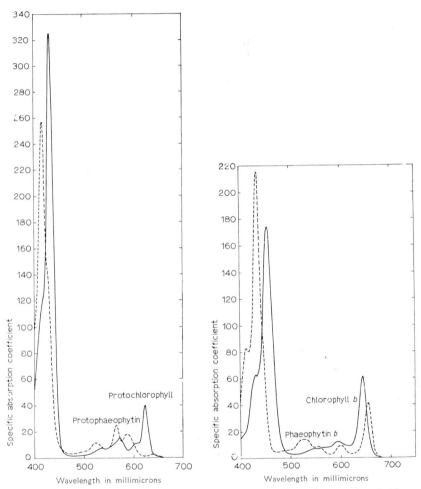

Fig. 2. The absorption spectra of protochlorophyll and protophaeophytin in ether[14].

Fig. 3. The absorption spectra of chlorophyll *b* and phaeophytin *b* in ether[14].

of absorption and values of the corresponding specific extinction coefficients are given in Table I. The absorption spectra given in Figs. 1–4 are taken from Smith and Benitez[14]. The specific absorption coefficient α is defined as

$$\alpha = \frac{1}{dC} \log \frac{I_0}{I}$$

where d is the length of the absorption cell, C is the concentration of the pigment in grams per litre, I_0 and I are the light intensities transmitted by the pure solvent and the solution, log is ^{10}log.

TABLE I

ABSORPTION MAXIMA AND SPECIFIC ABSORPTION COEFFICIENTS OF CHLOROPHYLLS AND
PHAEOPHYTINS a AND b IN 80% ACETONE ACCORDING TO VERNON[15]

Chlorophyll a	665	618	582	536	433	mμ
	90.8	19.6	11.6	4.78	101.5	l/g · cm
Phaeophytin a	666–667	610	536	505	409	mμ
	55.2	11.6	12.8	14.6	127.3	l/g · cm*
Chlorophyll b	648–649	600	558	536	460	mμ
	52.5	14.3	7.91	6.37	148.0	l/g · cm
Phaeophytin b	655	600	558	527	436	mμ
	34.8	10.4	9.25	14.5	176.3	l/g · cm

* The specific extinction coefficients of the phaeophytins are given in form which yields the concentrations as equivalent concentrations of chlorophyll.

(b) Spectrophotometric determination of chlorophyll

For estimation of chlorophyll in chloroplast suspension, four volumes of acetone are added to the suspension (containing less than 1 mg chlorophyll/ml). The insoluble material is spun off at once, and washed by resuspending in 80% acetone and centrifuging. The second supernatant is combined with the first and the whole made up to a convenient volume with 80% acetone. If necessary, aliquots are taken for further dilution with 80% acetone so that the final concentration of chlorophyll is about 1 mg/200 ml.

For estimation in plant tissues rapid grinding with acetone may be safely used in a number of cases. Smith and Benitez[14] recommend the addition of magnesium carbonate to the tissue when the cell sap is acid, in order to avoid the formation of phaeophytin. The chlorophyll in whole cells of *Chlorella* is not extracted with acetone owing to the nature of the cell wall. Methanol, however, may be used. If the *Chlorella* cells are completely broken then acetone will extract the chlorophyll.

The extracts so obtained contain a mixture of chlorophylls a and b. The total concentrations of a and b can be determined by measuring the absorption at two wavelengths. In practice the absorption is determined at positions corresponding to the red absorption peaks of the two separate components, although other combinations of wavelengths are possible. Providing the measurements are made in the longer wavelength range, there is virtually no interference due to the yellow plastid pigments which are extracted with the chlorophylls.

The following pair of simultaneous equations adapted from MacKinney[16] may be used for the determination of chlorophyll *a* and *b* in 80% acetone. The extinction E $(= {}^{10}\log I_0/I)$ is measured at the wavelengths given in mμ. The concentrations are obtained in mg/l.

$$C_a = 12.7\, E_{663} - 2.69\, E_{645}$$

$$C_b = 22.9\, E_{645} - 4.68\, E_{663}$$

This method cannot be safely applied if the chlorophyll solution also contains phaeophytin. If, however, a little of the chlorophyll has been converted into chlorophyllide, the effect is negligible as the removal of phytol has only a slight effect on the absorption spectrum. When phaeophytin is present it has been recommended that oxalic acid should be added, and after storage in the dark to complete the removal of magnesium, the phaeophytins *a* and *b* can be determined by an analogous method depending on the extinction coefficients at two different wavelengths. The following pair of simultaneous equations has been given by Vernon[15] for this purpose:

$$C_a = 20.15\, E_{666} - 5.87\, E_{655}$$

$$C_b = 31.90\, E_{655} - 13.40\, E_{666}$$

The equations yield the concentrations of phaeophytins in mg/l. In order to compare these with the equivalent concentrations of the chlorophylls, allowance for the loss of magnesium must be made.

Vernon[15] has also given a complete method for determining both the phaeophytins and the chlorophylls in the same solution; this depends on readings of the extinction values at six different wavelengths.

(c) Preparation of phaeophytin a and b and conversion of phaeophytin a into protophaeophytin

(Based on Willstätter and Stoll[4], Noack and Kiessling[17] and unpublished work by the author)

Phaeophytin *a* and *b* can easily be obtained from fresh leaves in a pure form. The leaves, grass or *Urtica*, are minced finely and to 100 g of mince 30 ml of acetone are added immediately with stirring. The mass, after 20 min standing, is filtered off on a Buchner funnel and the cake of minced tissue is pressed gently. This is covered with 90% ethanol and the rest of the acetone is displaced by gentle suction. When the ethanol begins to filter through, the first fluid is rejected, and then the concentrated solution of plastid pigments in 90% ethanol is collected. When the chlorophyll is extracted the filtrate is acidified with concentrated hydrochloric acid diluted with nine volumes of ethanol containing 1% $CaCl_2$ until the green colour becomes a brownish green. About 3 ml of the alcoholic HCl is required for 100 ml of leaf extract. After mixing and standing for 20 min the bulk of the phaeophytin is precipitated and can be centrifuged. The precipitate is washed with 90% ethanol and finally with a small volume of 96% ethanol and then dried. The yield is from 0.5–1 g of phaeophytin a plus b from 1 kg of fresh leaves.

The phaeophytin a plus b is treated with about 15 times its weight of 95% formic acid containing about 1% calcium formate. This dissolves the phaeophytin a giving a solution which appears blue in thin layers. The phaeophytin b is less soluble and can be filtered off. For conversion to protophaeophytin some of the solution of phaeophytin is put in a Thunberg tube, 0.3–0.5 g of iron powder is added and the vessel evacuated. On shaking, the blue colour of the fluid soon changes to a reddish purple. This is a dihydrophaeophytin and is immediately reoxidised to phaeophytin on exposure to air. On standing at room temperature in the absence of air the fluid gradually becomes reddish brown. At this stage it contains a tetrahydro derivative of the porphyrin protophaeophytin. It is then poured into ether and the ether washed with small quantities of water. Oxidation in the ether solution occurs through a green dihydroporphyrin stage to the red solution of protophaeophytin. In light the oxidation is much more rapid and the intermediate green stage may not appear. The extra hydrogen atoms on these reduced compounds appear to be in the inner part of the porphyrin structure. They differ in reactivity from those in positions 7–8 as in phaeophytin. Prolonged exposure to the iron causes some reduction of the vinyl group and the 90% formic acid slowly hydrolyses the phytol ester, giving the protophaeophorbide.

3. Photochemistry of chlorophyll

In photosynthesis the reduction of carbon dioxide and the corresponding oxidation of the hydrogen donor requires the absorption of radiant energy by the photosynthetic pigments. For the green plant, as oxygen is produced as a result of the process, the ultimate hydrogen donor has been identified with water (Van Niel[18]; Hill[19,20]). In bacterial photosynthesis where oxygen is never produced, certain inorganic compounds or even organic compounds may serve as ultimate hydrogen donors. When hydrogen itself is the ultimate hydrogen donor the process can be concerned simply with the conversion of the radiant energy into the form of ATP, that is, into "active" phosphate groups (Losada et al.[21]). However, in all cases including the last, the primary conversion of the radiant energy is generally considered in terms of hydrogen transport or electron transport. Thus it is the photochemistry of chlorophyll, in relation to hydrogen transport systems, which has the more immediate biochemical significance. All aspects of photochemistry of chlorophyll are fully considered by Rabinowitch[3] and the subsequent developments by Livingston[22].

When light is absorbed by chlorophyll in solution, part of the energy is emitted as fluorescence within an interval of 10^{-8} second; the other part, about 85% of that absorbed, is lost as heat. Livingston[22] applied the methods of flash photolysis, developed by Norrish (Norrish and Porter[23]; Norrish, Porter and Thrush[24]), to solutions of chlorophyll. It was found that the chlorophyll molecules could be converted into a metastable state with a life of about 10^{-3} second, several orders longer than the fluorescent state. The conversion was perfectly reversible provided all traces of oxygen could be removed. In the presence of oxygen the metastable state is quenched very efficiently and a small fraction of the chlorophyll is irreversibly destroyed. By analogy with a variety of other organic compounds this metastable form of chlorophyll is regarded as being a triplet state of the molecule. The absorption spectrum is completely different from that of chlorophyll; there is a complete absence of the red and blue maxima; the change in absorption is as profound as in the case of the phase test. Allomerised chlorophyll gives a result by the flash photolysis method similar to the native chlorophyll, so that the energy excess temporarily stored in the molecule in both cases might be expressed as a disturbance of the conjugate bond system of the chlorin nucleus. The singlet and the triplet states of chlorophyll could each be considered as being able to act simultaneously both as a potential oxidising and reducing agent.

The clearest demonstration of this aspect of chlorophyll photochemistry was provided by Krasnowski[25]. He discovered that chlorophyll dissolved in pyridine in presence of ascorbic acid and a little water could be reduced in light. The reduced form had a pink colour and a diffuse absorption spectrum which was similar to, but not identical with, a phase test intermediate. The reduced form was immediately reoxidised by oxygen. Reoxidation also took place in the dark in absence of oxygen, but this was a slow process. The oxidation and reduction of the chlorophyll in this way is reversible, but not completely so. During each cycle there is a partial loss of the magnesium resulting in phaeophytin formation. Krasnowski and Brin[26] were able to show that the photochemically reduced chlorophyll was reoxidised by the coenzyme NAD. It is therefore possible to conclude that the chlorophyll

References p. 96

photocatalyses the reduction of the coenzyme by ascorbic acid with the conversion of a definite fraction of the light energy absorbed into a chemical form. It is possible to replace the chlorophyll by phaeophytin or by porphyrins, in which case the system preserves its reversibility. While phaeophytin can be reduced in the dark by a suitable reagent to the pink or purple red dihydro form there does not seem to be any reagent which can be used to reduce the magnesium compound, chlorophyll, in this way; the absorption of light appears to be essential.

Vernon[27] has been able to carry out the same type of photocatalysed reaction in aqueous media. He found that with chlorophyll as a finely dispersed preparation the coenzyme could be reduced in light in the presence of ascorbate and a crude preparation of a specific protein from the plant. The protein was originally found by Davenport, Hill and Whatley in the search for a natural hydrogen acceptor for chloroplast preparations and it was independently found by San Pietro and Lang as an essential factor for the reduction of the coenzyme NADP by illuminated chloroplast preparations. The system described by Vernon gives a model which might refer to a part of the actual process of photosynthesis.

The first well defined reversible oxidation–reduction reaction involving chlorophyll was discovered by Rabinowitch and Weiss[28].

Chlorophyllide or chlorophyll in solution in methanol was bleached to a yellowish colour when small amounts of ferric chloride (in methanol) were added. The chlorophyll was regenerated on addition of ferrous chloride or other reducing agent. In the presence of a mixture of ferrous and ferric salts the equilibrium was more in favour of the bleached chlorophyll during exposure to light. The conclusion was that the chlorophyll is oxidised by ferric chloride to a somewhat unstable "oxidised chlorophyll". Over periods of a few minutes the oxidation and reduction process was found to be truly reversible. The presence of water lowered the stability of the oxidised product and the reversibility was lost. Allomerised chlorophyll also shows these changes, so that they may be referred to the properties of the magnesium tetrapyrrole structure and do not have any direct connection with the reactions involved in the phase test concerning ring V.

There is good evidence that chlorophyll can form covalent compounds by addition of a molecule of a variety of substances on either side of the plane of the tetrapyrrolic ring. The property depends on the presence of the magnesium atom and resembles the property of haem in the formation of haemochromogens. Pure chlorophyll is found to contain water which is only removed with great difficulty. This is not the case with phaeophytin. In the case of magnesium phthalocyanine (a compound in many respects analogous to chlorophyll) Barrett, Dent and Linstead[29] found that the anhydrous crystals obtained by sublimation *in vacuo* gave a powder of a dihydrate in moist air. Livingston found that chlorophyll does not fluoresce when it is dissolved in benzene with all traces of water removed but that this scarcely affects the conversion to the metastable state observed by flash photolysis. The absorption spectrum of the chlorophyll in the absence of water or other polar solvents differed from that observed in their presence. The absorption was more diffuse in character. The order of one molar equivalent of water was enough to restore the fluorescence and the normal appearance of the absorption spectrum.

The magnesium and the zinc derivatives of the porphyrins and of related macrocyclic compounds give a magnificent red or orange-red chemiluminescence with aliphatic hydroperoxides. The reaction was described by Cook[30] and by Helberger[31] with magnesium phthalocyanine dissolved in hot tetralin (tetrahydronaphthalene); Rothmund[32] described the reaction with chlorophyll. The light emitted corresponds to the spectrum of the fluorescence of the pigment concerned. The free porphyrins, although they may show strong fluorescence, do not give this luminescent reaction; neither is the reaction shown by the porphyrin derivatives of Cu, Co, Ni, or Fe. The reaction depends on a catalysis of the decomposition of the hydroperoxide (vii) by the pigment, to give the corresponding ketone (viii) and water.

Tetralin hydroperoxide   Tetralone

The kinetics of this reaction for the zinc compound of tetraphenylporphin were studied by Linschitz and Abrahamson[33]. The results could be explained by assuming that the pigment loses one hydrogen equivalent when the hydroperoxide loses one hydroxyl equivalent, giving water; the two radicals then react to give the ketone and the pigment in its first excited singlet state; the excess energy appears as fluorescence as the pigment returns to its ground state. It was stated that this mechanism would be precisely the reverse of photosensitisation when it is assumed that an excited dye molecule reacts with an acceptor to yield a pair of radicals. This inverse relationship between photosensitisation and chemiluminescence would appear to be shown by living green cells and by chloroplast preparations. Strehler and Arnold[34] discovered, by using sensitive methods for light detection, that after illumination the cells showed an after-glow. This could be detected for several minutes during the dark period. The light emitted was subsequently found to correspond with the fluorescence spectrum of the chlorophyll in the chloroplast. Observations of the after-glow under a variety of conditions are in accord with the assumption that back reactions between photochemical products can supply energy required to excite the chlorophyll molecules concerned. The initial intensity of the after-glow would correspond to about a millionth of the light absorbed by the chlorophyll and is far too low to be observed visually.

The state of chlorophyll in the chloroplast

In contrast with the iron porphyrins, the chlorophylls have not yet been shown to be in the form of any compounds with specific proteins which are readily characterised. Bacterial chlorophyll shows a complex absorption spectrum in the living cell. Duysens in his classical work was able to study the behaviour of these spectroscopically distinct forms of the pigment. As only the one chlorophyll component is present it has to be concluded that in the bacterial chromatophores the pigment can be bound in different ways. The environmental conditions which influence the spectroscopic properties of the pigment might be arbitrarily divided into three types. (1) The state of aggregation of the pigment molecules influences the character and position of the absorption bands. These effects were studied in the case of haem and its derivatives and the copper porphyrin, turacin, by Keilin[35]. Rabinowitch[3] and colleagues (1956, see p. 1815) have made a detailed study with chlorophyll and derivatives. With both series of pigments the α-band or that of the lower transition frequency is displaced to the red with increasing aggregation. With the formation of a crystalline aggregate the displacement is considerably increased. (2) The position of the absorption bands can be influenced by the nature of the protein connected to the pigment. An example of this is the difference in position of the α-band of oxyhaemoglobin and oxymyoglobin. Oxyhaemoglobin from mammalian blood has four haem groups and a molecular weight of 67,000, the α-band position is 576 mμ. Oxymyoglobin has one haem group and molecular weight of 17,000 and yet the α-band position is 581 mμ. (3) When chlorophyll is in solution the character of the absorption spectrum is influenced by the solvent. There is a displacement to the red with increasing refractive index and the polar and non-polar solvents fall into two classes.

In the chromatophores and chloroplasts all these three types of environmental conditions have been considered, for the chlorophyll is present in high concentration and is associated with both protein and with lipids.

It may be assumed that the chlorophylls are an essential component of the layered structure of the chloroplast as interpreted by electron microscopy. Goedheer[36] has been able to show by optical methods that the chlorophylls and carotenoids show a degree of orientation in a single chloroplast which is related to the layered structure. This aspect is discussed by Thomas[37]. The chloroplasts can be fragmented by a variety of methods and the chlorophyll-containing particles separated. In some experiments the smallest chlorophyll-containing particles appear to have a lower chlorophyll–protein ratio than would be indicated by the upper range of the ratios found with whole chloroplasts. This might suggest that the chlorophyll is not all related in the same way with proteins. The efficient transfer of excitation energy between pigment molecules in chloroplasts or in bacterial chromatophores suggests that the number of sites of photochemical action is far less than the number of pigment molecules. The classical work of Emerson and Arnold[38] with photosynthesis in *Chlorella* indicated that about 1500 chlorophyll molecules could cooperate in the production of one oxygen molecule. In its natural state the red band of chlorophyll *a* can be observed visually with the microspectroscope to be complex as compared with chlorophyll *a* in solution. French and colleagues (Brown and French[39]; Myers and French [40,41]) made detailed studies of the fine structure of the chlorophyll absorption spectrum in living cells and in chloroplasts. They suggest a relationship between the action spectrum of the Emerson enhancement effect (Emerson[42]) and different spectroscopic forms of the chlorophyll *a*. It could be concluded that the "forms" were structurally related to sites of two different photochemical processes and that one of the forms of chlorophyll *a* is in close relation to the chlorophyll *b*.

The absorption spectrum of the chlorophyll as observed in cells or in chloroplasts is immediately altered by heating above 60° or by exposure to a variety of organic solvents. Treatment of chloroplast preparations with a hydrocarbon solvent such as *n*-octane does not appreciably affect the absorption spectrum although carotene and other lipid materials are removed.

In the chloroplasts the red absorption band of chlorophyll *a* has its maximum at a longer wavelength than the band of chlorophyll *a* in a solution with any of the usual solvents. The maximum of the fluorescence spectrum of chlorophyll in the leaf is also displaced to a longer wavelength as compared with a solution. In the living cell the intensity of fluorescence in relation to light absorbed is less than 1/10th of that observed in solutions of chlorophyll. Kautsky and Hirsch[43] discovered that the intensity of fluorescence in the green plant was subject to variations which corresponded with the time relation of the induction period of photosynthesis. These observations have lead to a variety of studies which are fully dealt with by Rabinowitch[3] and could only be considered in relation to the process of photosynthesis. The development of the biochemistry of the chlorophylls in their functional form is one of the vistas open to the future.

4. Fate of chlorophyll in animal nutrition

Chlorophyll when present in the food associated with plant material, is not absorbed from the gut. It is first converted into phaeophytin by loss of magnesium and then mainly into phaeophorbides in the digestive tract; these products are excreted in the faeces. There is also a conversion to a porphyrin, phylloerythrin (ix), discovered by Marchlewski[44]. The formation

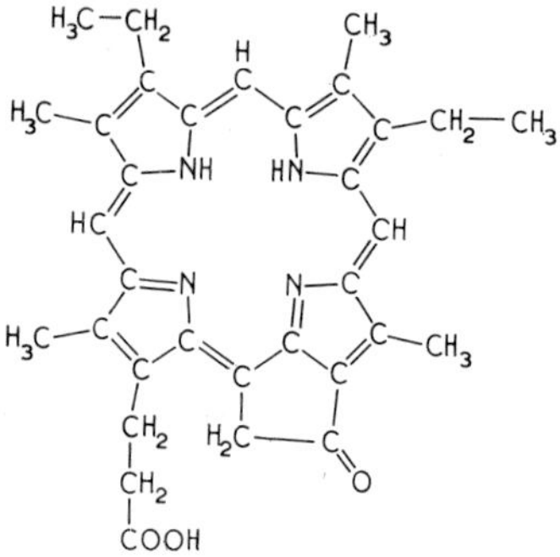

(ix)

Phylloerythrin

of phylloerythrin and also a number of other pyrrole derivatives depends mainly on the presence of micro-organisms (Quin, Rimington and Raets[45]). Fischer showed that phylloerythrin could be produced in small yield from phaeophytin by prolonged boiling in hydrochloric acid. The formation of phylloerythrin from phaeophorbide *a* involves reduction of the vinyl group and loss of the carboxyl group at C-10. The absorption spectrum is very similar to "protophaeophytin" and to the magnesium-free derivative of chlorophyll *c*.

In the sheep or ox some of the phylloerythrin which is formed from chlorophyll in the rumen is absorbed by the gut and excreted by the liver. Phylloerythrin is found as a normal constituent of the bile of these ruminants when chlorophyll is present in the food. The concentration of this porphyrin in the blood is normally insufficient to cause photosensitivity. In South Africa the disease of cattle known as Geeldekkop was shown by Rimington and Quin[46] to be due to the poisonous action of a plant *Tribulus* in the fodder, producing dysfunction of the liver. The phylloerythrin absorbed then remained in the blood causing photosensitisation typical of free porphyrins.

5. Chlorophyll in food technology

In the sterilisation of canned green vegetables precautions may have to be taken to avoid the formation of phaeophytin which causes loss of green colour. Blair and Ayres[47] have recommended the addition of magnesium carbonate; this, while raising the pH value, was found not tó produce an adverse influence on the texture of the material. It was, however, stated that spores of *Clostridium botulinum* are relatively resistant at the higher range of pH: they were not sterilised after 3 h at 100°. An older method for preserving the green colour was to add a trace of a copper salt; this would give the green copper compound of phaeophytin which is stable to acid. The addition of copper, however, is unsatisfactory, especially when sealed metal containers are used. The addition of a green dye to counteract the brown colour of phaeophytin overcomes the main technical difficulty but the presence of dye in the product is not altogether free from objection.

6. Other chlorophyll compounds

(a) Chlorophyll c

This pigment was found as a minor chlorophyll component in the brown algae by Strain and Manning[48] and in Diatoms and Dinoflagellates by Strain, Manning and Hardin[49]. The structure has been considered to be that of a magnesium phaeoporphyrin. The absorption spectrum is similar to that of protochlorophyll and after removal of magnesium is similar to that of protophaeophytin. It does not appear to contain a phytol group and is very easily extracted from its solution in petroleum ether by aqueous methanol. Chlorophyll *b* appears to be absent from the brown algae.

(b) Chlorophyll d

This pigment has only been found in certain species of red algae (Manning and Strain[50]). The absorption band in the red and the fluorescence spectrum are both at longer wavelengths than those of chlorophyll *a*. Because of the spectroscopic properties it has raised problems connected with the function of chlorophyll *a* in certain species, an aspect which has been discussed by Rabinowitch[3]. Chlorophyll *d* gives a positive phase test. Holt and Morley[51] converted chlorophyll *a* into the 2-desvinyl 2-formyl derivative. The product was considered to be identical with chlorophyll *d*.

(c) The bacterial chlorophylls

One of the main characteristics of bacterial photosynthesis seems to be that the mechanism for producing oxygen is absent. All the organisms which produce oxygen in photosynthesis contain chlorophyll *a* as the principal chlorophyll component. So far, chlorophyll *a* has not been found in bacteria.

References p. 96

(i) Bacteriochlorophyll

Bacteriochlorophyll (x) from *Rhodospirillum* was shown by Fischer to be chemically related to chlorophyll *a*. It contains two pyrrolene residues and thus is to be regarded as derived from tetrahydroporphin. Ring II is re-

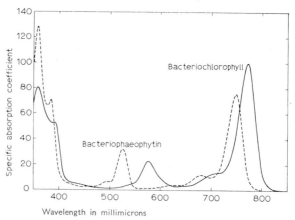

(x)

Bacteriochlorophyll

duced by the addition of H to C-3 and C-4 while the vinyl group at C-2 is oxidised to $-COCH_3$. The presence of two reduced pyrrole residues involves a displacement of the main absorption band into the near infrared, while the absorption band in the violet is relatively less intense. Solutions of the pigment have a blue colour and compared with equivalent solutions of chlorophyll *a* or *b* are less intensely coloured as the second main absorption band is in the infrared. The two hydrogen atoms in the ring II are apparent-

Fig. 4. The absorption spectra of bacteriochlorophyll and bacteriophaeophytin in ether[14].

ly easily removed by oxidation during the extraction of the chlorophyll from the bacteria and unless precautions are taken, a considerable amount of a green product resembling the chlorophylls *a* and *b* may be produced. This is considered to be 2-desvinyl 2-acetyl chlorophyll *a* which would result from the dehydrogenation of ring II.

(ii) Chlorobium chlorophyll (660)

The chlorophyll characteristic of the green bacteria resembles that in green plants as being a dihydroporphin but differs from the chlorophylls *a* and *b* in not giving a positive phase test. The pigment has been described under the name of bacterioviridin. Recently Stanier and Smith[52] were able to compare two strains of *Chlorobium thiosulphatophilum*; they found each to contain a single distinct type of chlorophyll. The main absorption maxima in ether solution were at 650 mμ and 660 mμ respectively. The 650-type was only found in the one strain which had originated in Oxford where it was isolated by Lascelles. A partial structure for *Chlorobium*-chlorophyll which has a propyl side chain at position 6 is given by Holt and Morley[53]. The absence of ring V in a photosynthetic chlorophyll alters the former approach to the problem of the significance of ring V in the chlorophylls.

7. Biosynthesis of chlorophyll

A landmark in the development of this study was provided by the experiments of Granick[54], described in his Harvey Lecture. A series of artificial

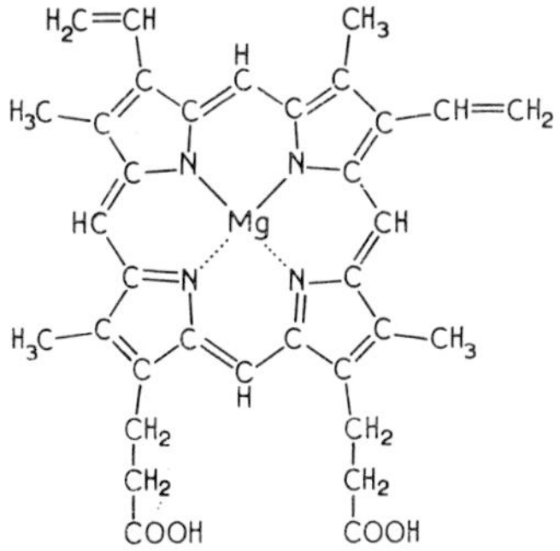

(xi)

Magnesium protoporphyrin IX

mutants of *Chlorella* which did not form chlorophyll and could be grown heterotrophically in the dark were produced by X-ray treatment. One of them produced protoporphyrin and from another, magnesium protoporphyrin (xi) was isolated. This finding of the magnesium analogue of the iron protoporphyrin haem, suggested that chlorophyll and haem may possess a common pathway of biosynthesis until the stage at which the metal is introduced into the molecule. Magnesium protoporphyrin, which here might be termed "protophyllin", gives bright bluish-red solutions showing a marked orange-yellow fluorescence; its absorption spectrum shows, in the visible region, two very strong and sharply defined bands similar to the α and β bands of oxyhaemoglobin. The magnesium protoporphyrin, if it is a precursor of chlorophyll, would have to undergo several further reaction stages during conversion to protochlorophyll (Granick and Mauzerall[55]). In studies of the biosynthesis of bacteriochlorophyll with *Rhodopseudomonas spheroides* by Lascelles[56,57] it was found that with relative absence of iron in the growth medium the chlorophyll production was suppressed and co-proporphyrin III accumulated. This suggested that in this case the presence of iron was necessary for the production of bacterial chlorophyll as well as for haem. The presence of light and absence of oxygen are also conditions required by this organism (*R. spheroides*) for normal production of bacterio-chlorophyll. Conversion of coproporphyrin to protoporphyrin and also to bacteriophaeophytin would, however, require an oxidative process. The lack of chlorophyll in green plants caused by iron deficiency has been known from early times. The occurrence of chlorotic vines on calcareous soils and the rapid recovery after spraying with iron salts is the classical example. These plants, however, do not appreciably accumulate porphyrin.

The last stage in the biosynthesis of chlorophyll a is, in the majority of cases, a photochemical reaction, involving protochlorophyll. This has been studied in detail by Smith[58] (1958) in a brilliant series of investigations. He has been able to purify from etiolated plant tissues an active protochloro-phyll–protein compound. He has termed this compound protochlorophyll a holochrome. Conversion of the pigment to chlorophyll a *in vitro* is rapidly brought about by light. The action spectrum of conversion corresponds with the protochlorophyll absorption spectrum. It was found that two quanta of the light energy absorbed were required. The source of the two hydrogen atoms transferred to the protochlorophyll to give chlorophyll a remains undetermined. It might be supposed that a dismutation involving a half-reduced protochlorophyll radical with another component or compo-nents in the holochrome would be involved, if one equivalent of hydrogen is transferred per quantum. The conversion to chlorophyll will occur at low temperatures, but is not completed at liquid air temperature. The holo-chrome loses all activity on heating and then the protochlorophyll cannot be converted into chlorophyll a. Thus the holochrome resembles somewhat a very undissociable enzyme–substrate compound.

Consideration of this very high quantum efficiency serves to emphasise the care which had to be taken in Smith's work to avoid exposure to even a faint light throughout the growth of the plant material and all the subsequent manipulations. The light absorption of protochlorophyll in the green regions of the spectrum is, however, relatively small and a dim green safe light can be used sparingly.

When chlorophyll formation is followed in the living plant it is found that the first chlorophyll a to appear is not active for photosynthesis. The red band of the chlorophyll first formed, 684 mμ, is slightly to the red of the final position, 677 mμ. The process has been examined in detail by Shibata[59]. He emphasises the potentialities in the use of partially green leaves for the study of the different forms of chlorophyll a found in the chloroplast.

The appearance of chlorophyll b in the greening of etiolated plants follows that of chlorophyll a and some of the chlorophyll-deficient varieties of plants have a very low b/a ratio. The mechanism of formation of chlorophyll b in the plant is at present unknown.

In a few cases among plants chlorophyll can be formed in the dark. This occurs with *Chlorella* grown heterotrophically and with seedlings of *Citrus* and *Pinus*. Schmidt[60] found that the so-called endosperm of the germinating pine seed supplied a necessary factor for the greening of the embryo. The isolated embryos were capable of growth in the dark. Chlorophyll could be made to appear by placing fragments of the endosperm in contact with the embryo. Bogorad[61] showed that the isolated embryos, however, were capable of greening in the light without any contact with the endosperm. When the growth of the normal seedlings is continued in darkness the later growth loses the capability for greening, unless it is exposed to light. No evidence was found for a factor which could be extracted from the endosperm.

ACKNOWLEDGEMENTS

The writer is very grateful to Dr. and Mrs. D. S. Bendall for their help with this article and to the Agricultural Research Council, London for their support.

References p. 96

REFERENCES

[1] R. B. WOODWARD, W. A. AYER, J. M. BEATON, F. BICKELHAUPT, R. BONNETT, P. BUCHSCHACHER, G. L. CLOSS, H. DUTLER, J. HANUCK, F. P. HAUCK, S. ITÔ, A. LANGEMANN, E. LE GOFF, W. LEIMGRUBER, W. LWOWSKI, J. SAUER, Z. VALENTA AND H. VOLZ, *J. Am. Chem. Soc.*, 82 (1960) 3800.

[2] M. STRELL, A. KALOGANOFF AND H. KOLLER, *Angew. Chem.*, 72 (1960) 169.

[3] E. I. RABINOWITCH, *Photosynthesis*, Interscience, New York, Vol. I, 1945; Vol. II, Part I, 1957; Vol. II, Part II, 1956.

[4] R. WILLSTÄTTER AND A. STOLL, *Untersuchungen über Chlorophyll*, Springer, Berlin, 1913.

[5] H. FISCHER AND H. ORTH, *Die Chemie des Pyrrols. II. Pyrrolfarbstoffe*, Part I, Edwards, Ann Arbor, Mich., 1943.

[6] H. FISCHER AND A. STERN, *Die Chemie des Pyrrols. II. Pyrrolfarbstoffe*, Part 2, Edwards, Ann Arbor, Mich., 1943.

[7] S. KROL, *J. Org. Chem.*, 24 (1959) 2065.

[8] R. B. JOHNS AND R. P. LINSTEAD, *J. Chem. Soc.*, (1956) 2273.

[9] A. STOLL AND E. WIEDERMANN, *Helv. Chim. Acta*, 16 (1933) 307.

[10] A. S. HOLT, *Canad. J. Biochem. Physiol.*, 36 (1958) 439.

[11] M. TSWETT, *Ber. deut. botan. Ges.*, 24 (1906) 316.

[12] E. E. JACOBS, A. E. VATTER AND A. S. HOLT, *Arch. Biochem. Biophys.*, 53 (1954) 228.

[13] A. S. HOLT AND E. E. JACOBS, *Am. J. Botany*, 41 (1954) 718.

[14] J. H. C. SMITH AND A. BENITEZ, in K. PAECH AND M. V. TRACEY (Eds.), *Modern Methods of Plant Analysis*, Vol. IV, Springer, Berlin, p. 142.

[15] L. P. VERNON, *Anal. Chem.*, 32 (1960) 1144.

[16] G. MACKINNEY, *J. Biol. Chem.*, 140 (1941) 315.

[17] K. NOACK AND W. KIESSLING, *Z. physiol. Chem.*, 182 (1929) 48.

[18] C. B. VAN NIEL, *Arch. Mikrobiol.*, 3 (1931) 1.

[19] R. HILL, *Nature*, 139 (1938) 881.

[20] R. HILL, *Proc. Roy. Soc. (London)*, B, 127 (1939) 192.

[21] M. LOSADA, A. V. TREBST, S. OGATA AND D. I. ARNON, *Nature*, 186 (1960) 753.

[22] R. LIVINGSTON, *Quart. Revs. (London)*, 14 (1960) 174.

[23] R. G. W. NORRISH AND G. PORTER, *Nature*, 164 (1949) 658.

[24] R. G. W. NORRISH, G. PORTER AND B. A. THRUSH, *Proc. Roy. Soc. (London)*, A, 216 (1953) 165.

[25] A. A. KRASNOWSKI, *Doklady Akad. Nauk S.S.S.R.*, 60 (1948) 421. (AEC translation 2156).

[26] A. A. KRASNOWSKI AND G. P. BRIN, *Doklady Akad. Nauk S.S.S.R.*, 67 (1949) 325. (Translated by E. I. RABINOWITCH, 1956, U.S. AEC).

[27] L. P. VERNON, *Acta Chem. Scand.*, 15 (1961) 1650.

[28] E. I. RABINOWITCH AND J. WEISS, *Proc. Roy. Soc. (London)*, A, 162 (1934) 25.

[29] P. A. BARRETT, C. E. DENT AND R. P. LINSTEAD, *J. Chem. Soc.*, (1936) 1719.

[30] A. H. COOK, *J. Chem. Soc.*, (1938) 1845.

[31] J. H. HELBERGER, *Naturwiss.*, 26 (1938) 316.

[32] P. ROTHMUND, *J. Am. Chem. Soc.*, 60 (1938) 2005.

[33] H. LINSCHITZ AND E. W. ABRAHAMSON, *Nature*, 172 (1953) 909.

[34] B. L. STREHLER AND W. ARNOLD, *J. Gen. Physiol.*, 34 (1951) 809.

[35] D. KEILIN, *Proc. Roy. Soc. (London)*, B, 100 (1926) 129.

[36] J. C. GOEDHEER, *Biochim. Biophys. Acta*, 16 (1955) 471.

[37] J. B. THOMAS, *Progr. Biophys. Biophys. Chem.*, 5 (1955) 109.

[38] R. EMERSON AND W. ARNOLD, *J. Gen. Physiol.*, 15 (1952) 391.

[39] J. S. BROWN AND C. S. FRENCH, *Biophys. J.*, 1 (1961) 549.

[40] J. MYERS AND C. S. FRENCH, *Plant Physiol.*, 35 (1960) 963.

[41] J. MYERS AND C. S. FRENCH, *J. Gen. Physiol.*, 43 (1960) 723.

[42] R. EMERSON, *Science*, 127 (1958) 1059.

[43] H. KAUTSKY AND A. HIRSCH, *Naturwiss.*, 19 (1931) 964.

[44] M. L. MARCHLEWSKI, *Bull. soc. chim. biol.*, 6 (1924) 404.

[45] J. I. QUIN, C. RIMINGTON AND G. C. S. RAETS, *Onderstepoort J. Vet. Sci. Animal Ind.*, 4 (1935) 463.

[46] C. Rimington and J. I. Quin, *Onderstepoort J. Vet. Sci. Animal Ind.*, 1 (1933) 469.
[47] J. S. Blair and T. B. Ayres, *Ind. Eng. Chem.*, 35 (1943) 85.
[48] H. H. Strain and W. M. Manning, *J. Biol. Chem.*, 144 (1942) 625.
[49] H. H. Strain, W. M. Manning and G. Hardin, *J. Biol. Chem.*, 148 (1943) 655.
[50] W. M. Manning and H. H. Strain, *J. Biol. Chem.*, 151 (1943) 1.
[51] A. S. Holt and H. V. Morley, *Canad. J. Chem.*, 37 (1959) 507.
[52] R. Y. Stanier and J. H. C. Smith, *Biochim. Biophys. Acta*, 41 (1960) 478.
[53] A. S. Holt and H. V. Morley, *J. Am. Chem. Soc.*, 82 (1960) 500.
[54] S. Granick, *Harvey Lectures*, Ser. 44 (1950) 220.
[55] S. Granick and D. Mauzerall, *J. Biol. Chem.*, 233 (1958) 1119, 1141.
[56] J. Lascelles, *Biochem. J.*, 62 (1956) 78.
[57] J. Lascelles, *Biochem. J.*, 72 (1959) 508.
[58] J. H. C. Smith, *Brookhaven Symposia in Biol.*, No. 11 (1958), The Photochemical Apparatus: Its Structure and Function.
[59] K. Shibata, *J. Biochem. (Tokyo)*, 44 (1957) 147.
[60] A. Schmidt, *Botan. Arch.*, 5 (1924) 260.
[61] L. Bogorad, *Botan. Gaz.*, 111 (1950) 221.
[62] L. R. Blinks, *Plant Physiol.*, 34 (1959) 200.
[63] L. Bogorad, *Comparative Biochemistry of Photoreactive Systems*, Vol. I, Academic Press, New York, 1960.
[64] K. Noack and W. Kiessling, *Z. physiol. Chem.*, 193 (1930) 97.
[65] R. G. W. Norrish, *British Association for the Advancement of Science*, No. 74, 1961.

Chapter IV

Bile Pigments

C. H. GRAY

Department of Chemical Pathology, University of London and King's College Hospital, London (Great Britain)

1. Introduction

Although the bile may contain small quantities of porphyrins, chlorophyll degradation products and other pigments, the term *bile pigments* is usually restricted to those compounds possessing a linear tetrapyrrolic structure, each of the four pyrrole rings of which are bridged by a single carbon atom[1]. They are bilanes, bilenes, biladienes and bilatrienes, according to the number of bridge carbon atoms present as —CH= groups. The positions of the bridge carbon atoms are indicated by the letters a, b and c in parentheses (Fig. 1), and correspond to the β, γ and δ (and not the α, β and γ) bridge

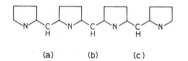

(a)   (b)   (c)

Fig. 1. Linear tetrapyrrolic structure.

carbon atoms of protoporphyrin. Passing from the bilanes, in which all three bridge carbon atoms are —CH₂— groups, to the bilatrienes, the number of conjugated double bonds throughout the chain increases, the light absorption changes to longer wave lengths and the colour progressively changes. The bilanes are colourless, the bilenes and biladienes are yellow, orange, red or violet, while the bilatrienes are green or blue. Some naturally occurring bile pigments are shown in Table I.

It is convenient to regard biliverdin, a typical bilatriene, as the parent bile pigment. Hitherto, the two end α-positions have been considered to carry hydroxyl groups, but hydroxypyrroles are now known to be unstable and rapidly tautomerise to a keto form[2]. Recent determinations of spectrophotometric titration curves of the bile pigments and dipyrrylmethanes and di-

Bile pigment	Source and occurrence	Colour	Spectral absorption
Bilirubin	Product of haemoglobin breakdown; present in bile, gall stones, haematomata, haemorrhagic infarcts and in faeces of newborn; in small quantities in normal serum, increased in jaundice when present also in urine and tissues.	Orange	Broad spectral absorption λ_{max} in CHCl₃ 450–455 mμ
Mesobilirubin	Probably present in small intestine.	Orange/yellow	Broad spectral absorption λ_{max} in CHCl₃ 425 mμ
Biliverdin	In bile of some animals, egg shells of many birds (oocyan), placenta of some mammals (uteroverdin), haematomata; prosthetic group of some catalases.	Blue-green	λ_{max} in 5% HCl in MeOH 680 and 377 mμ
Glaucobilin	Probably present in haemolymph and integuments of some insects (coelenterates), molluscs and annelids.	Blue	λ_{max} in 5% HCl in MeOH 670 and 373 mμ
"Urobilinogens" mesobilinogen stercobilinogen d-urobilinogen	In intestinal contents and faeces and in pathological urines and bile.	Colourless	—
Urobilinoids	In intestinal contents and faeces and in pathological urines and bile; dehydrogenation products of urobilinogens.	Reddish-orange	Hydrochloride In MeOH λ_{max} Zinc complex In MeOH
urobilin-IXα (a)			492 mμ 510 mμ
stercobilin (b)			496 mμ 510 mμ
d-urobilin (c)			492 mμ 510 mμ
Mesobiliviolin	In intestinal contents and faeces; probably derived from urobilin-IXα; prosthetic group of phycocyanins (chromoproteins of red and blue algae).	Violet	λ_{max} in 5% HCl 598 mμ and 325 mμ
Mesobilirhodin	In intestinal contents and faeces; probably derived from urobilin-IXα; prosthetic group of phycocyanins (chromoproteins of red and blue algae).	Red	λ_{max} in 5% HCl 560 mμ and 495 mμ

Reproduced from Gray[37] by permission of the publishers.

pyrrylmethenes support this view[3]. In the present article the keto form will be presented throughout. All the naturally occurring bile pigments are derived from protoporphyrin-IX by removal of the α-methene group so that the nature and order of the side chains in the β-positions are the same as in the protoporphyrin molecule[4]. In some bile pigments, however, the vinyl groups are reduced to ethyl groups; the pigments are then known as meso-compounds.

The two vinyl groups are readily hydrogenated to ethyl groups leading to the formation of a mesobiliverdin, which because of its blue colour receives the trivial name, glaucobilin. Both biliverdin and glaucobilin are readily hydrogenated at the centre methene bridge forming bilirubin and mesobilirubin, both of which are biladienes-(a,c) (Fig. 2).

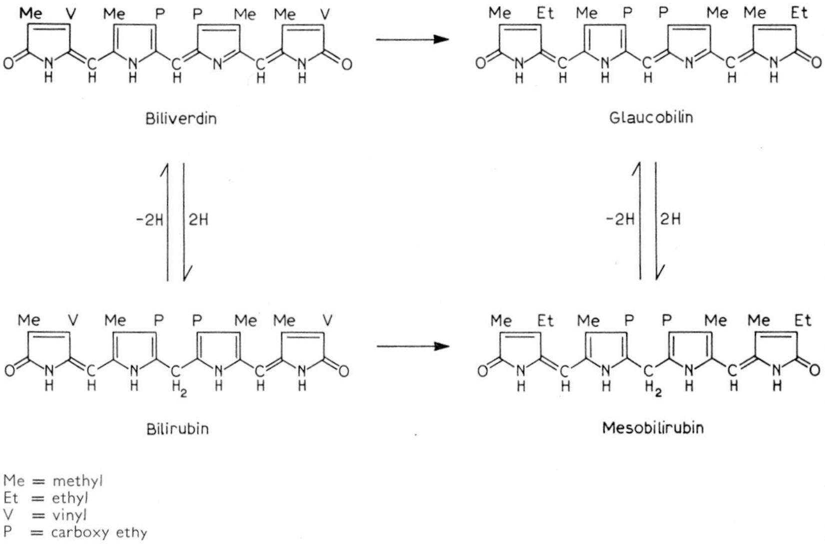

Me = methyl
Et = ethyl
V = vinyl
P = carboxy ethy

Fig. 2.

When bilirubin is reduced with sodium amalgam the two vinyl groups are reduced to ethyl groups and the two methene groups to methane groups. The resulting colourless compound has been given the trivial name, meso-bilirubinogen, and has the fully saturated mesobilane structure. On standing in air the central bridge carbon atom is dehydrogenated giving a mesobilene-(b), which receives the trivial name, urobilin-IXα. This is an unsatisfactory name since all naturally occurring bile pigments are IXα pigments. The structure of urobilin-IXα was confirmed by synthesis by Siedel and Meier[5]. *In vivo* a similar reduction of bilirubin to a urobilinoid pigment occurs in

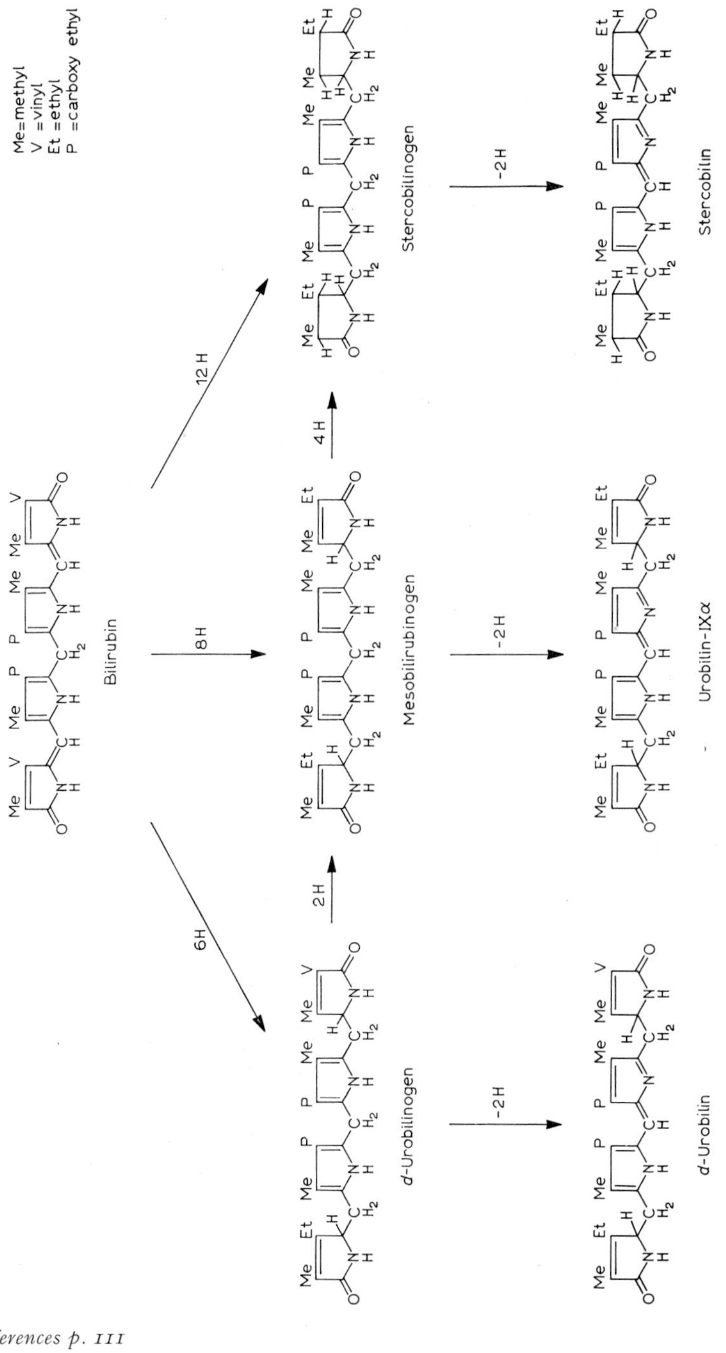

Fig. 3.

TABLE II

THE UROBILINS

Pigment	No. of H atoms in molecule	Absorption max. (E in parenthesis) in CHCl₃	Specific rotation [α]p in CHCl₃	Stability	Product of ferric chloride oxidation
Urobilin-IXα	42	498 (1,150)	inactive	The least stable of the urobilins	Mainly violins together with some glaucobilins. Glaucobilin predominates after prolonged oxidation.
d-Urobilin-IXα	42	499	+4,900		Not known
d-Urobilin	40	498 (1,500)	+5,000	Less stable than stercobilin, more stable than urobilin-IXα. Isomerises in alkali.	Mainly glaucobilin, together with some violin. Violin predominates under mild conditions. Sometimes purpurins.
Racemised d-urobilin	probably 40	499	inactive		Not known
Stercobilin	46	496 (1,500)	−4,000	The most stable of the urobilins.	Not oxidised.

the gut, but in addition to urobilin-IXα and mesobilirubinogen, two other urobilinoid pigments and their colourless chromogens are produced[6]. These are stercobilin and d-urobilin and their chromogens, stercobilinogen and d-urobilinogen. The relationship of these compounds is shown in Fig. 3. Stercobilin and stercobilinogen contain four hydrogen atoms more than urobilin-IXα and mesobilirubinogen respectively. Stercobilinogen is, therefore, a tetrahydromesobilane and stercobilin is a tetrahydromesobilene-(b). The four additional hydrogen atoms in these compounds are probably situated at the two β-positions of each end ring, which are, therefore, pyrrolidone units[7].

d-Urobilin contains two hydrogen atoms less than urobilin-IXα; its chemical behaviour is, nevertheless, typical of that of the urobilinoid pigments. The position of the extra unsaturation has not yet been elucidated, although it is known to be in, or attached to, one end ring; in this pigment, one of the vinyl side chains may not have been reduced to the ethyl group[7].

Some of the urobilinoid pigments show marked optical activity (Table II), the origin of which remains a fascinating problem of stereochemistry. Certainly, urobilin-IXα cannot be a racemic mixture of the enantiomorphs of stercobilin and d-urobilin. The enormous values of specific optical rotation are due to the proximity of the wave length of maximum light absorption to the wave length at which the optical rotation is usually measured[8]. This is a well known effect shown by most compounds containing a chromophoric group capable of interaction with the structural centre responsible for optical activity.

Hitherto, urobilin-IXα, stercobilin and d-urobilin have been the only three members of the urobilinoid series which had been isolated. Recently, catalytic hydrogenation followed by oxidation of d-urobilin has provided a new dextro-rotatory urobilin which is assumed to be an isomer of urobilin-IXα. The last pigment, therefore, is possibly a racemic mixture from which a laevo-rotatory urobilin, distinct from stercobilin, may eventually be isolated[9]. After standing in alkali, d-urobilin is found to be converted into a compound chemically similar to d-urobilin but which is optically inactive; it is probably racemised d-urobilin[9].

A number of tetrapyrrolic pigments are known in which one or more of the carbon bridges have been oxidised to hydroxymethyl or carbonyl groups. Thus, biladien-(a,b)-ones-(c) and biladiene-(a,b)-diols have been called purpurins by Siedel and type 3 biliviolins by Lemberg. The choletelins are related bilene-(b)-diones and tetrols[10].

The reactions of the bile pigments are summarised in Table III. The Gmelin reaction, given only by bilatrienes and biladienes-(a,c) (*i.e.*, by biliverdin, bilirubin and their analogous meso-compounds) produces a characteristic series of colour changes and is brought about by oxidation with

TABLE III

REACTIONS OF SOME BILE PIGMENTS

		Gmelin	Diazo	Ehrlich	Schlesinger fluorescence
Bilatrienes	Biliverdin Glaucobilin	+	—	—	—
Biladienes (a,c)	Bilirubin Mesobilirubin	+	+	—	—
Bilidienes (a,b) and (b,c)	Mesobiliviolin Mesobilirhodin	—	—	—	red
Bilenes (b)	Urobilin-IXα Stercobilin d-Urobilin	—	—	—	green
Bilanes	Mesobilirubinogen Stercobilinogen d-Urobilinogen	—	—	+	green after dehydrogenation

nitric acid, ferric chloride, hydrogen peroxide and other oxidising agents. A series of dehydrogenation and prototropic changes takes place[1,10-12].

The diazo reaction is given only by biladienes-(a,c) (*i.e.*, by bilirubin and mesobilirubin) with diazotised sulphanilic acid or related diazonium compounds. The tetrapyrrolic chain is cleaved into two dipyrryl fragments which then couple with the diazo reagent to form a mixture of two closely related isomeric red pigments. The reaction is also given by monopyrroles with a free α-position[1,11].

The Ehrlich reagent is a solution of p-dimethylaminobenzaldehyde in acid, and reacts with bilanes and pyrrylmethanes generally (as well as monopyrroles, such as porphobilinogen) to form a red pigment. The elements of water are removed from the carbonyl group of the reagent and the two hydrogen atoms of the central methane bridge of the bilanes[1,11].

The Schlesinger reaction consists of the formation of a green fluorescing zinc complex and is characteristic of all bilenes-(b), as well as of dipyrrylmethenes generally. In this reaction it is probable that a planar molecule is formed between the complexing zinc ion and two molecules of the bile pigment[1,11].

2. Haemoglobin breakdown

It is now generally accepted that the bile pigments are formed from the breakdown of the haem of haemoglobin in the cells of the reticuloendothelial system of the body[1,10,13]. The ready conversion *in vitro* of haemoglobin to haematin by acids and alkalis suggested that haematin and protoporphyrin might be intermediaries in the normal breakdown of haemoglobin. The oxidative removal of the α-methene bridge of protoporphyrin would thus lead to the formation of biliverdin. The evidence of this pathway is very doubtful because the excretion of labelled bile pigment after the administration of ^{15}N-labelled haematin or protoporphyrin[14,15] can be interpreted in other ways, for example, the reformation of haematin from protoporphyrin and of a haem protein from the haematin. On the other hand, it has long been known that haemoglobin and its derivatives in solution in the presence of a reducing agent form green pigments on oxidation. Haemoglobin leads to the formation of choleglobin and haematin to verdohaems. In these compounds, the iron is still co-ordinated to the pyrrole rings of the tetrapyrrolic compounds; verdohaem is a bile pigment iron complex and choleglobin is a denatured globin haemochromogen of a cyclic tetrapyrrolic pigment closely related to protoporphyrin[10,16], but with one methene bridge oxidised to a carbonyl group. Lemberg believed that under physiological conditions the haemoglobin of the red cells and the ascorbic acid in the presence of oxygen lead to the formation of choleglobin. He found that after haemolysis was induced with phenylhydrazine, there were increased amounts of the choleglobin-like precursors of bile pigments in the blood of rabbits. Gardikas and his colleagues[17], however, believe that the formation of bile pigment in this way, from rabbit red cells, is not of physiological significance. Unfortunately, the postulated intermediaries can be recognised only spectroscopically and cannot be isolated in the pure state; tracer experiments cannot, therefore, be performed to assess the quantitative part played by this pathway in the normal breakdown of haemoglobin.

3. Biosynthesis of bile pigments

For many years, bile pigments were believed to be formed only from the haemoglobin of red cells at the end of their life span, but the use of isotopes has shown another source of origin. Shemin and Rittenberg[18] had shown that ^{15}N-labelled glycine was specifically incorporated into the haemoglobin of circulating red cells, and showed that the curve of incorporation of the isotope into haem could not be explained in terms of synthesis and degradation of haemoglobin, but indicated a definite life span of the haemoglobin. This was soon followed by studies on the incorporation of labelled glycine into the faecal stercobilin, the one end product of haemoglobin metabolism which can be isolated in the pure state. The incorporation of the isotope into the stercobilin showed a high peak about 120 days after the glycine feeding, i.e., at the time when labelled haemoglobin was being broken down; a lower peak occurred 2–4 days after the glycine feeding and there was a small but significant labelling between the two peaks[19-26]. The high peak was clearly due to the catabolism of haemoglobin of red cells breaking down at the end of their life span and has been called the catabolic bile pigment. The fraction of the bile pigment which is labelled soon after the glycine feeding must be formed by a rapid biosynthetic process, closely related in time to the synthesis of haem of haemoglobin. It has, therefore, been called the haemopoietic bile pigment[27]. It might be due to the breakdown of newly formed red cells before release to the circulation, to a disproportionate synthesis of globin and haem, the excess of the latter being eliminated as bile pigment, or to the anabolism and catabolism of haemoglobin occurring simultaneously in immature red cells. Maturation of the red cells would occur because anabolism is greater than catabolism; the catabolised haemoglobin would lead to bile pigment. The labelling between the two peaks was at first thought to be a third metabolic source of bile pigment but is now known to be due to labelled glycine persisting longer in the body than had been expected[28]. Mathematical analysis of the results has revealed that normally about 10–15% of the bile pigment is haemopoietic in origin, while about 85% is catabolic. Similar isotope experiments in subjects with disease have shown that the proportion of haemopoietic bile pigment is increased to 80–85% in congenital porphyria[23], pernicious anaemia[19], sickle-cell anaemia[29] and thalassaemia[30], but the reason for this remains unknown.

4. Quantitative aspects of haemoglobin breakdown

Many attempts have been made to relate the rate of haemoglobin breakdown to the results of estimation of the faecal urobilinogen[1,13], but because in some diseases haemopoietic bile pigment can contribute to different extents to the faecal urobilinogen, the correlation can be only approximate. Moreover, faecal urobilinogen consists of a complex mixture of the three urobilinoid compounds and their precursors. The proportions of these three groups of compounds in the faeces is different from patient to patient and probably depends on the intestinal flora and perhaps on the diet. Of the three faecal urobilins, urobilin-IXα is highly labile, while stercobilin is relatively stable; the extent of breakdown in the gut of bile pigment to compounds which are not measured cannot, therefore, be readily assessed. Measurements of faecal urobilinogen can, therefore, provide only an approximate measure of haemoglobin breakdown.

5. Jaundice

In jaundice there is pigmentation of the cells and tissues of the body by bilirubin. The concentration of this pigment in the plasma is then increased above the normal value of about 0.8 mg/100 ml. Bilirubin in normal plasma consists of the pigment passing from the cells of the reticuloendothelial system to the liver where it is excreted in the bile after conjugation with glucuronic acid and perhaps with other compounds. Table IV summarises the differences between bilirubin and conjugated bilirubin.

TABLE IV

DIFFERENCES BETWEEN BILIRUBIN AND CONJUGATED BILIRUBIN

(after Billing[34])

	Bilirubin	Conjugated bilirubin
Direct diazo reaction	negative	positive
Solubility in chloroform	soluble	insoluble
Ease of oxidation	less easily	very easily
Occurrence in urine during regurgitation jaundice	absent	present
Occurrence in bile	absent	present
Affinity for brain tissue	strong	none

When haemoglobin breakdown is greatly increased from some haemolytic process affecting the red cells, the liver may be unable to remove the bilirubin sufficiently quickly from the blood stream. The concentration of bilirubin in the blood, therefore, increases and a retention jaundice of haemolytic type results. In certain rare individuals, there is a failure in the conjugation of bilirubin by the liver, sometimes because of a deficiency of the necessary enzymes. Bilirubin is retained in the blood; there is then a non-haemolytic form of retention jaundice[31].

On the other hand, if there is obstruction of the biliary passages, these become dilated above the site of obstruction and the whole biliary system becomes distended with bile. In the substance of the liver, where the biliary passages are very thin, they will rupture and bile is then regurgitated into the venous sinuses and reaches the blood stream. The resulting obstructive jaundice is associated with the presence of conjugated bilirubin in the blood. This also occurs in hepatogenous jaundice, in which the necrosis and damage to the liver cells results in distortion of their architecture. Again, the finer bile ducts inside the liver become obstructed and rupture, so that regurgitation of bile also occurs. Obstructive and hepatogenous jaundice are, therefore, more conveniently referred to as mechanical and parenchymatous forms respectively of regurgitation jaundice.

In both forms of regurgitation jaundice, conjugated bilirubin accumulates in the blood which, therefore, gives a positive diazo reaction (*i.e.*, in the absence of ethanol), in contrast to the bilirubin in retention jaundice which does not give a direct diazo reaction (*i.e.*, the reaction only occurs in the presence of ethanol). The glucuronide radical of the conjugated bilirubin makes the pigment sufficiently soluble for the reaction to occur without the addition of alcohol.

Lathe and Billing and their colleagues[32-34] have done much to elucidate the nature of the bile pigments in jaundice — and have shown that the conjugated bilirubin of the blood in regurgitation jaundice is partly a di-glucuronide and partly a monoglucuronide; recently, evidence has been accrued that conjugation with sulphate also occurs. Bollman has shown that while conjugation of bilirubin occurs mainly in the liver, formation of the monoglucuronide may take place, at any rate in part, in extrahepatic tissues, for the monoglucuronide accumulates in the plasma of hepatectomised dogs[35].

The low renal threshold of the conjugated bilirubin is responsible for its appearance in the urine of patients with both forms of regurgitation jaundice and its absence in the urine of subjects with retention jaundice is on account of the high renal threshold of the unconjugated pigment. There has been much discussion regarding the source of the urinary urobilin and urobilinogen which appear in the urine in certain forms of jaundice. They almost certainly arise from reabsorption from the gut of "faecal urobilinogen". A high proportion of the reabsorbed chromogen can be disposed of by the normal liver. This is not possible when the liver is damaged and the chromogen, and its associated pigment, is then excreted in increased amounts in the urine. The nature of the disposal by the liver is unknown. Detection of excess urinary urobilinogen and urobilin is of considerable value in the differential diagnosis of the two forms of regurgitation jaundice, providing that bile pigment is reaching the gut. If liver damage were so severe that this is not the case, then urinary urobilin and urobilinogen would disappear (Table V).

TABLE V

BILE PIGMENTS IN EXCRETA

	Urine		Faecal urobilinogen
	Bilirubin (conjugated)	Urobilinogen and/or urobilin	
Normal	o	trace	+ +
Haemolytic jaundice	o	trace or +	+ + + +
Non-haemolytic retention jaundice	o	o	o — +
Obstructive jaundice	+	o	o — +
Liver damage: mild	+	+	o — +
severe	+	o	o
Obstructive jaundice and infection	+	+	o — +

6. Biosynthesis of conjugates of bilirubin

The microsomes of liver cells contain an enzyme, bilirubin glucuronyl transferase, which transfers the glucuronyl radical from uridine diphosphoglucur-

onic acid (UDPGA) to bilirubin[33,36,37]. The UDPGA in turn is formed by
a uridine diphosphoglucose (UDPG) dehydrogenase present in the nucleus
(Fig. 4). Transfer of bilirubin from blood to bile is thus a highly complex
process[38], for it arrives at the liver cell surface as a bilirubin albumin complex;

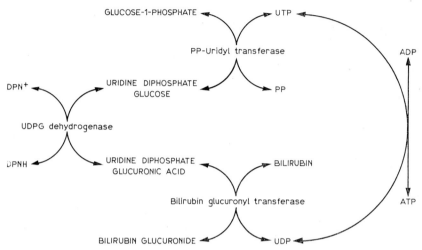

Fig. 4. Mechanism of formation of bilirubin glucuronide.

in the liver cell it is conjugated with glucuronic acid by the microsomes, and
is then transferred to the intracellular biliary canaliculi. Meanwhile, the
UDPG is synthesised in the nucleus, is converted to UDPGA in the particle-
free cytoplasm and then has to be utilised by the microsome. There may be
a deficiency of the bilirubin glucuronyl transferase in some human subjects
with non-haemolytic retention jaundice, but in others this enzyme appears to
be present in normal amounts and there is some evidence of an abnormality
of the transport of the bilirubin from the plasma to the microsomes[39,40].
Bilirubin glucuronyl transferase is also deficient in the livers of a strain of
rats with an hereditary form of retention jaundice[41]. The fate of the bile
pigments in these cases remains to be elucidated.

7. Jaundice in infancy

During the first few days of life most infants show a mild jaundice, due to the
destruction of the excess red cells present during intra-uterine life. The liver
of the newborn, particularly if the infant is premature, is deficient in transferase and other enzymes concerned with conjugating bilirubin[38]. Free bilirubin, therefore, accumulates in the blood and jaundice results. This con-

trasts with the adult liver which can deal easily with even the most severe haemolytic episodes so that plasma bilirubin seldom increases to more than 3 or 4 mg/100 ml. In haemolytic disease of the newborn there has been a transplacental transfer into the foetus of maternal antibodies formed in response to the foetal red cells, which were incompatible with those of the mother. Very severe haemolysis occurs, haemoglobin is converted to bilirubin and because of the enzyme deficiency in the immature liver, a severe retention jaundice results. There may be concentrations of free bilirubin in the blood exceeding 20 mg/100 ml. In regurgitation jaundice, bilirubin concentrations of this magnitude are frequently encountered, but the pigment never passes the blood–brain barrier to reach the brain tissues because it is in the conjugated form. The high concentrations of free bilirubin in haemolytic disease of the newborn are accompanied by selective absorption of this pigment by the brain tissues, particularly by the basal nuclei with consequent permanent brain injury. This is called kernicterus and can frequently be anticipated if the blood group of the mother is determined before birth. If haemolytic disease is expected, repeated bilirubin estimations during the early days of life must be carried out and if the concentration in the plasma exceeds 20 mg/100 ml, the red cells of the child must be replaced by exchange transfusions with blood of an appropriate compatible group.

REFERENCES

1 C. H. GRAY, *The Bile Pigments*, Methuen and Co., London, 1953.
2 H. PLEININGER AND M. DECKER, *Ann. Chem., Liebigs*, 598 (1956) 198.
3 C. H. GRAY, A. KULCZYCKA AND D. C. NICHOLSON, *J. Chem. Soc.*, (1961) 2264, 2268, 2276.
4 C. H. GRAY, D. C. NICHOLSON AND R. A. NICOLAUS, *Nature*, 181 (1958) 183.
5 W. SIEDEL AND E. MEIER, *Z. physiol. Chem., Hoppe-Seyler's*, 242 (1936) 102.
6 C. J. WATSON, *The Harvey Lectures*, Charles C. Thomas, Springfield, Ill., 1948, p. 41.
7 C. H. GRAY AND D. C. NICHOLSON, *J. Chem. Soc.*, (1958) 3085.
8 C. H. GRAY, P. M. JONES, W. KLYNE AND D. C. NICHOLSON, *Nature*, 184 (1959) 41.
9 C. H. GRAY AND D. C. NICHOLSON, *Nature*, 181 (1958) 483.
10 R. LEMBERG AND J. W. LEGGE, *Haematin Compounds and Bile Pigments*, Interscience, New York, 1949.
11 H. FISCHER AND H. ORTH, *Die Chemie des Pyrrols*, Akademische Verlagsgesellschaft, Leipzig, 1937.
12 W. SIEDEL, *Ber. deut. chem. Ges., Abt. A*, 77 (1944) 21.
13 C. J. WATSON, *Downey's Handbook of Haematology*, Hamish Hamilton, London, 1938.
14 I. M. LONDON, *J. Biol. Chem.*, 184 (1950) 373.
15 I. M. LONDON, M. YAMASAKI AND A. G. SABELLA, *Federation Proc.*, 10 (1951) 217.
16 R. LEMBERG, *Revs. Pure and Applied Chem.*, 6 (1956) 1.
17 C. GARDIKAS, J. E. KENCH AND J. F. WILSON, *Biochem. J.*, 46 (1950) 85.
18 D. SHEMIN AND D. RITTENBERG, *J. Biol. Chem.*, 166 (1946) 621, 627.
19 I. M. LONDON, D. SHEMIN, R. WEST AND D. RITTENBERG, *J. Biol. Chem.*, 179 (1949) 463.
20 I. M. LONDON, R. WEST, D. SHEMIN AND D. RITTENBERG, *Federation Proc.*, 7 (1948) 169.
21 M. GRINSTEIN, R. A. ALDRICH, V. HAWKINSON AND C. J. WATSON, *J. Biol. Chem.*, 179 (1949) 983.
22 C. H. GRAY, A. NEUBERGER AND P. H. A. SNEATH, *Biochem. J.*, 45 (1949) xP.
23 C. H. GRAY, A. NEUBERGER AND P. H. A. SNEATH, *Biochem. J.*, 47 (1950) 87.
24 I. M. LONDON, R. WEST, D. SHEMIN AND D. RITTENBERG, *J. Biol. Chem.*, 184 (1950) 351.
25 I. M. LONDON AND R. WEST, *J. Biol. Chem.*, 184 (1950) 359.
26 I. M. LONDON, R. WEST, D. SHEMIN AND D. RITTENBERG, *J. Biol. Chem.*, 184 (1950) 365.
27 C. H. GRAY AND J. J. SCOTT, *Biochem. J.*, 71 (1959) 38.
28 N. I. BERLIN, C. HEWITT AND C. LOTZ, *J. Biochem.*, 58 (1954) 498.
29 G. WATSON JAMES AND L. D. ABBOTT, *Proc. Soc. Exptl. Biol. Med.*, 88 (1955) 398.
30 M. GRINSTEIN, R. M. BANNERMAN, J. B. VAVRA AND C. V. MOORE, *Am. J. Med.*, (1960) in the press.
31 L. SCHIFF AND B. H. BILLING, *Gastroenterology*, 37 (1959) 595.
32 G. H. LATHE AND B. H. BILLING, *Am. J. Med.*, 24 (1958) 111.
33 C. H. GRAY, *Brit. Med. Bull.*, 13 (1957) 94.
34 B. H. BILLING, *Advances in Clinical Chemistry*, Academic Press, New York, London, 1960.
35 H. N. HOFFMANN, F. F. WHITCOMB, H. R. BUTT AND J. L. BOLLMAN, *J. Clin. Invest.*, 39 (1960) 132.
36 R. SCHMID, L. HAMMAKER AND J. AXELROD, *Arch. Biochem. Biophys.*, 70 (1957) 285.
37 C. H. GRAY, *Bile Pigments in Health and Disease*, Charles C. Thomas, Springfield, Ill., 1960.
38 G. H. LATHE AND M. WALKER, *Biochem. J.*, 70 (1958) 705.
39 R. SCHMID, J. AXELROD, L. HAMMAKER AND R. L. SWARM, *J. Clin. Invest.*, 37 (1958) 1123.
40 R. SCHMID AND L. HAMMAKER, *New Engl. J. Med.*, 260 (1959) 1310.
41 R. SCHMID, *J. Clin. Invest.*, 36 (1957) 927.

Volume 9

Part B

ISOPRENOID COMPOUNDS

Chapter V

Chemistry of Isoprenoid Compounds

A. J. HAAGEN-SMIT AND C. C. NIMMO

Division of Biology, California Institute of Technology,
Pasadena, Calif. (U.S.A.)

1. Introduction

The chemical analysis of plant and animal material has shown the occurrence of a large number of compounds with a molecular structure which can be constructed from isoprene or isopentane units. This type of structure appears frequently in volatile oils of plants, the so-called essential oils, valued since early history because they carried the *Quinta essentia*, the fragrance of the plants. The occurrence of this type of compound in oil of turpentine impressed upon them the name "terpenes". Through the work of Wallach, Semmler and Perkin around the turn of the century, the chemical nature of many of the terpenes became well understood, and at present we know about 150 different structures of the general formula $C_{10}H_{16}$ and their oxygen derivatives.

Higher boiling fractions of the oils contained closely related compounds which received the name of sesquiterpenes, because their formula contained one and a half times as many carbon atoms as the monoterpenes. Rapid development in the study of these terpenes with 15 carbon atoms was initiated by Ruzicka about 35 years ago and has since been extended by the work of Simonsen, Sorm, and many others.

A still higher boiling fraction of the oils contained diterpenes of the general formula $C_{20}H_{32}$. Their oxygen derivatives were found in the distillation residues of the oleoresins.

The recognition that a group of the saponins, as well as the yellow and orange pigments found in plants and animals, the carotenes and xanthophylls, and also rubber obey the same building principle has extended the terpene group to the following classes: C_5, hemiterpenes; C_{10}, monoterpenes; C_{15}, sesquiterpenes; C_{20}, diterpenes; C_{30}, triterpenes; C_{40}, tetraterpenes; and C_{5n}, polyterpenes.

In recent years a few terpenoid compounds with 45 and 50 carbon atoms arranged in isoprene units have been found.

The variety in structure of the terpenoids is caused not only by the number of isopentane or isoprene units, but also by the way in which carbon atoms of the units are interlocked. Diagrammatic illustration of this is presented in Figs. 1 and 2, in which the carbon–carbon linkages of the naturally occurring mono- and sesquiterpenes are accounted for in one formula. Further variations in these structures are caused by presence and location of double bonds and functional groups.

Fig. 1. Sesquiterpenes, carbon–carbon linkages.

Fig. 2. Monoterpenes, carbon–carbon linkages.

Greatly improved isolation techniques in the fields of distillation and the broad field of chromatography, as well as the vastly increased use of spectroscopic methods to assist in identification, have not only revealed many more representatives of this group, but have also shown that the isoprene "rule" is not always strictly adhered to. Ruzicka[1] proposed in 1953 that the carbon skeleton of natural terpenic compounds can be deduced from postulated precursors with regularly arranged isopentane units, using accepted reaction mechanisms. Deviations from this rule would imply that molecular rearrangements had taken place. Biochemical studies with precursors labeled with radioactive carbon atoms have given experimental justification for the classification of the terpenes and structurally related compounds in one large group of isoprenoids or terpenoids. These related compounds may be derived from the terpenes by rearrangements, oxidation and reduction or by combination with non-terpenoid structures. Examples of these are some of the bitter substances, terpene alkaloids, chromanes and quinones and various terpenoids of mixed biogenetic origin occurring in fungi. Steroids, although biogenetically related to the triterpenoids, are usually for practical reasons classed separately.

Recognition of the biosynthesis of the terpenoid from acetate units establishes a definite relationship of this to fats, as well as to the seven-carbon ring substances, tropolones, which differ in the way in which the acetate units were joined initially in the biochemical formation. A regular, "head-to-tail" union of the acetate units leads to the fatty acid family, whereas branching and cyclization yielded the terpenes and their relatives the steroids. The name *acetogenins* has been proposed for both groups, accounting thereby for their common origin.

Systematic surveys of the terpenes of essential oils have been compiled by Guenther[2] (Vol. II). The occurrence and the technical production of the more important commercially produced oils are found in the subsequent volumes. The most detailed treatise on the chemistry of the terpenoids has been compiled by Simonsen[3], in collaboration with others. Several reviews on terpenoids were included in *The Encyclopedia of Plant Physiology*[4]. Other recent reviews are by Barton[5] and Mayo[6]. Absolute configuration and spatial arrangement can now be assigned to many of the terpenoids, as a result of applications of X-ray, conformational analysis and other physical measurements such as nuclear magnetic resonances and optical rotatory dispersion[6]. Reviews of progress in this field have been made by Mayo in Simonsen[3], Barton[7], Hückel[8] and Birch[9] and Klyne[10]. Absolute stereochemical configurations of many of the terpenoids have been related to L-glyceraldehyde through the oxidation products (—)-methylsuccinic acid (1) and(—)-isopropylsuccinic acid (2).

(—)-Methylsuccinic acid   (—)-Isopropylsuccinic acid
(1)   (2)

The configuration of substituents is indicated by dotted and thick bonds, which are respectively below and above the plane of the paper.

Effect of structure on reactivity of terpenoids has been a subject of long and increasing interest among organic chemists, in relation to molecular rearrangements and cyclization to form higher molecular weight compounds in the series. Recent discussions in this field have been made by Ruzicka[11] and by Mayo[6].

Nomenclature for the complicated structures found in the terpenoids has always presented a difficult problem. Trivial names, assigned to a large number of the oil compounds before their structures were established, have carried through to the present time. A more systematic nomenclature for the monoterpene hydrocarbon fundamental structures has been approved by the American Chemical Society[12]. This system uses standard, recognized naming and numbering rules for acyclic and gem-dimethylcyclohexane type terpene compounds. Frequently occurring mono- and bicyclic structures are named according to skeleton type, such as menthane and oleanane, with fixed numberings for each type. These will be mentioned in the appropriate section.

2. Hemiterpenoids and related substances

In view of the abundance of structures consisting of multiples of C_5H_8, as a basic structure, in the terpenoids, one might reasonably expect to find isoprene itself accompanying the essential oils. It has not been found, however, in plants, even though it is easily formed in the laboratory by pyrolysis of limonene.

Oxygen-containing isopentane derivatives are often found in terpene sources free or as esters and others combined with higher terpenes. Of special interest is the natural occurrence of the hydrolysis products of the biogenetically important isopentenyl pyrophosphates: β,β'-dimethylallylalcohol and 2-methyl-3-buten-2-ol. These alcohols are the hemiterpene analogs of the alcohol pairs: geraniol, linalool and farnesol, nerolidol of the mono- and sesquiterpene series. β,β'-Dimethylallylalcohol is often found as ester or ether combined with phenol or coumarins, as in feniculin (3) and imperatorin (4). Other five-carbon compounds are isoamyl alcohol, isovaleraldehyde, isovaleric acid, 2-methylbutyric acid and the unsaturated acids, isopropylidene acetic, angelic and tiglic acids. Their combination with other terpenes is illustrated by the sesquiterpene ester laserpitin (5). Analogous cases involving the monoterpene alcohol, geraniol, and the sesquiterpene alcohol, farnesol, in bergamottin and umbelliprenin justify the name of hemiterpenoids for the C_5 compounds.

The isopentenyl is often recognized as part of non-isoprenoid structures of mixed biogenetic origin[19]. Typical examples are the bitter substances from oil of hops (*lupulone*) (6), the ergot alkaloids and various constituents of fungi[13].

Feniculin (3)   Imperatorin (4)   Laserpitin (5)   Lupulone (6)

In plant species of the genus *Senecio* (*Compositae*) occur a number of branched-chain acids, free and bound to alkaloids, which form a bridge from the hemiterpenes to the monoterpenes. Isotope experiments have established that acetate residues are transformed into these branched acids, similar to their incorporation into the higher terpenes. A few examples of these acids are shown by the coupling of heliotridine with angelic and lasiocarpic acid in lasiocarpine (7), dicrotalic (8) and trichodesmic (9) acid. The present status of our knowledge of these "necic" acids has been reviewed by Leonard[14].

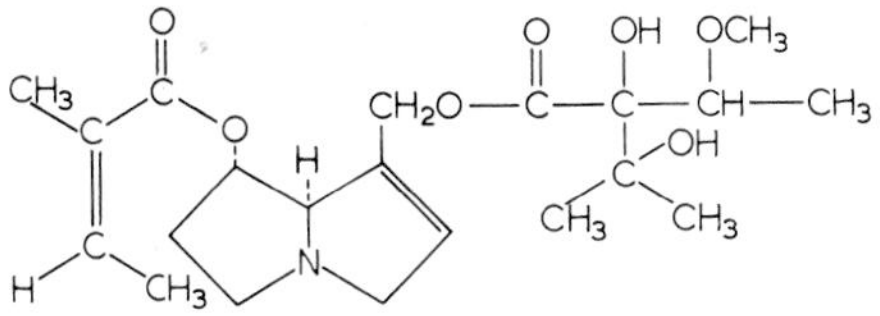

Lasiocarpine (7)
Angelic and lasiocarpic ester of heliotridine

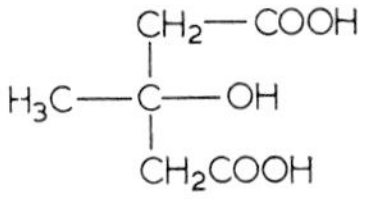

Dicrotalic acid (8)

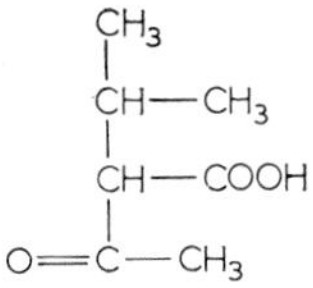

Trichodesmic acid (9)

3. Monoterpenoids

(a) General

The main source of monoterpenes are essential oils, obtained from plants by steam distillation, extraction with low boiling solvents or fats or pressing. Fractionation of the oils by distillation is used for the separation of individual terpenes and their oxygen-containing derivatives. In recent years chromatographic methods, especially gas chromatography, have been used to obtain far better separation than was possible in the past. Spectroscopic analysis, especially the use of the infrared region, has greatly increased the reliability of the studies on the composition of the oils[15].

A large percentage of many oils consists of hydrocarbons and oxygen-containing derivatives which can be constructed of two isoprene units. In principle several ways are possible to combine these units by a carbon–carbon bond. Schinz and Bourquin[16] list ten of these structures of which several have been synthesized. After scores of monoterpenes had been assigned their structural formula, it was clear that in the pattern of combination of isopentane or isoprene units the so-called "head-to-tail" arrangement predominated, as in 2,6-dimethyloctane. An example of such arrangement is found in the metabolically important alcohol, geraniol (18) and its *cis* isomer, nerol.

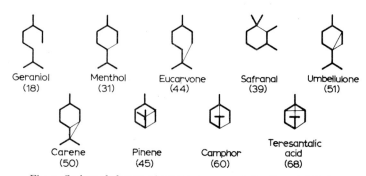

Fig. 3. Carbon skeletons of monoterpenes and the Geraniol Rule.

Carbon skeletons of the types shown in Fig. 3 account for most of the known terpenes. A common example is named for each skeleton. The geraniol chain is indicated with a heavy line, while secondary linkages leading to cyclic compounds are indicated with thin ones. Number and position of double bonds, hydroxyl, carbonyl, carboxyl, oxide and even peroxide functions account for about 150 monoterpenes which have been well characterized.

In the course of time a few exceptions to a head-to-tail structure were found in lavandulol (10) from the oil of *Lavandula officinalis*, artemisiaketone (11) from *Artemisia annua* and some of the necic acids. An ortho-menthane derivative, carquejol, has been identified in oil of carqueja[16]. Biochemical studies will be needed to determine the reasons for these deviations. For the irregular structure of fenchyl alcohol (12) we can suspect a rearrangement of the Wagner type from a pinane structure. In other cases it is reasonable to assume a decarboxylation or oxidative removal of one of the carbon atoms, as in santene (70) from sandalwood oil and isopropylhexenes with a hydroxyl or keto group in the para position as in cryptol, cryptone and the isopropylphenol, australol, from Eucalyptus oils.

Abnormally constituted terpenoids with tropolone ring structures, the thuja-plicins (13), occur in the heartwood of conifers[17]. α- and β-Ionone (14) with 13 and the irones (15) with 14 carbon atoms are probably oxidation products of higher terpenoids.

(b) Acyclic monoterpenes

The variety of structures in this series are related to geraniol (18) through dehydrations, hydrogenation and the introduction of oxygen, as shown for the olefin myrcene (16), the alcohol citronellol (19) and the aldehyde citral (17). Oxide rings are present in linalool monoxide (20), elsholtzione[18] (21), and in the aglycone of gentiopicrin (22), a part of the structure of the bitter substance from gentian root (*Gentiana lutea*[19]).

Myrcene (16) 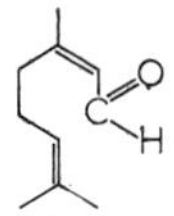   Citral (17) 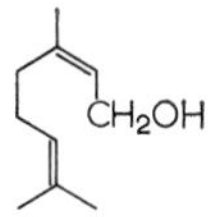   Geraniol (18) 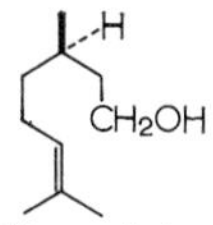   (+)-Citronellol (19)

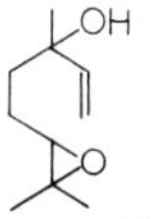

Linaloolmonoxide (20) 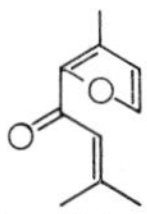   Elsholtzione (21) 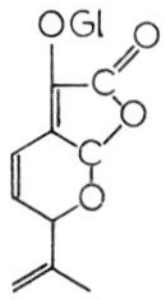   Gentiopicrin (22)

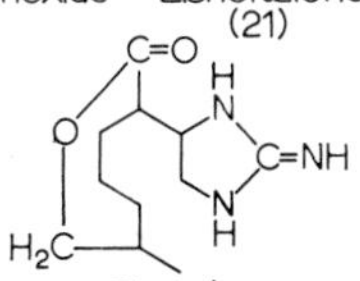

Chaksine (23) 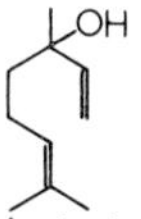   Linalool (24)

A recent addition to this group is the guanidine derivative chaksine (23) from a monoterpene alkaloid from *Cassia absus*[20].

Allyl rearrangement converts geraniol (18) to linalool (24) and vice versa, a process of biochemical as well as of industrial importance in the production of valuable perfume ingredients. Geraniol of variant origin differs in physical constants and odor due to the presence of isomers. The double bond between carbon atoms 2 and 3 makes the existence of *cis* and *trans* isomers possible, and the relative ease of ring formation permits one to distinguish between these forms, which have been called nerol and geraniol according to their origin from oil of neroli and oil of geranium. The double bond near the ter-

minal isopropyl group is a prominent feature of many terpenes and frequently carries a double bond in either the isopropylidene or the isopropenyl form.
Chemical evidence, in which both acetone and formaldehyde were released
on ozonolysis led to the conclusion that the naturally occurring acyclic monoterpenes were mixtures of the two forms. Infrared spectroscopic investigations have shown that they contain less than $2-3\%$ of the isopropenyl form.

(c) Monocyclic carbon systems

Acyclic terpenes are readily converted to members of the monocyclic group
with menthane (27) or cyclogeraniol (25) structures.

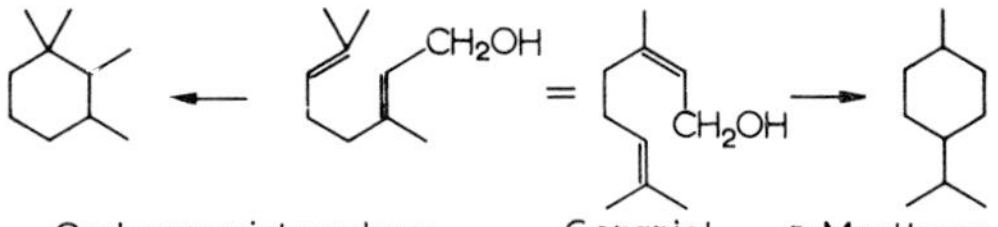

Cyclogeraniol nucleus   Geraniol   p-Menthane nucleus
(25)   (26)   (27)

Representation in the menthane group varies from fully saturated p-menthane to exhaustively dehydrogenated methylisopropenyl benzene (28) from
Cannabis indica. Especially frequent in essential oils are the menthadienes
such as limonene (29) and the terpinenes (30).

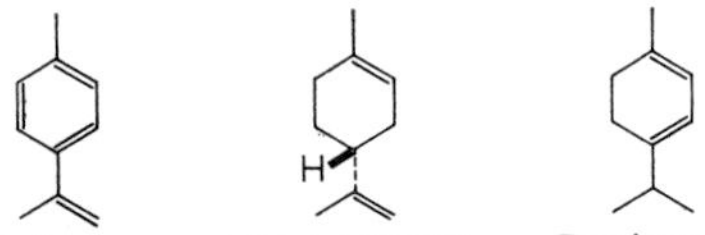

Methylisopropenyl   (+)-Limonene   α-Terpinene
benzene
(28)   (29)   (30)

Many members of the menthane group are substituted by hydroxyl, aldehyde or keto groups or may contain oxide, lactone or peroxide ring systems.
This, coupled with the variation in number and position of the double bonds,
leads to a large number of possible structures. 35 of these have been listed,
not counting stereoisomeric forms, as occurring in nature, and examples
in formulae (28–38) illustrate this variety.

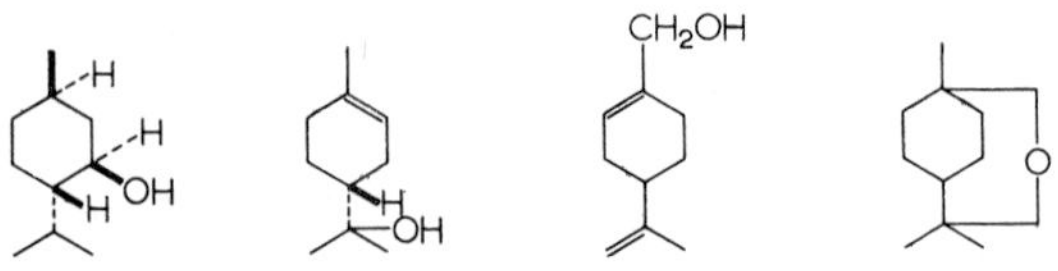

(-)-Menthol   (+)-α-Terpineol   Perillylalcohol   1,8-Cineole
(31)   (32)   (33)   (34)

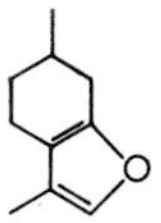

Menthofuran (35) 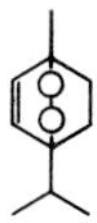 Ascaridole (36) 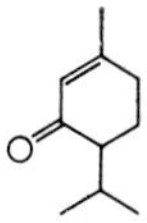 Piperitone (37) 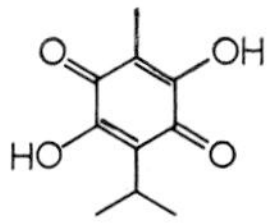 Dihydroxy thymoquinone (38)

A ring closure of a geraniol chain leading to a 1,1',2,3-tetramethylcyclo-hexane structure, frequently met in the higher terpenes, has been found in only a few monoterpenoids. Examples of these are safranal (39) derived from the aglucon of the bitter principle picrocrocin from saffron (*Crocus sativus*) and the α- and β-ionones (14) with 13 and the irones (15) with 14 carbon atoms, from, respectively, *Boronio megastigma* and *Costus* oil. Dihydro-γ-ionone occurs in ambergris and its fully hydrogenated form has been isolated from urine of pregnant mares and the scent glands of the Canadian beaver. Their origin as degradation products from carotenoids is likely.

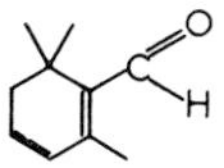

Safranal (39) 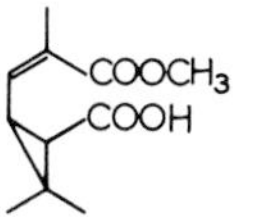 Chrysanthemum monocarboxylic ester (40)  3-Isopropylidene-1-acetylcyclopentene-5 (41)

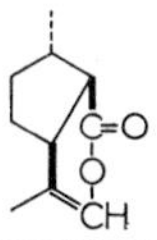

Nepetalactone (42) 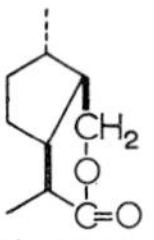 Iridolactone (43) 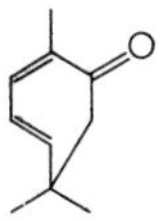 Eucarvone (44)

Monocyclic terpenes with cyclopropane, -pentane and -heptane structure

These can be considered as oxidation or rearrangement products of the menthane group. For example, chrysanthemum monocarboxylic acid (40), the acid part of the insecticide pyrethrin from *Chrysanthemum cinaerarifolium* is probably derived from a carene type structure by oxidation. The same holds for the monoterpenes with cyclopentane ring, 3-isopropylidene-1-ace-tylcyclopentene-5 (41) from *Eucalyptus globulus*, the enol lactone nepeta-lactone[21] (42), the active principle of catnip, iridolactone (43) and iridodial isolated from ants. Closely related are the alkaloids, actinidine and skytan-thin, in which the ring oxygen in the ant lactone has been replaced by a nitrogen atom[22].

References p. 164

Seven-membered rings are found in eucarvone (44) from *Asarum sieboldi*[23]. This ketone is formed from carvone by ring enlargement through the intermediate formation of a carane type anion, by treatment of carvone hydrobromide with alkali. Related structures are probably those of shonanic acid[24] from the wood of *Libocedrus formosana* and thujic acid[25] from *Thuja plicata*.

(d) Bicyclic carbon systems
Carane, thujane, pinane, bornane and trimethylnorbornane types

Bicyclic monoterpenes contain, in addition to a six-membered ring, three-, four-, or five-membered rings. Formally we can derive these systems from menthane by connecting carbon atom 8 with carbon atoms 5, 6, or 1, or by linking carbon atoms 4 and 6. Fig. 4 shows how these linkages yield the basic ring systems carane, pinane, bornane and thujane. These groups are noted for their tendency to form new ring systems through pinacol–pinacolone type rearrangements.

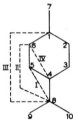

Fig. 4. Cyclisations in menthane structure. I. Carane; II. Pinane; III. Bornane; IV. Thujane.

The facility with which these carbon–carbon bonds are broken and new linkages established demonstrate clearly the limitation of our ordinary chemical formulae. The investigation of the fused ring structures of the terpenes and their analogues enjoys a lively interest among theoretical organic chemists in the study of reaction mechanisms and the nature of the carbon–carbon bond.

The rearrangements in this series involve the formation of carbonium ions and electron shifts. These are discussed in their application to the transformations in the bicyclic monoterpenes by Mayo[6]. Presented in a simplified form, protonation of the double bond in α-pinene (45) results in the formation of a carbonium ion. Subsequent 1,2-shifts, and loss of a proton or the addition of a hydroxyl or chloride ion stabilizes the new structure. This simplified version cannot explain the retention of stereochemical specificity and the concept of bridged ions was therefore introduced. Using localized classical carbonium ions, the Wagner–Meerwein and Nametkin rearrangement of α-pinene are presented in Fig. 5. By treatment of α-pinene (45) with anhy-

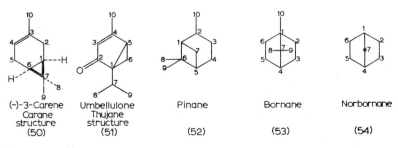

α-Pinene (45)

Bornylchloride (46)

Camphene (47)

Fig. 5.

drous hydrogen chloride, a chloride is obtained, which does not have the original ring structure, but is converted to a bornane system. When this bornyl chloride (46) is treated with base it rearranges again and camphene (47) is formed.

(+)-Camphene (48)   **(−)-Camphene (49)**

The movement of the electrons were in this case within the ring, and the resulting structural change has become known as the Wagner or Wagner– Meerwein rearrangement. A transfer of a methyl group as in the formation of (+)-camphene (48) to (—)-camphene (49) is connected with the name of Nametkin.

The carane group represented by 3-carene (50) from *Pinus longifolia* contains a three-membered ring fused to a cyclohexane ring. In thujane a cyclopropane ring is joined with a cyclopentane ring, as shown for umbellul- one (51) from *Umbellularia californicum*. α-Pinene (45), a common constituent of many essential oils has a fused four- and five-membered ring system, which received the name of pinane (52). The numbering of these ring systems is indicated in formulae 50–54. Borneol (59) has a bornane (53) and camphene (47) a norbornane (54) ring structure.

All three groups show a tendency to rupture of the more strained smaller

(−)-3-Carene
Carane
structure
(50)

Umbellulone
Thujane
structure
(51)

Pinane

(52)

Bornane

(53)

Norbornane

(54)

ring. In the case of carane structures this may lead to cyclopentane or men-thane structures. The breaking of the 6–7 bond in carene leads to the for-mation of a *meta*-menthane, sylvestrene, in the distillation of some pine oils. This terpene is now considered as an artefact and has not been found to occur in nature. α-Pinene is readily converted to the menthane structure as in limonene, and to several other bicyclic ring systems. Its many rearrange-ments and the formation of oxidation products still containing the cyclo-butane ring suggests a biogenetic relationship between many constituents, which often occur together in essential oils. Fig. 6 illustrates the relations within this pinene family. Oxidation of pinene leads to formation of verben-one (55), myrtenal (56), myrtenol (57) and chrysanthenone[26] (58). Fission of the cyclobutane ring leads to monocyclic terpineol (62) and related com-pounds, dipentene (63), 1,4-cineole (64), and other menthane type structures. Wagner–Meerwein rearrangements are involved in the formation of borneol (59), camphor (60), camphene (61), fenchyl alcohol (65) and fenchone (66) with bornane and norbornane type structures.

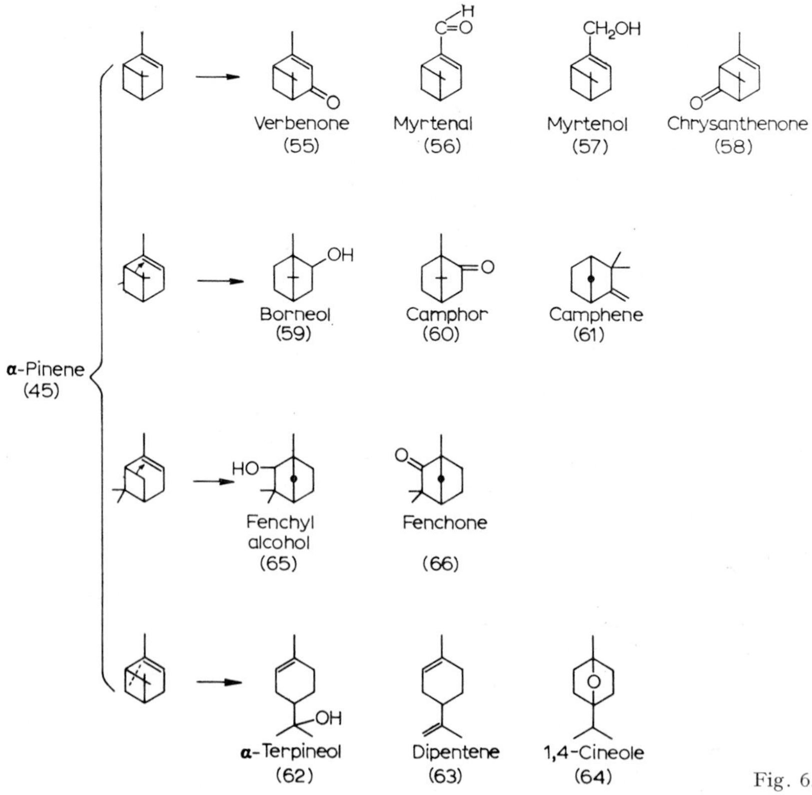

Verbenone (55)   Myrtenal (56)   Myrtenol (57)   Chrysanthenone (58)

Borneol (59)   Camphor (60)   Camphene (61)

α-Pinene (45)

Fenchyl alcohol (65)   Fenchone (66)

α-Terpineol (62)   Dipentene (63)   1,4-Cineole (64)

Fig. 6.

(e) Tricyclic carbon systems

The oil of sandalwood (*Santalum album*) contains an interesting small family of tricyclic compounds which can be constructed from the bornane skeleton by linking carbon atoms 2 and 6. Representatives with a tricyclane structure are teresantalol (67) and teresantalic acid (68). Several imperfect isoprene type structures occur in the oil.

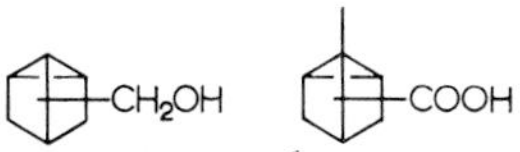

Teresantalol	Teresantalic acid	Tricyclane
(67)	(68)	(69)

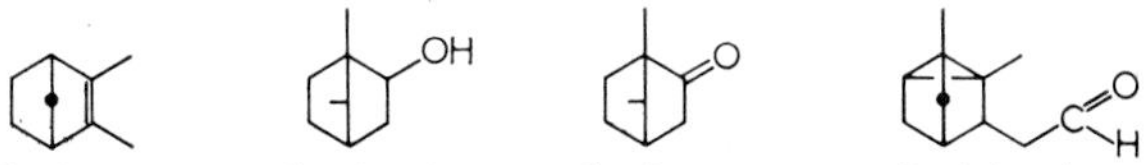

Santene	Santenol	Santenone	Nortricyclo-ekasantalal
(70)	(71)	(72)	(73)

Santene (70), santenol (71) and santenone (72) consist of only 9 carbon atoms, whereas nortricycloekasantalal (73) contains 11. Their structure indicates a relationship to teresantalic acid and the sesquiterpene alcohol santalol, from which they can be derived by decarboxylation, oxidation and rearrangements common in the bicyclic terpenes.

4. Sesquiterpenoids

(a) General

At present about 150 sesquiterpenes are listed with complete structural formulae assigned to half of them. With exception of acyclic farnesol (74) and nerolidol (75) and a few related structures, most members of this group are mono-, bi-, tri- and tetracyclic. Dehydrogenation with sulfur, introduced by Ruzicka in the structure determinations of sesquiterpenes, allowed them to be characterized by their ability to yield the naphthalene hydrocarbons cadalene (4,7-dimethyl-1-isopropylnaphthalene) and eudalene (1-methyl-7-isopropylnaphthalene), and the colored azulenes with 5- and 7-membered ring system. This method served as a useful indication of the nature of the carbon skeleton of the original terpene. Subsequent oxidative degradation had to be used to determine the position of double bonds and functional groups and to settle structural problems caused by secondary rearrangements during the dehydrogenation experiments. Great difficulties had to be overcome in the elucidation of structures which did not yield readily identifiable products upon dehydrogenation, and it is only in recent times that the baffling problems of the structure of compounds such as cedrene, caryophyllene and many others have been solved. The introduction of modern methods of separation, such as chromatography, countercurrent distribution, and the use of infrared spectroscopic analysis and X-ray analysis has contributed greatly to the increase in our knowledge in this field. New types of structures are being added at an increasing rate. The results of configurational analysis

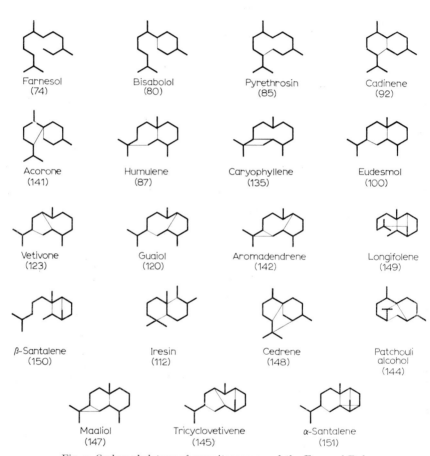

Fig. 7. Carbon skeletons of sesquiterpenes and the Farnesol Rule.

has been incorporated in many of the examples to illustrate the building principles of this group. In recent years several extensive reviews have been published on sesquiterpenes in general[27,28] and on the perhydroazulene subgroup[29-32].

Fig. 7 shows the carbon skeletons of several sesquiterpene types, illustrating correspondence to a "Farnesol Rule" analogous to the "Geraniol Rule".

(b) Acyclic carbon systems

The building principle of head-to-tail union of the isopentane units generally holds for the sesquiterpene series. Acyclic farnesol (74) and nerolidol (75) are related as geraniol (18) and linalool (24) are in the monoterpene series.

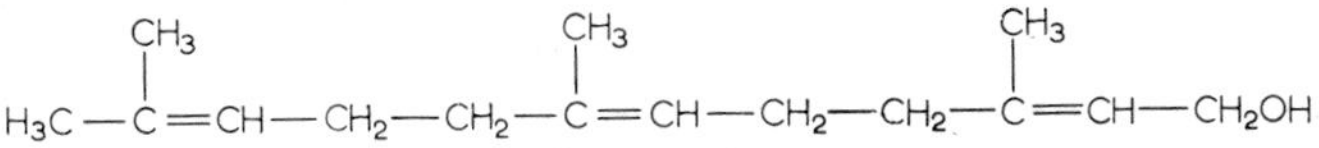

Farnesol (74)

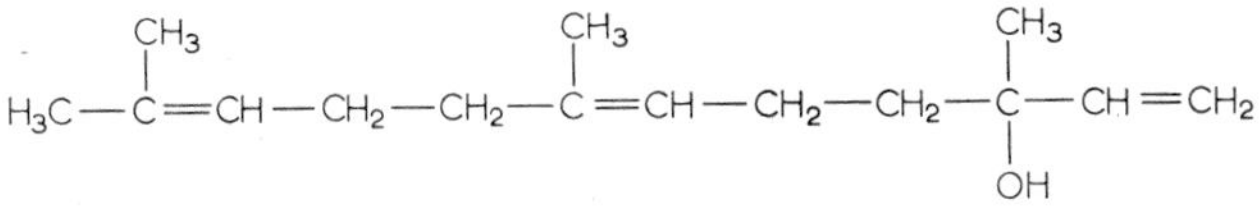

Nerolidol (75)

Other acyclic representatives are farnesene and also furanosesquiterpenes isolated from black-rotted sweet potatoes, ipomeamarone (76) and its *trans* isomer, ngaione from the New Zealand tree *Myoporum lactum*[33]. Closely related compounds are myoporone (77) from *Myoporum bontioides*[34] and the odorous substance dendrolasin[35] (78) from the plant *Lasius* (*Dendrolasius*) *fuliginosus*.

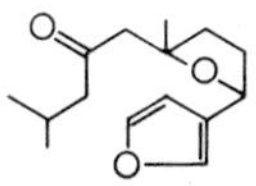

Ipomeamarone
(76)

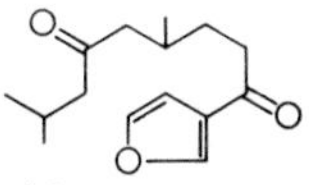

Myoporone
(77)

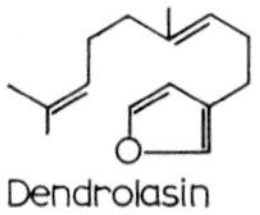

Dendrolasin
(78)

(c) Monocyclic carbon systems

Acyclic sesquiterpenes readily form cyclic structures and many of these cyclizations have been carried out in the laboratory. Similar enzymatically regulated cyclizations are responsible for the diversity of the naturally occurring C_{15} compounds. Ruzicka, Eschenmoser[36] and especially Schinz[37] have studied the laboratory transformations of farnesyl and similarly built chains to cyclic systems. When nerolidol (79) is treated with formic acid, a monocyclic sesquiterpene alcohol, bisabolol (80), is formed. This cyclization follows along the lines found in the monoterpene series, since bisabolene can be constructed from a farnesol chain by cyclizations comparable to the formation of dipentene from geraniol.

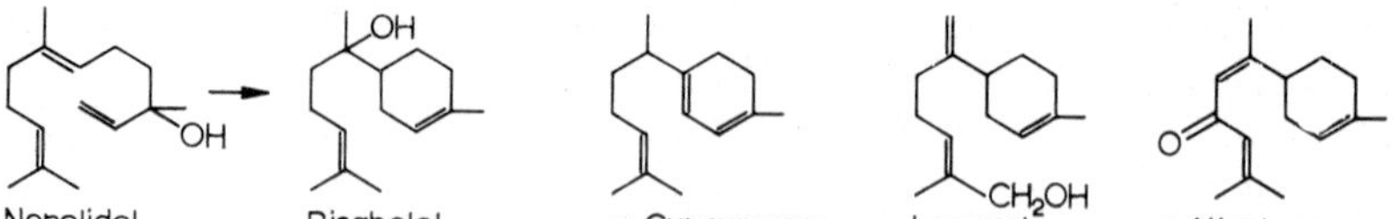

| Nerolidol (79) | Bisabolol (80) | γ-Curcumene (81) | Lanceol (82) | α-Atlantone (83) |

Examples of similarly constituted monocyclic structures are shown for the hydrocarbon γ-curcumene (81) from *Curcuma aromatica*, the alcohol lanceol (82) from *Santaluma lanceolatum* and the ketone α-atlantone (83) present in the volatile oils of several species of *Cedrus*.

In recent years new types of monocyclic ring structures, containing 10- and 11-membered rings have become known. Representatives of this cyclo-decane series are arctiolide and its β-hydroxy-α-methyl propionic ester arctiopicrin[38] (84) from *Arctium minus* and pyrethrosin[39] (85) from *Chrysanthemum cinaerariaefolium*.

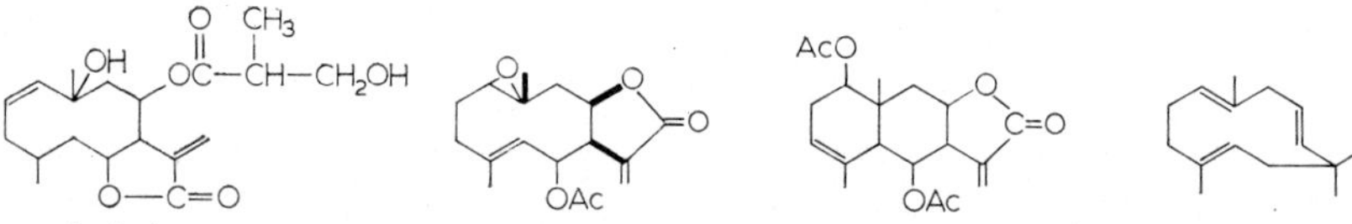

| Arctiopicrin (84) | Pyrethrosin (85) | Cyclisation product (86) | Humulene (87) |

Their conversion to bicyclic lactones structures (86) corresponding to those found in santonin (106) and related compounds has suggested a possible biogenetic relationship. Humulene[40] (87) from oil of hops and zerumbone[41] (88) from wild ginger contain 11-membered ring systems. Monocyclic elemol (89) isolated from Manila oil of Elemi cannot be built of a farnesol chain. It was therefore suggested that a ring opening from a eudalene type structure took place in its formation. The discovery of the ready transformation of

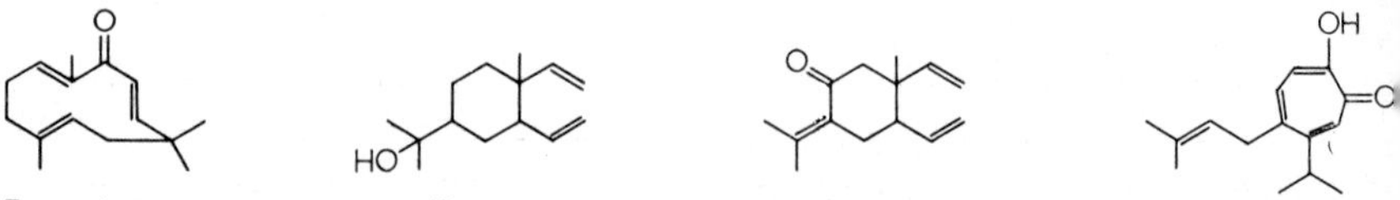

| Zerumbone (88) | Elemol (89) | β-Elemenone (90) | Nootkatin (91) |

monocyclic germacrone (146) to β-elemenone (90) present in the same zdravets oil of *Bulgaria* makes its formation through the primary formation of a 10-membered ring system plausible[42]. A more distantly related compound is an isoprene homologue of the thujaplicins, nootkatin, found in *Chamaecyparis nootkatensis*[43] (91).

(d) Bicyclic carbon ring systems

(i) Cadalene type

Bicyclic sesquiterpenes with a perhydrocadalene ring structure occur widely in essential oils. The 20 well-established structures differ in position of double bonds and their functional groups. Chromatographic methods have allowed the isolation of some of the double bond isomers in pure condition. Such separation methods resulted in the resolution of the complex of cadinenes (92–96) and cadinols (97–98) by Sorm et al.[44] and by Soffer et al.[45] into the several isomers.

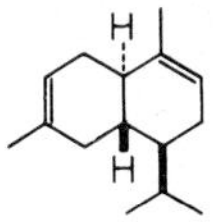

(–)-β-Cadinene (92)	(+)-γ-Cadinene (93)	(–)-γ-Cadinene (94)	(+)-δ-Cadinene (95)

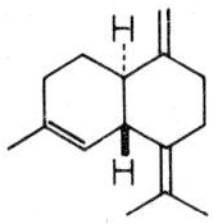

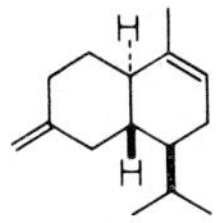

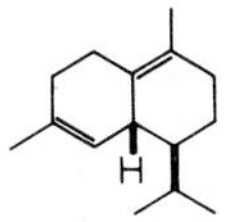

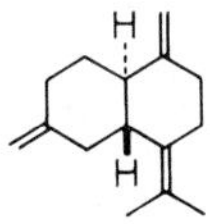

(+)-ε-Cadinene (96)	(–)-α-Cadinol (97)	(–)-δ-Cadinol(pilgerol) (98)	Calamendiol (99)

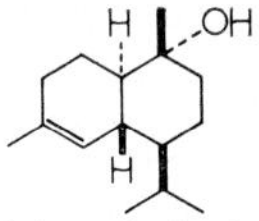

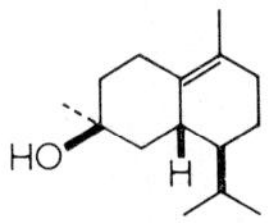

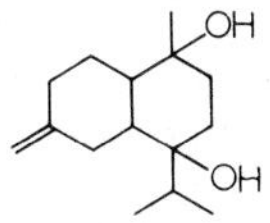

Other cadinene type sesquiterpenes differ in position and number of double bonds and number and presence of hydroxyl or keto groups, as for example, calamendiol (99) from *Acorus calamus*, a dihydroxy derivative of dihydro-γ-cadinene.

(ii) Eudesmol type

Ruzicka[46] established the presence of hydronaphthalene structure differing from that of cadinene, by dehydrogenating eudesmol (100). The naphthalene hydrocarbon, eudalene (101), contains one carbon atom less than cadalene. It was subsequently shown that in the dehydrogenation process a bridge methyl group was lost from the original sesquiterpene.

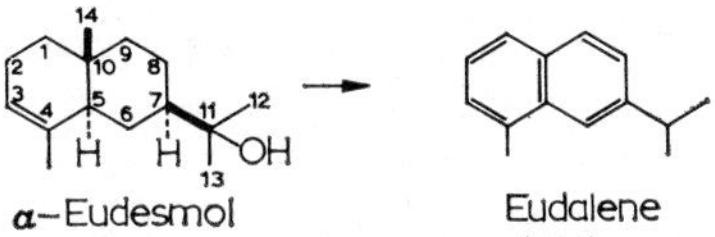

α–Eudesmol (100)	Eudalene (101)

Typical representatives of this group are, in addition to α- and β-eudesmol[47], α-cyperone (102), costol (sesquibenihiol[48]) (103), junenol[49] (104) from juniper oil and occidentalol[50] (105) from *Thuja occidentalis*.

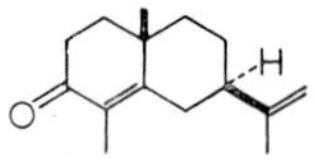

| (+)-α-Cyperone (102) | Costol (103) | Junenol (104) | Occidentalol (105) |

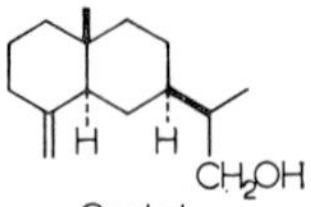

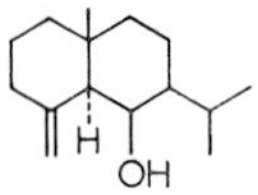

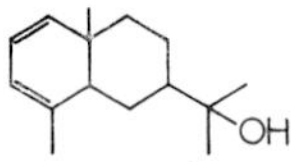

To this group belong the commercially important santonins[51] (106), arte-misin[52] (108) from various species of *Artemisia* and the alantolactones[53] (109). The structures of these compounds suggest a biogenetic relationship with the previously mentioned monocyclic lactones arctiopicrin (84) and pyrethrosin (85), as well as the perhydroazulene type lactones helenalin (125), matricin and tenulin.

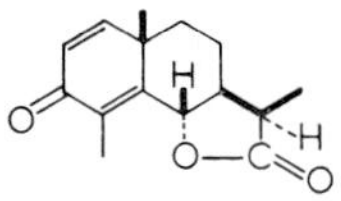

| (−)-α-Santonin (106) | Perhydroazulenelactone (107) | Artemisin (108) | Alantolactones (109) |

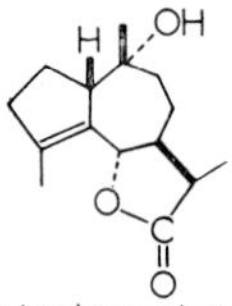

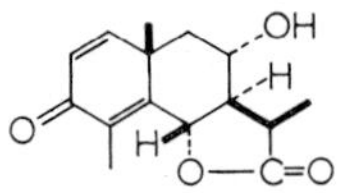

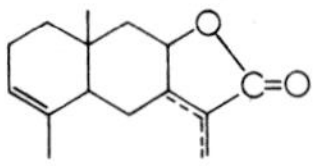

Photochemical rearrangement of α-santonin to a sesquiterpene lactone of the perhydroazulene series (107) has been shown to occur by Barton[54].

Related to this group is irregularly built eremophilone (110), present in the wood oil from *Eremophila mitchelli*, which shows an abnormal position of the bridge methyl groups[55]. A methyl shift for eremophilone from a regular eudalene type structure has been discussed by Ruzicka[1].

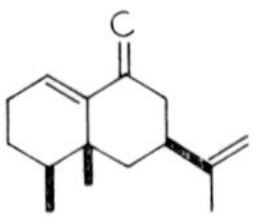

Eremophilone (110)

(*iii*) *Iresin group*

The cadinene group can be constructed from a farnesol chain (111) by two dipentene ring closures, whereas one cyclization of this type followed by a cyclogeraniol forms a eudesmol structure. Djerassi[56] found in iresin (112) and related compounds from *Iresine celioides*, a new type which could be formed by two cyclogeraniol type structures. Iresin establishes a link between the sesqui- and higher terpenes, where this type of cyclization is most common. It is noteworthy that iresin has abnormal configuration at C-10 as have the diterpenes cafestol and eperuic acid in the diterpenes series.

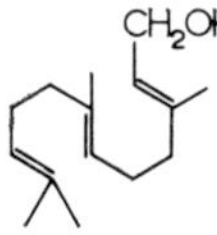

Farnesol
(111)

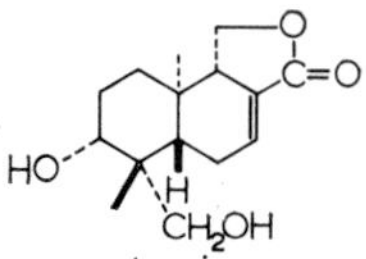

Iresin
(112)

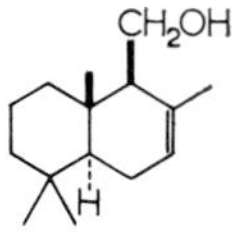

Drimenol
(113)

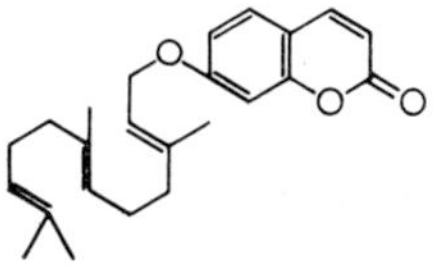

Umbelliprenin
(114)

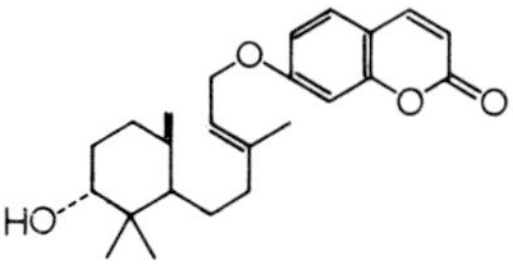

Farnesiferol-B
(115)

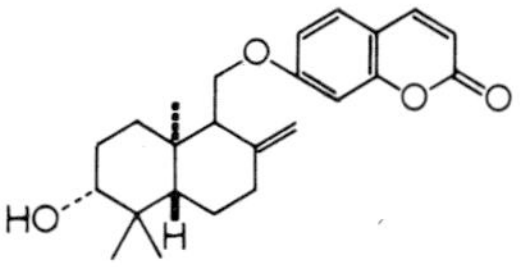

Farnesiferol-A
(116)

Recent additions to the iresin group are drimenol[57] (113) from the bark of *Drimys winteri*, and the complex terpenoids farnesiferol-A (116) and -B (115) from *Asa foetida*[58]. Including the uncyclized farnesyl ether of umbelliferone, umbelliprenin (114), all three stages in this cyclization are now known. Farnesiferol-A shows an unusual coupling of rings A and B, similar to that present in iresin, pointing to a common feature of the cyclization process in their biogenetic origin.

(iv) Azulene type

The observation of blue and green colors in the distillation products of plant materials led to the discovery of a new type of ring system among the sesquiterpene family. The blue color of camomile, spike and blue camphor oil can be readily removed from the higher boiling fractions with concentrated phosphoric acid, and by the formation of crystalline addition products with picric acid or trinitrobenzene. Chromatographic methods are particularly useful. The intensely blue hydrocarbons removed from the oils are quite stable, and their structure has been shown to consist of a fused five- and seven-membered ring system, in which 5 conjugated double bonds are present. Related colorless compounds occur in many oils, and are converted to azulenes through dehydrogenation with sulfur or selenium. The most prevalent azulene-type structure is guaiazulene (118) formed from guaiol, and crystalline constituent of oil of *Guaiacum officinalis*. The oxidative degradation of this well-defined sesquiterpene alcohol by Pfau and Plattner led to the discovery of the true nature of the azulenes and the structure of the precursors. The precursors of the azulenes can be constructed from a farnesyl chain folded as indicated in (117) and (121). Dehydrogenation of these cyclized products gives rise to methyl- and isopropyl-substituted azulenes, such as the most frequently occurring guaiazulene from guaiol (120) and from kessoglycol (119). Vetivazulene (122) is formed from β-vetivone (123).

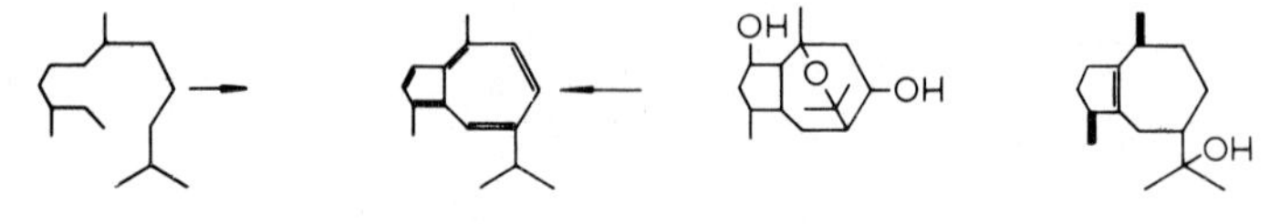

| Farnesol chain | Guaiazulene | Kessoglycol | Guaiol |
| (117) | (118) | (119) | (120) |

| Farnesol chain | Vetivazulene | β-Vetivone |
| (121) | (122) | (123) |

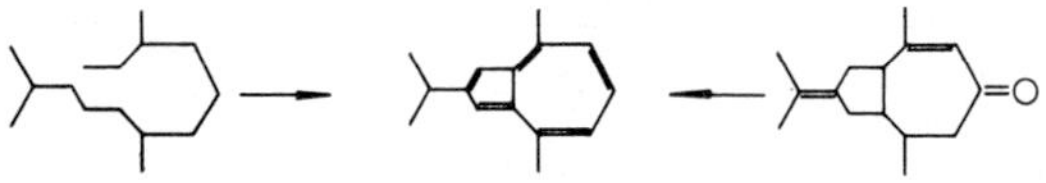

The variations in structure within this group are caused by position and number of double bonds and the presence of diverse functional groups. Oxide bridges are present in kessyl alcohol and kessoglycol (119). In other guaiazulene precursors, one of the methyls of the isopropyl group is converted to a carboxyl group, as in guaiazulenic acid[59] found in yarrow (*Achillea millefolium*). With a hydroxyl group at C-6 or C-8, adjacent to a carboxyl-carrying side chain, lactone formation has been established in many instances. This group has become known as the *guaianolide series* and is represented by artabsin (124), lactucin[60] (126), helenalin (125) and geigerin (127).

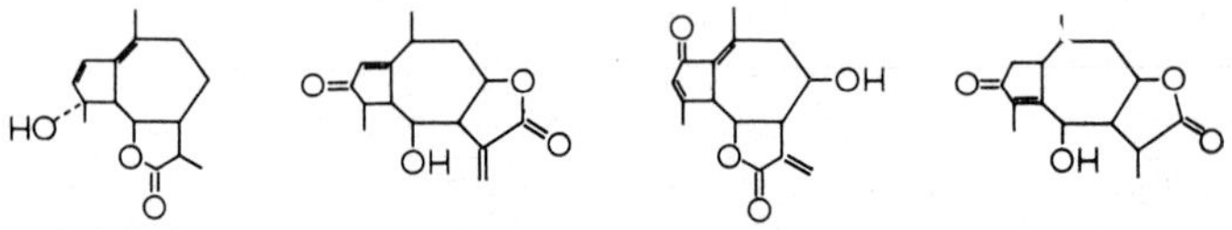

| Artabsin | Helenalin | Lactucin | Geigerin |
| (124) | (125) | (126) | (127) |

In some azulene-type compounds, the isopropyl group has participated in forming a furane ring fused to the seven-membered ring at C-6 and C-7. These compounds give linderazulene (129) on dehydrogenation. Fusion at C-7 and C-8 occurs in a similarly built compound, artemazulene (128). The fungus *Lactarius deliciosus* yields two additional azulenes, lactaroviolin (130) and lactarazulene (131).

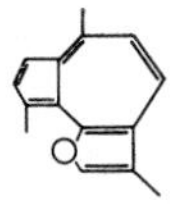

Artemazulene	Linderazulene	Lactaroviolin	Lactarazulene
(128)	(129)	(130)	(131)

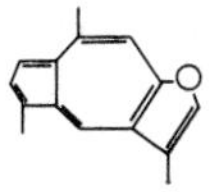

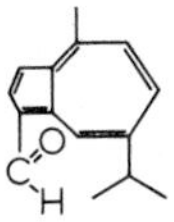

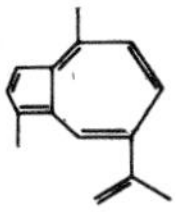

A recent addition to the perhydroazulene type structures with irregular position of the bridge methyl group is carotol[61] (132). A monocyclic cyclo-heptane ring is found in xanthinin (133) from *Xanthium pennsylvanicum*[62]. Its structure is related to the guaianolides and may be linked to that group by oxidative opening of the five-membered ring.

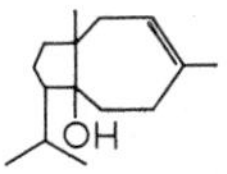

Carotol	Xanthinin
(132)	(133)

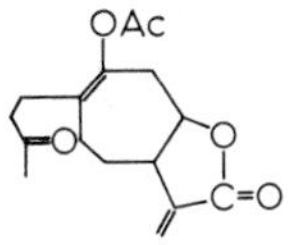

(v) *Miscellaneous bicyclic structures*

Oil of cloves contains an interesting structure with an 11-membered ring humulene (α-caryophyllene) (134), *cis-* and *trans-*caryophyllene (135) with fused 4- and 9-membered ring systems. The readiness of these structures to undergo further cyclization in the preparation of derivatives is evident in the formation of β-caryophyllene alcohol (136), clovene (138) and pseudo-clovene (137).

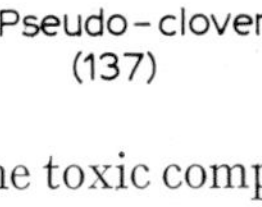

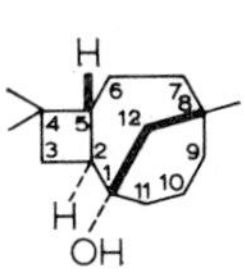

Humulene (α-caryophyllene)
(134)

Caryophyllene *(trans)*
(β-caryophyllene)
(135)

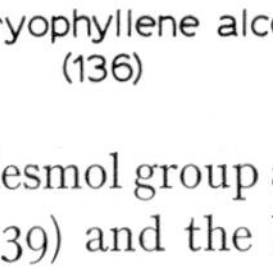

β-Caryophyllene alcohol	Pseudo-clovene	Clovene
(136)	(137)	(138)

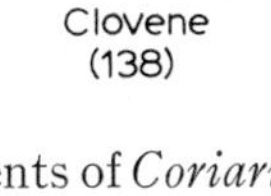

Related to the eudesmol group are the toxic components of *Coriaria japonica*, coryamyrtion[63] (139) and the bitter principle from *Cocculus indicus*, picrotoxinin (140) and picrotoxic acid[64]. A spirane structure was established in acorone[65] (141) from sweet flag oil. Dehydrogenation of the corresponding diene yields both cadalene and a 1,7-dimethyl-4-isopropylnaphthalene also obtained from carotol (132).

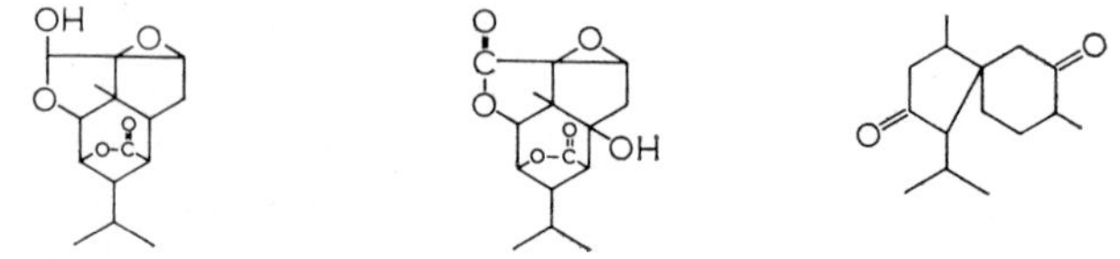

Coriamyrtion
(139)

Picrotoxinin
(140)

Acorone
(141)

(e) Tricyclic carbon systems

Several members of this series contain structures which have a close relationship to the azulenes. Fused 5- and 7-membered rings with an additional cyclopropane ring are found in aromadendrene (142), α-gurjunene (143) and maaliol[67] (147). A bridging of the 7-membered ring has taken place in patchouli alcohol (144) and in tricyclovetivene (145).

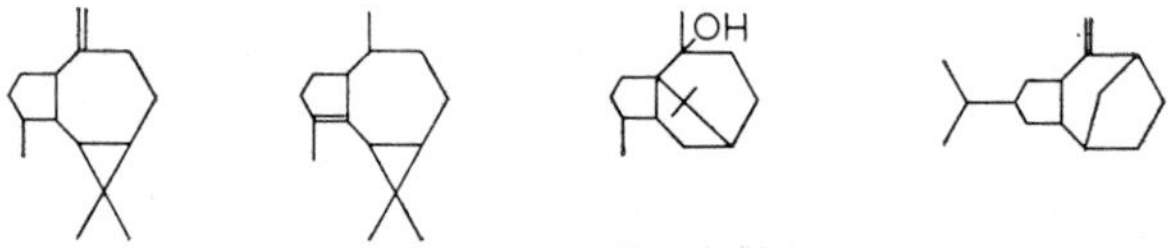

Aromadendrene   α-Gurjunene   Patchouli alcohol   Tricyclovetivene
(142)   (143)   (144)   (145)

The discovery of germacrone[66] (146) established a link between previously discussed groups. Germacrone is readily converted into β-elemenone (90) of elemane structure. Dehydrogenation yields eudalene (101), vetivazulene (122) and guaiazulene (118) through ring closures as indicated in (146a).

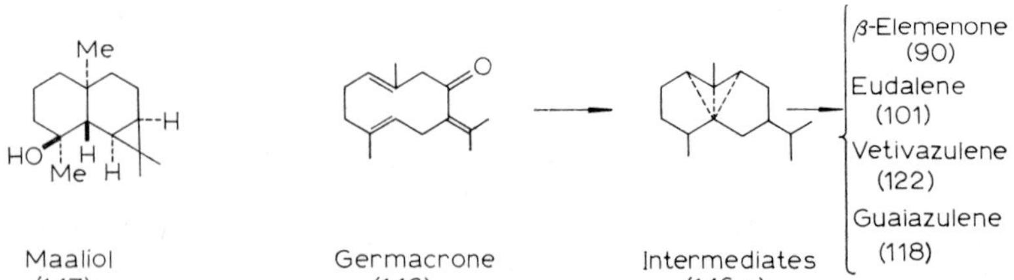

Maaliol
(147)

Germacrone
(146)

Intermediates
(146 a)

β-Elemenone
(90)
Eudalene
(101)
Vetivazulene
(122)
Guaiazulene
(118)

Tricyclic sesquiterpenes which do not readily yield naphthalene or azulenes upon dehydrogenation are cedrene (148) from cedar oil, which possesses two 5-membered rings fused with a 7-membered ring, and longifolene (149) with a different arrangement of this ring system. The latter can be considered as an isoprene homologue of camphene, whereby the third isoprene unit has its "tail" joined to the *exo* member of the gem-dimethyl group of camphene. This structure is related to that of bicyclic β-santalene (150). However, in longifolene the isoprene head is cyclized to form a 7-membered ring. α-Santalene (151) can be regarded as an isoprene homologue of the tricyclic teresantalic acid structure (68).

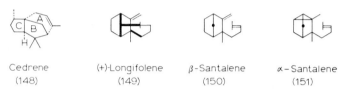

Cedrene	(+)-Longifolene	β-Santalene	α–Santalene
(148)	(149)	(150)	(151)

5. Diterpenoids

(a) General

Diterpenoids are often present in high boiling fractions of essential oils and in the residues of the distillation of oleoresins, such as colophony obtained from pine trees. Related are a number of bitter substances[19], the plant hormone gibberellic acid[90] and the diterpene alkaloids[129]. The number of fully established naturally occurring ring members of this group is still relatively small. This is in part due to the experimental difficulties in their isolation, formation of mixed crystals, sensitivity to oxidation and difficulties in characterization of their degradation products.

Historically our knowledge of structures consisting of four isopentane units developed from the investigation of the resin acids. As early as 1903 sulfur dehydrogenation of abietic acid by Vesterberg[68] led to recognition of retene (152) as the carbon skeleton of a number of diterpenes. Twenty years later Ruzicka and Balas[69] isolated a different hydrocarbon, pimanthrene (153) from the dehydrogenation products of pimaric acid, itself isolated from

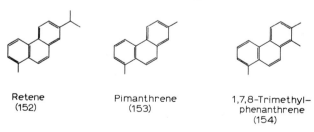

Retene	Pimanthrene	1,7,8-Trimethyl–
(152)	(153)	phenanthrene
		(154)

galipot, a rosin from *Pinus maritima*. A third type of phenanthrene, 1,7,8-trimethylphenanthrene (154), was obtained from the resin of *Agathus alba*, Manila copal.

Oxidative degradation established the position of double bond, substituent methyl and isopropyl groups as well as those of functional groups. In recent years many of the diterpene molecules were assigned their absolute configuration and spatial arrangement. These extensions from the classical formulations are of great importance in establishing the biogenetic relationships among the diterpenes and their precursors[36].

In the description of the acyclic and monocyclic structures accepted rules of nomenclature are followed. The more complex ring systems have received the names of 7,8-seco-pimarane (155), pimarane (156) and abietane (157). A numbering system which brings out the relationship with triterpenes and steroids has been suggested by Klyne[70]. The stereochemical configurations of the fundamental hydrocarbons are shown in formulae 155–157. If inversion has taken place at a ring junction, this is indicated by a prefix giving the number of the carbon atom and the Greek letter α or β. Levopimaric acid is thus described as 13β-abieta-6,8(14)-dien-15-oic acid.

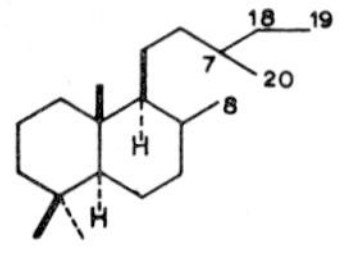

7,8-Seco-Pimarane (155)   Pimarane (156)   Abietane (157)

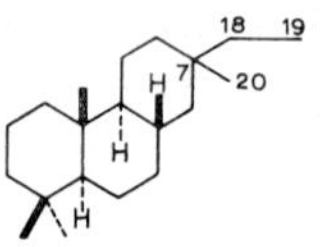

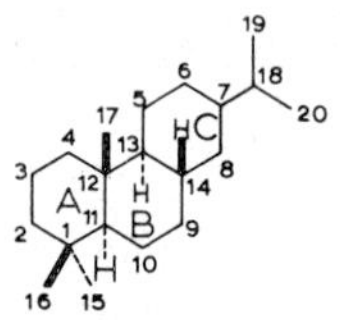

(b) *Acyclic and monocyclic diterpenoids*

Phytol (158) is at present the only naturally occurring representative of the acyclic series. Its occurrence in green plants as part of the chlorophyll molecule makes it one of the most widespread of the diterpenes. Its formation and occurrence in plants has been studied by Fischer *et al.*[71] and its synthesis has been accomplished[72]. Phytol has *trans* configuration and its stereochemical description[73] is: 3,D-7,D-10,15-tetramethylhexadeca-*trans*-2-en-1-ol.

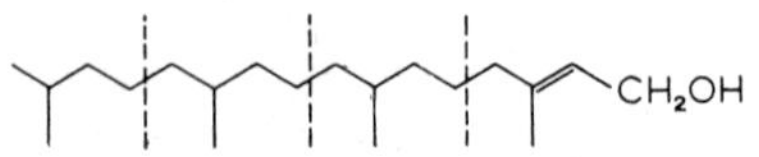

Phytol (158)   Phytadiene (159)

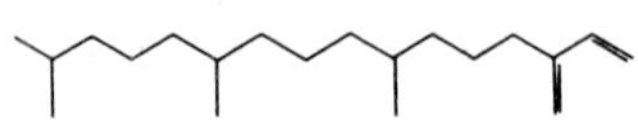

Dehydration leads to a mixture of phytadienes; one of these, neo-phytadiene (159) has been isolated from aged flue-cured tobacco leaves and is probably of secondary origin[74].

The number of monocyclic structures in this group is small. Only a few members contain a menthane-type structure, which is the most common type in the monoterpenes and forms the basic structure of a large number of the preceding group of sesquiterpenes. This type is represented by a diterpene (160) isolated from wormwood oil by Sorm *et al.*[75]. Another monocyclic diterpene is α-camphorene (161) from camphor oil. It can be described as a condensation of two geraniol chains. Other monocyclic diterpenes containing a cyclogeraniol structure are widespread in the animal kingdom and are vitamin A (162) and its several *cis* forms, such as neovitamin A and the corresponding aldehyde retinene[76].

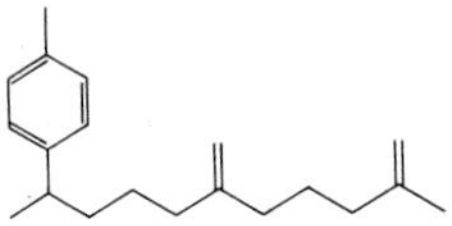

Wormwood diterpene   α-Camphorene   Vitamin A₁
(160)   (161)   (162)

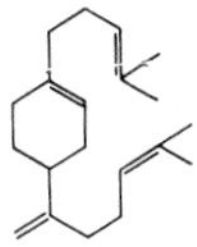

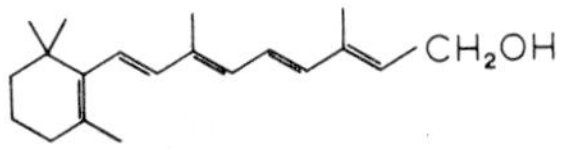

(c) Bicyclic carbon systems

Bicyclic diterpenes are found in Kauri copal, manila and other resins. Manool (163) and its derivative manoyloxide and ketomanoyloxide from *Dacrydium colensos* can be constructed from a phytol chain by cyclization. Other representatives of this type are agathenedicarboxylic acid from *Agathus australia*[77], sclareol (164) from *Salvia sclarea*, labdanolic acid (165) from gum labdanum and marrubiin (166), the bitter principle present in *Marrubium vulgare* of the family *Labiatae*.

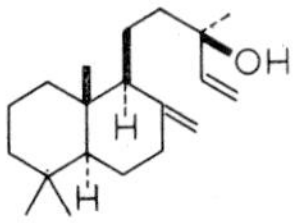

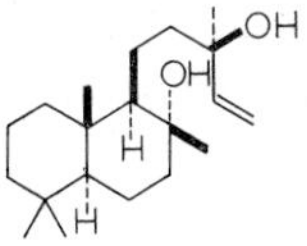

Manool   Sclareol   Labdanolic acid   Marrubiin
(163)   (164)   (165)   (166)

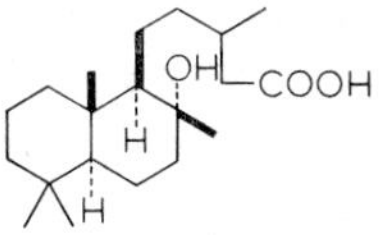

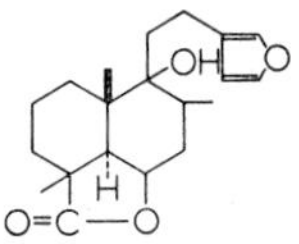

Eperuic acid (167) found in *Eperua falcata* has a structure very similar to that of manool, except that rings A and B are fused differently[78]. The interrelations of members of this group have been well established and conversion

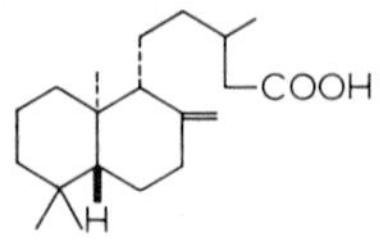

Eperuic acid	Elliotinol	Columbin
(167)	(168)	(169)

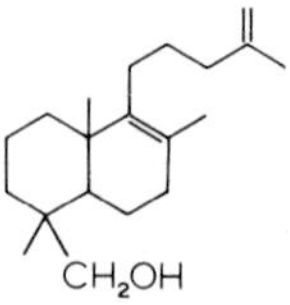

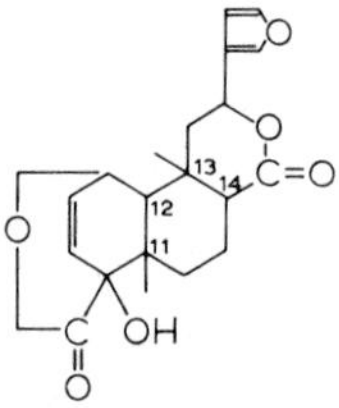

among its members have been carried for example by the conversion of sclareol into manool and labdanolic acid[79,80].

Related to the manool group, but differing in position of the methyl groups are elliotinol (168) from *Pinus elliotti*[81] and the bitter substance columbin[82] (169) present in Colombo root (*Jatrorrhiza palmata*). In columbin methyl shifts comparable to those seen in the sesquiterpene ketone eremophilone brought the methyl group across the ring fusions from C-14 to C-13 and from C-12 to C-11.

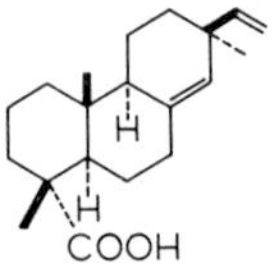

Dextropimaric acid	Rimuene	Isopimaric acid	Abietic acid
(170)	(171)	(172)	(173)

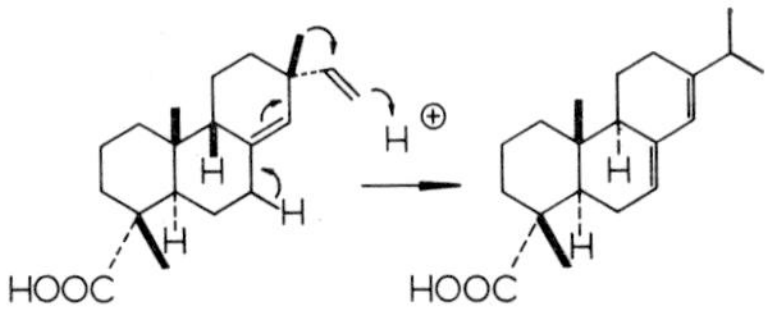

(d) Tricyclic carbon systems

Additional ring formation in the previous group leads to the resin acids dextropimaric acid (170), a major constituent of galipot, and the hydrocarbon rimuene (171) from *Dacrydium cupressinum* (*Podocarpaceae*). The oleo resin from *Pinus palustris* contains abietic acid (173), which cannot be constructed from a phytol chain without shifting one of the methyl groups to form an isopropyl group, characteristic for the abietane carbon skeleton. This shift was postulated by Ruzicka[1] in the biogenesis of the abietane group from the regularly built pimarane structure and was presented by Wenkert[83] as a concerted rearrangement of pimaradienes as indicated in formulae 172 and 173. This conversion takes place with concentrated sulfuric acid on either pimaric or isopimaric acid, whereby 5- and 6-membered lactones of the abietadiene series are formed[84].

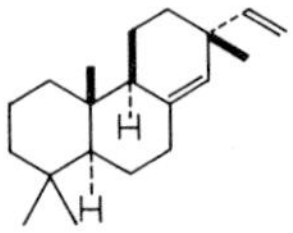

The relationship of the bicyclic manool group has been established by a laboratory conversion of manool, by Jeger *et al.*[85], to a tricyclic abietic acid derivative (174) which can also be obtained from abietic acid by reduction of the carboxyl group to a methyl group and the aromatization of ring C.

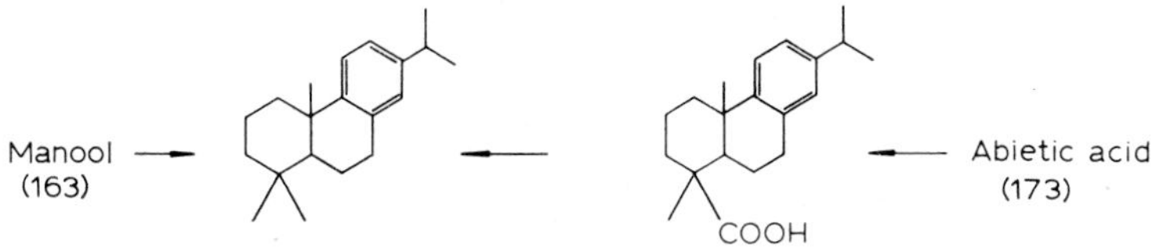

Manool
(163)

Abietic acid
(173)

Dehydro-abietane
(174)

Dehydro-abietic acid
(175)

Representatives of the abietane group are, in addition to abietic acid, isomers with different positions of the double bonds, such as neoabietic acid, levopimaric acid (176) and the aromatic tricyclics ferruginol (177) from *Podocarpus ferrugineus*[86] and its 7-keto derivative, sugiol, from *Cryptomeria japonica*[87].

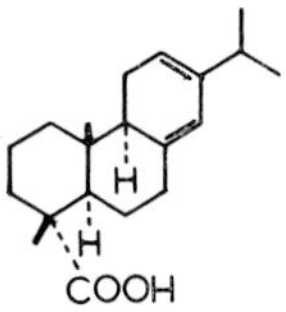

Levopimaric acid
(176)

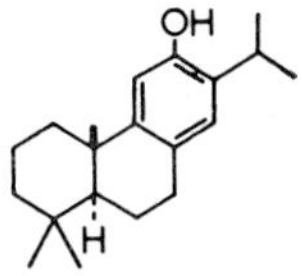

Ferruginol
(177)

The totally saturated fossil resin, fichtelite (178) could be included in this group although it lacks one of the methyl groups at C-1. Other abnormal structures are found in cassaic acid (179), which is a part of a number of alkaloids, totarol from *Podocarpus totara*[88] (180) and podocarpic acid (181) which resembles the abietane structure but lacks the isopropyl group.

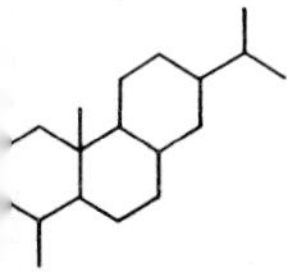

Fichtelite
(178)

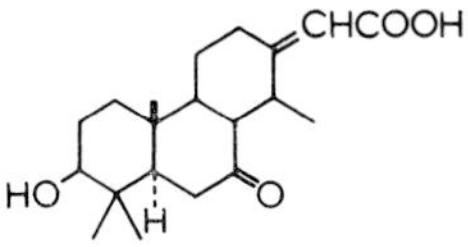

Cassaic acid
(179)

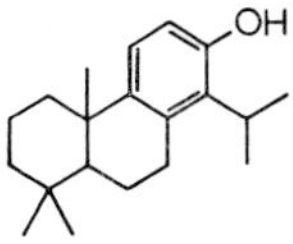

Totarol
(180)

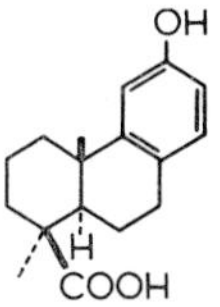

Podocarpic acid
(181)

Other related diterpenes are vinhaticoic acid (182) from the heartwood of *Plathymena reticulata* and rosenolactone[89] (183) from the mycelium of *Tri-*

cothetium roseum. Although the position of the methyl group in rosenolactone differs from that required for a pimarane structure, experiments with labeled mevalonic acid-[2-^{14}C] leave no doubt of its terpenoid nature, and suggest a methyl shift from position C-12 to C-13.

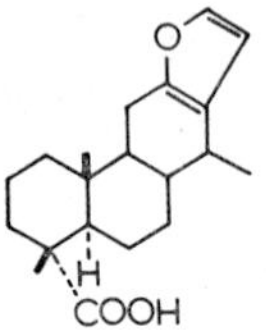

Vinhaticoic acid   Rosenolactone
(182)   (183)

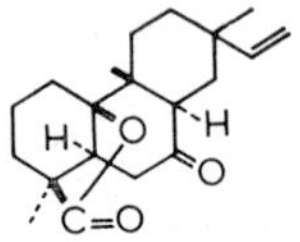

The formation of similar lactones (185, 186) with simultaneous transfer of a methyl group from C-12 to C-13 has been shown to occur by treatment of dihydro*dextro*pimaric acid (194) with sulfuric acid[84].

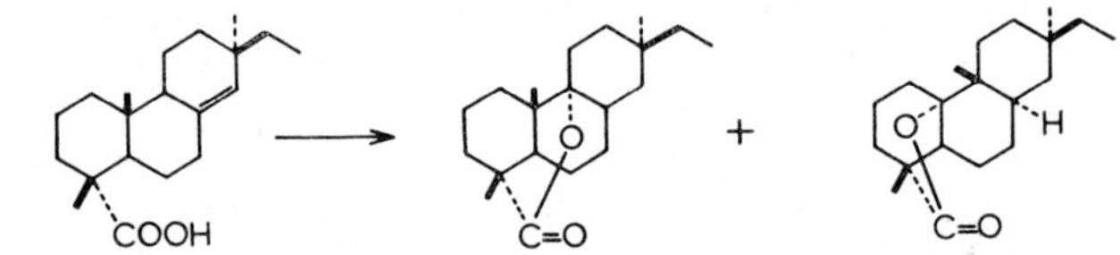

Dihydro*dextro*pimaric   95% 6-Lactone   5% 5-Lactone
acid (184)   (185)   (186)

(*e*) *Tetracyclic carbon systems*

Ring closure between carbon atoms 14 and 18 in a pimarane structure leads to tetracyclic diterpenes phyllocladene (187) and isophyllocladene, present in the higher boiling fractions of many essential oils, and to steviol (189), the aglycon of stevioside, the sweet principle of *Stevia rebaudia*. Deviations from the regular structure of a cyclized phytol chain is found in cafestol (188) from coffee bean oil. A 1,2-shift of the methyl group at C-1 has apparently taken place and led to the formation of a furane ring; also of interest is the unusual orientation of the methyl group at the bridge position C-12.

Several rearrangements of a pimarane structure are necessary to arrive at the structural formula of the plant hormone gibberellic acid (190). Experi-

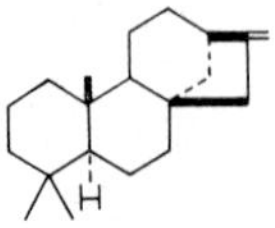

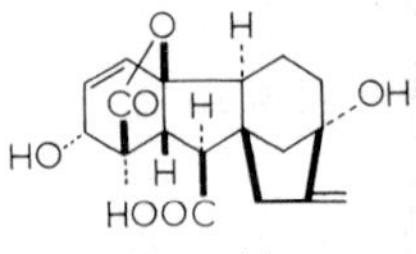

Phyllocladene   Cafestol   Steviol   Gibberellic acid
(187)   (188)   (189)   (190)

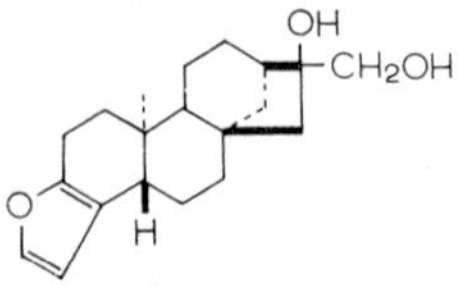

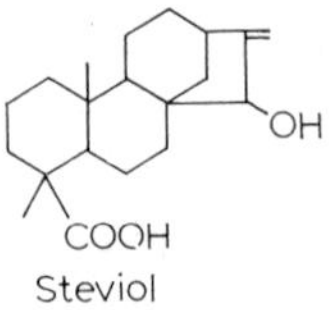

ments with isotope labeled acetate and mevalonic acid have shown that its formation involves an opening of ring B of the pimarane structure[90].

Napellonine
(191)

Atisine
(192)

The phyllocladene group is related to the *Garrya* and *Aconite* diterpene alkaloids[91]. These structures are represented here by napellonine[92] (191) and atisine[93] (192).

6. Triterpenoids

(a) General

The structural formulae of triterpenes contain 30 carbon atoms and can be constructed from 6 isopentane units. Many compounds fulfill this requirement for only a part of the structure and have been classed as triterpenoids. Those include lanosterol and fungoid acids with 31 carbon atoms, as well as abnormally constituted alnusenone, friedelin and cerin. Established biochemical relationships between the C_{30} compounds and steroids would justify their joint discussion, but practical considerations have grouped the steroids in a separate class. The historical development and present status of our knowledge of the chemistry of triterpenoids has been thoroughly reviewed by Simonsen and Ross[3], Barton[94], Mayo[6], and Steiner and Haltzem[95]. Triterpenes are found in many plants in the free state and in combination with sugars and with acids as esters. A widely distributed group are the saponins, which yield on acid hydrolysis their aglycones, the sapogenins. In animals the occurrence of undisputed triterpenes is limited, although squalene has been found to be more widespread than was at first suspected. Terpenoids such as lanosterol, and their descendants the steroids, are, however, of universal occurrence in the animal world.

The experimental difficulties in the study of the triterpenoids were considerable. Uncertainties in the analysis of compounds with a large number of carbon atoms, coupled with the property of many triterpenoids to crystallize with solvent, made revision of earlier empirical formulas necessary. Structure determinations were hampered by the presence of inert double bonds and the need to distinguish slight differences in the position of methyl groups attached to the large carbon skeleton.

A significant step in the total structure determination was the introduction of the dehydrogenation method with sulfur by Ruzicka *et al.*[96] (1929). The isolation of 1,8-dimethylpicene (194) and several methyl-substituted naphthalenes led to a presentation of the carbon skeleton of β-amyrin[97] as indicated in (193).

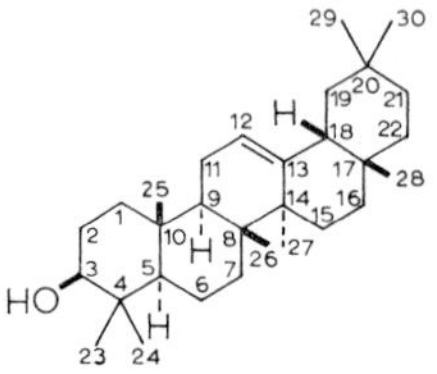

β-Amyrin   1,8-Dimethylpicene
(193)   (194)

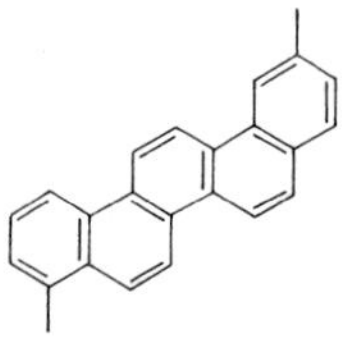

Oxidative degradations have confirmed dehydrogenation and pyrolysis results and established the position of double bonds and oxygen atoms in this series. Of great help has been the conversion of different triterpenoids into each other by rather simple reduction or oxidation steps. For example, reduction of the carboxyl group in oleanolic acid (206) to a methyl group leads to β-amyrin.

The work of Ruzicka, Jeger, Jones, Spring, Djerassi and many others has established the structure of about 70 triterpenes. This impressive accomplishment in relatively short time does not in any way exhaust the field, for there are about as many triterpenes listed of unknown or uncertain structure. Systematic investigations on plant and animal products will undoubtedly uncover many more of the triterpenoids.

As in the previous groups of terpenes, the variety in structure of the triterpenoids is caused by ring formation and substitution. In addition to acyclic squalene, bi-, tri-, tetra-, penta-, and hexacyclic structures have been well established.

(b) Acyclic, bi- and tricyclic carbon systems

Acyclic squalene,$C_{30}H_{50}$, (195), originally isolated from liver oils of sharks, was later found to occur in other fish oils and in animal products such as ovarian dermoid cysts, human earwax and hair oil. Its presence in vegetable oils and in fungi has been established. Squalene was shown to be a progenitor of cholesterol by Bloch[98], and is therefore probably of universal occurrence. Symmetrical arrangement of the 6 isopentane units, established by oxidative degradation, was confirmed by a synthesis from two moles of farnesyl bromide by Karrer and Helfenstein[99]. To the same end, others have synthesized squalene from 1,4-dibromobutane and two moles of *trans*-geranyl-acetone[100]. X-ray analysis has shown the all-*trans* configuration of the naturally occurring squalene[101].

In analogy with the properties found in the lower terpenes, cyclization occurs readily. The products obtained are not identical with any known natural product. Enzymatically, the cyclization to lanosterol has been accomplished by Bloch *et al.*[98]. The specificity of this reaction for all-*trans* squalene is used for the rigid identification of naturally occurring squalene (Tchen and Bloch[102]).

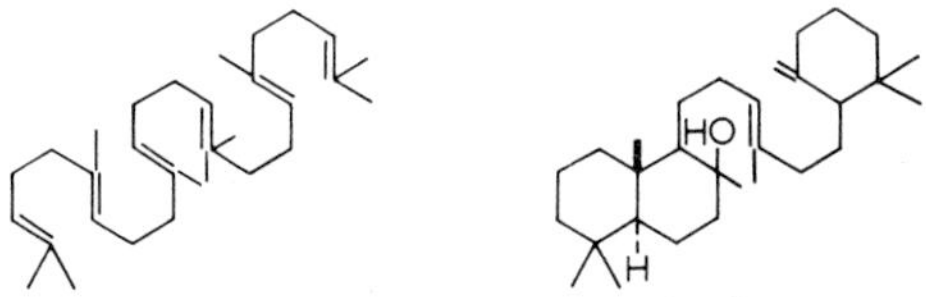

Squalene
(195)

Ambrein
(196)

The tricyclic triterpene ambrein (196) is a constituent of ambergris, used in the perfume industry. Through the investigations of Ruzicka[103] and Lederer[104] and their collaborators, its structure has been established and related to the sesquiterpene farnesol, the diterpene sclareol, and the triterpene oleanolic acid (206).

(c) *Tetracyclic carbon systems, onocerin and lanostane type*

Structurally related to tricyclic ambrein is onocerin (197) obtained from *Onosis spinosa*[105]. This symmetrically-built compound is of biochemical interest as a product of incomplete cyclization from squalene to pentacyclic structures. In the laboratory, such cyclizations have been carried out, leading to an isomer of the amyranes with different positions of the methyl groups[105] (198).

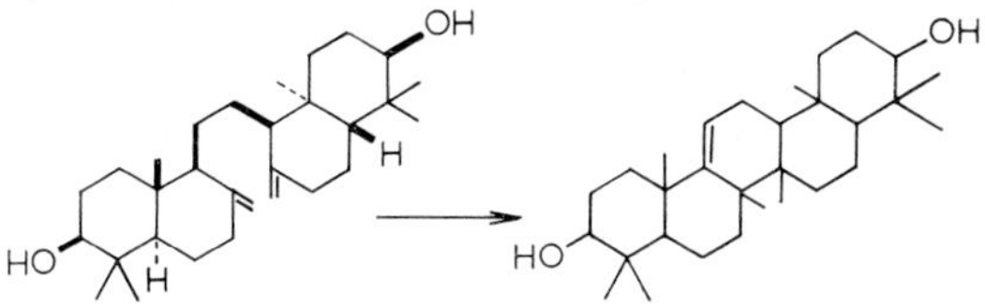

Onocerin
(197)

γ—Onocerin
(198)

Differently constituted tetracyclic structures with a lanostane carbon system are found in the unsaponifiable fraction of wool fat. This fat contains cholesterol (199) and the triterpene alcohols lanosterol (200), dihydrolanosterol, agnosterol and dihydroagnosterol. Related structures occur in a number of species of the *Euphorbiaceae*, in dammar and elemi resins. The variations in structures in this group are attributable to stereochemical differences, as in euphol (201) or to a redistribution of the methyl groups, as in dammaradienol (202). Several fungus triterpenoid acids are distinguished by an additional methylene group at C-24. Biosynthetic experiments of Dauben *et al.*, with eburicoic acid (203) have shown that this extra carbon atom does not originate from acetate in the biosynthesis, but is introduced from formate[106]. Closely related to the lanostane group are pentacyclic cyclo-artenol (204) and its ketone, cycloartenone. In these compounds carbon atoms 9, 10 and 19 of lanostane have formed a cyclopropane ring. The relation of the lanosterol group with pentacyclic terpenoids of α- and β-amyrane and lupane type and the steroids has been established through many conversions and the synthesis of lanosterol (200) from cholesterol by Woodward *et al.*[107].

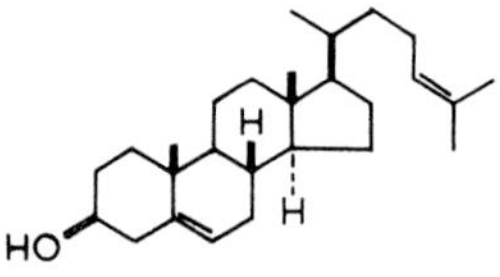

Cholesterol
(199)

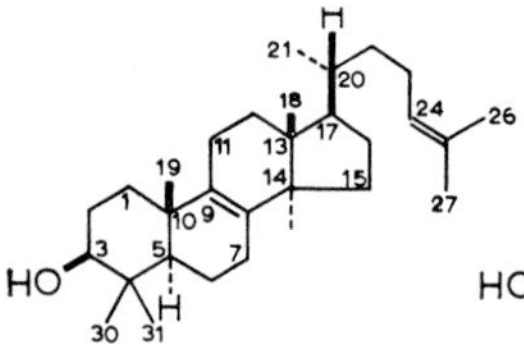

Lanosterol
(200)

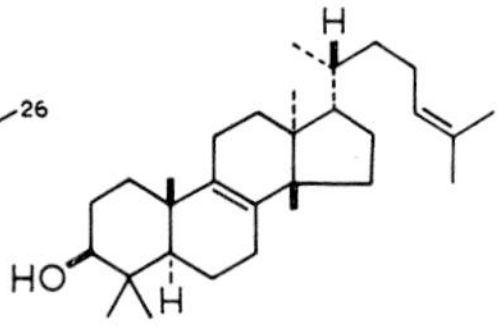

Euphol
(201)

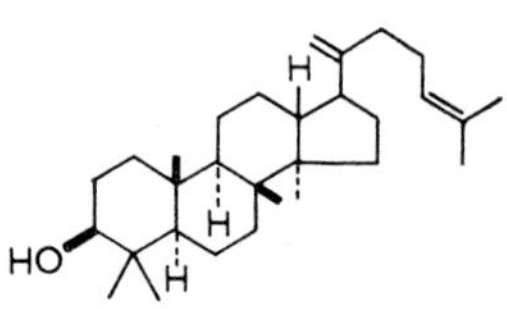

Dammaradienol
(202)

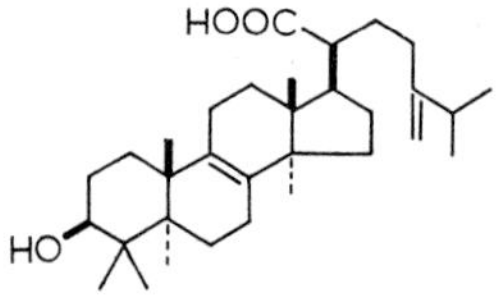

Eburicoic acid
(203)

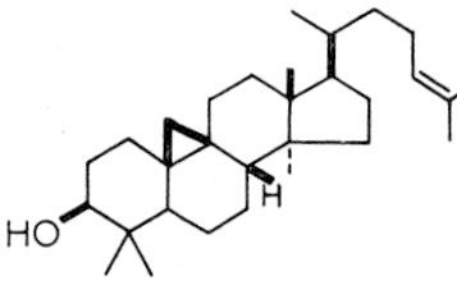

Cyclo artenol
(204)

(*d*) *Penta- and hexacyclic carbon systems*

(*i*) *Hydropicene (α- and β-amyrane) type*

Frequently occurring pentacyclic triterpenoids are derived from a hydro-picene substituted with 8 methyl groups or their oxygen derivatives and from a cyclo-pentenobenzophenanthrene ring system, lupane as in lupeol (215).

The hydropicene group developed historically from investigations of α- and β-amyrin (205, 193) present in elemi resin and triterpene acids such as oleanolic acid (206). The carbon skeletons are referred to as α-amyrane or ursane and β-amyrane or oleanane. To the α-amyrane group belong the well-known triterpene acid, boswellic acid, with a carbonyl group at C-23, present in incense, and ursolic acid, widely distributed in the wax coating of leaves and fruits. The hexacyclic triterpene alcohol phyllanthol (207) belongs structurally to the α-amyrane group in which carbon atoms 13, 14 and 27 have formed a cyclopropane ring[108].

A β-amyrane structure is found in hederagenin from ivy, siaresinolic acid from gum benzoin, and in many triterpenes isolated from cacti. The recent intensive activity in this field has revealed many naturally occurring triterpenoids which differ in the distribution of the methyl substituents in the ring system and in position and nature of the functional groups. Such abnormal structures are present in taraxerol (208), alnusenone (209) and the cork constituent friedelin (210)

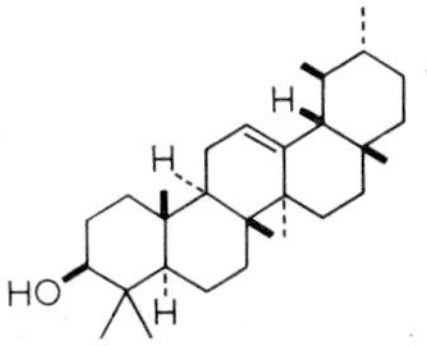

α-Amyrin
(205)

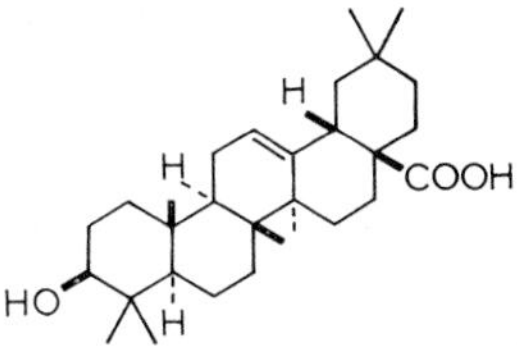

Oleanolic acid
(206)

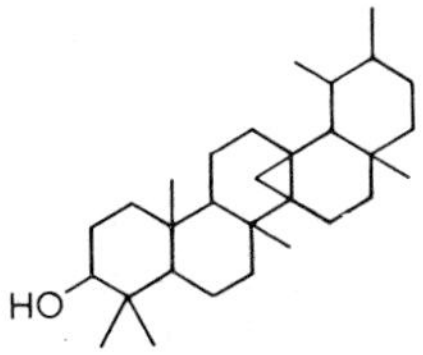

Phyllanthol
(207)

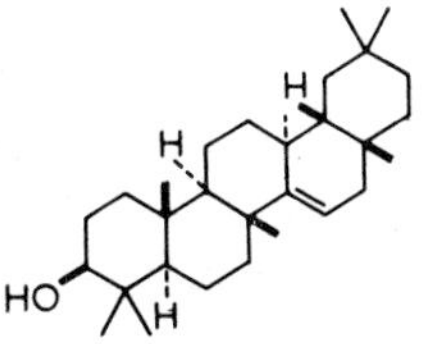

Taraxerol
(208)

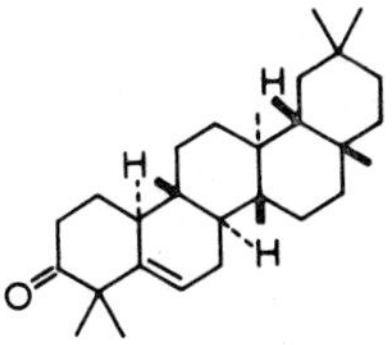

Alnusenone
(209)

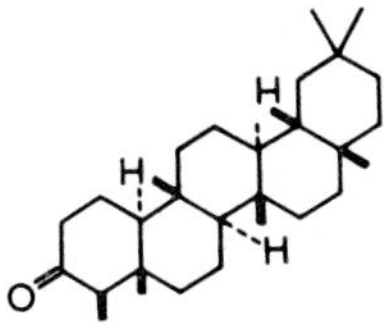

Friedelin
(210)

Table I shows schematically the presence, without regard to *cis-trans* position, of the substituent methyl groups at the ends of the condensed ring structure and at the bridge heads, as compared to the distribution of methyl groups without occurrence of methyl shifts in a cyclized squalene. The numbering is that shown in formula (193) and takes into account the course of the methyl shifts as predicted by Ruzicka and others. Several of these shifts have been realized in the laboratory, linking thereby the different structures in the series of lupane, α- and β-amyrane, other hydropicenes and lanostane. In the course of the structural investigations, relationships with most other members have been established by conversion into each other or into common

TABLE I

DISTRIBUTION OF METHYL GROUPS IN THE HYDROPICENE GROUP

Ring A	Ring junction				Ring E	Compound
	A/B	B/C	C/D	D/E		
23	25	—	—	28	29	Squalene arrangement
24	—	26	27	—	30	without shift
23	25	—	—	—	29	β-Amyrin (193)
24	—	26	27	28	30	
23	25	—	—	—	29	α-Amyrin (205)
24	—	26	27	28	30	
23	25	—	27	—	29	Taraxerol (208)
24	—	26	—	28	30	
23	—	25	27	—	29	Alnusenone (209)
24	—	—	26	28	30	
—	—	25	27	—	29	Friedelin (210)
23	24	—	26	28	30	

derivatives. These results are presented in schematic form by Barton[94]. The structure of the hexacyclic triterpene alcohol, phyllanthol (207) has been related to α-amyrin and quinovic acid[108]. Other conversions are described by Zurcher et al.[109].

A new type of transformation from a β-amyrane structure to a tricyclic one by opening of ring A has been found in the conversion of a β-amyrone to nyctanthic acid (212). A similar ring opening in the lanostane series led to dammarenolic acid[110] (211). The establishment of these structures has shown a precedent for biogenetic cleavage of the C-3 to C-4 portion of the triterpenoid skeleton, and has thereby been of corroborative value in studies cn the constitution of limonin (213), the citrus bitter principle[110]. Limonin is a triterpenoid of the euphol type (214) from which four side chain carbons have been removed, carbons C-20 to C-23 converted to a furane ring, and ring A cleaved between C-3 and C-4 with cyclization of the resulting carboxyl

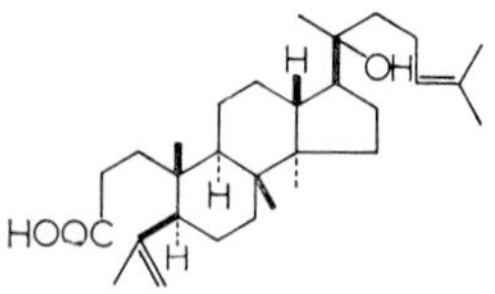

Dammarenolic acid
(211)

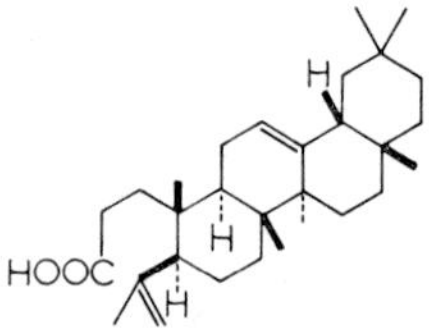

Nyctanthic acid
(212)

group to C-19. Oxidation in ring D and a methyl shift are indicated. Analogous bitter principles are nomilin and obacunone. The structure and molecular arrangement of limonin has been determined by X-ray studies.

This ring opening has its equivalent in the conversion by ultraviolet light of monocyclic menthone to the acyclic hydrogeranic acid. These interesting photochemical rearrangements are discussed by Barton[111].

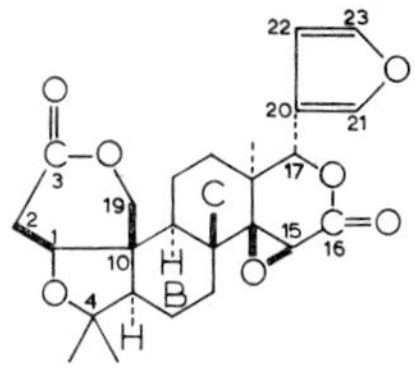

Limonin   Euphol
(213)   (214)

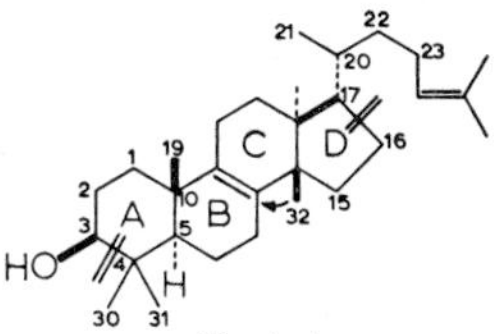

(ii) Lupane type

A different type of pentacyclic system is found in the lupane series. The parent alcohol of this group, lupeol (215), occurs in *Lupinus albus*, but is one of the most widely distributed of all triterpenoids. It has the hydroxyl group at C-3 in ring A, as do most other triterpenes. The double bond is located in the isopropenyl group at C-19.

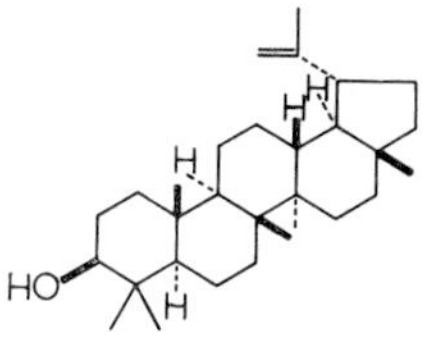

Lupeol
(215)

Conversion of lupeol into betulin and betulic acid established the relation between other members of this group, with the β-amyrane members morolic acid and germanicol and the α-amyranes taraxasterol, arnidiol and fara-diol[112].

(e) Stereochemistry of the triterpenoids

After the establishment of the carbon skeletons of a number of triterpenes, and the nature and position of the substitutents, there remained the problem of stereochemical configuration. As Simonsen and Ross[3] point out, in an extensive discussion of the subject, this is potentially extremely complex, since a parent hydrocarbon such as β-amyrane contains 8 centers of asymmetry, making it necessary to consider 256 possible configurations. This number is greatly increased when substituents are introduced into the alicyclic system. Some simplification of the problem was apparent when it was realized that the mode of locking of rings A/B, B/C and C/D was common to α-amyrane, β-amyrane, lupane and taraxastane derivatives. For the configuration of substituent groups in the individual triterpenes, reference is made to Simonsen and Ross[3] and to Mayo[6].

Members of the main triterpenoid groups such as α-amyrin oleanolic acid and lupeol possess *trans, trans* fusion of rings A/B and B/C. These arrangements correspond to those of the *trans* A/B steroids. Additional evidence of the correct configurations were obtained by X-ray analysis[113]. These relations have been confirmed by conversions of cholesterol into lanosterol, which in turn has been related to the amyrins. Since the total synthesis of cholesterol has been accomplished these conversions constitute a total synthesis of the tetracyclic terpenes.

Interesting speculations on the spatial distribution of the carbon atoms of *n,β*-amyranol (217) have been made by Klyne[114]. By assuming that all five rings adopt the more stable chair configuration, the structure takes the form presented in (216).

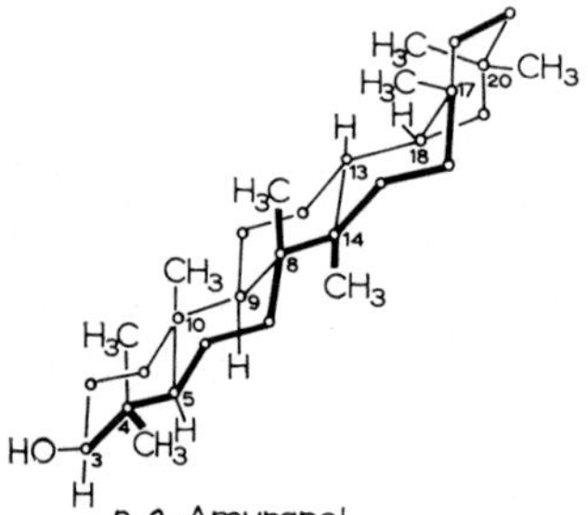

n,β–Amyranol
(216)

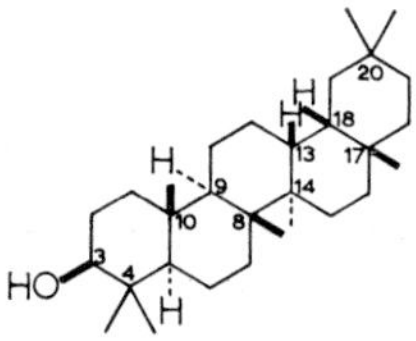

n,β–Amyranol
(217)

The biochemical studies on the formation of lanosterol and cholesterol from squalene and those of the C_{31} triterpenoid, eburicoic acid (203), from labeled acetate, established a common pattern in the biosynthesis of the steroids, lanosterol and other triterpenoids. To explain the various structures in this group, a scheme for the biogenesis of the triterpenoids, based on 1–2 Wagner shifts and the formation of carbonium ions, has been developed by Ruzicka *et al.*[1], and by Stork and Burgstahler[115]. This unified concept of the triterpene group furnished an explanation of the deviations in structure from the original arrangement of the isopentane units in squalene. Migration of methyl groups and ring enlargement and contraction leads to the formation of the lupane, α- and β-amyrane groups. Further methyl shifts on rings A and B connect these groups with alnusenone and friedelin. A presentation of these transformations was compiled by Mayo[6].

7. Tetraterpenoids

(a) General

Most of the known members of the tetraterpenoid group are found among the yellow and red pigments from plants and animals. These carotenoid and xanthophyll pigments contain isoprene type structures, in which the unit is repeated eight times. The two halves of the molecule are arranged in such a way that the carbon skeletons can be constructed from two phytol chains in mirror-like fashion. Extensive reviews on the occurrence and biochemistry of the eighty natural carotenoids have been written by Goodwin[116], Karrer and Winterstein[117]. The analytical methods have been reviewed by Paech and Tracey[118]. Chromatography has played a dominant role in the isolation procedures and particular methods used in this field has been compiled by Zechmeister[119] and by Strain[120]. Chemical behavior and synthesis are discussed by Zechmeister[121], and by Isler et al.[122].

The complex mixture of carotenoids obtained from extracts of plants or animals is separated by partition between two immiscible solvents, usually petroleum ether and 90% methanol. The upper phase contains the hydrocarbon carotenes, carotenoid waxes and xanthophyll esters, while xanthophylls and carotenoid acids are more soluble in the alcohol–water layer. Chromatographic procedures separate these crude fractions into their individual components. Solvent fractionation in the Craig countercurrent distribution apparatus divides the xanthophylls according to their degree of oxygenation and is used in conjunction with column chromatography.

Willstätter and Meig[123] established the formula $C_{40}H_{56}$ for the pigments from carrots and from green leaves. After Zechmeister and Cholnoky[124] had shown the presence of 11 double bonds in the carotene molecule, Karrer and

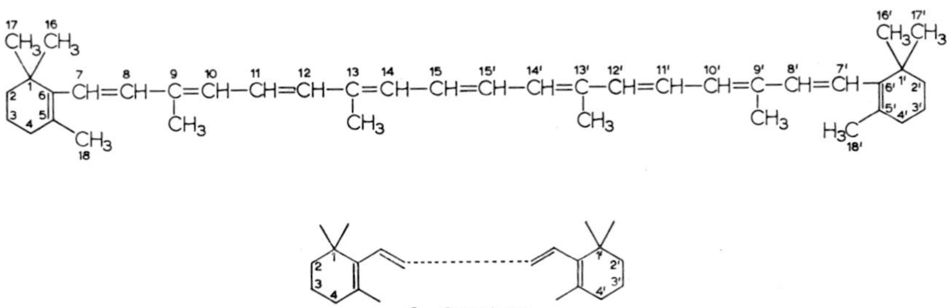

β–Carotene
(218)

others proposed a structure of 8 isopentane units arranged in such a manner that there is a center of symmetry in the molecule. The β-carotene molecule contains the nutritional activity of two molecules of vitamin A_1 into which it is split by oxidative processes. Connecting two vitamin A carbon skeletons through a double bond accounts for the 11 double bonds in β-carotene (218). β-Carotene is the most frequently encountered representative of this class. An abbreviated form such as (218) is often used, since most of the diversity in the members of this series is present in ten carbon structures at either end of the molecule and not in the central C_{20} chain.

As in the previous groups of terpenes we find acyclic and cyclic structures. The extensive conjugated system offers many possibilities for *cis–trans* isomerism. Most natural polyenes have the all-*trans* configuration. In recent years several *cis*-carotenoids have been found to occur in nature. Transformation of the *trans*-compound into *cis*-forms can be accomplished in the laboratory by iodine or acid catalysis and by thermal or photochemical isomerization[125].

In the stereoisomeric lycopene-set 40 well-defined *cis*-forms are known. Some of these were prepared by *in vitro* rearrangements of the all-*trans* forms, others by partial *cis–trans* isomerization of naturally occurring poly-*cis*-compounds, others by total synthesis and some were isolated from plants. As a rule *trans–cis* rearrangement involves a displacement of the main ultra-violet spectral absorption maxima toward shorter wave length, a decrease both in extinction values and the degree of fine structure of the main band. Even mono-*cis*-isomers differ sharply from the all-*trans* form in infrared spectra[126].

It was originally thought that *cis*-isomers could not exist at every double bond, those containing a methyl substituent on one of the α-carbon atoms being considered unstable or hindered. However, carotenoid isomers have been synthesized with the hindered structure, and the poly-*cis*-lycopenes present in *Pyracantha* berries may be naturally occurring hindered isomers[127].

(b) Acyclic carbon systems

Variations in structure in the acyclic series are caused by the number and position of double bonds and by the presence of hydroxyl or keto groups on one or both ends of the carbon chain. Examples are lycopene (219) with 13 double bonds, 11 of which are conjugated and the 3-hydroxy and 3-3'-dihydroxy derivatives: lycoxanthin (220) and lycophyll (221).

Lycopene
(219)

Lycoxanthin
(220)

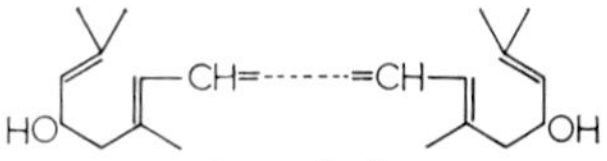

Lycophyll
(221)

Spirilloxanthin
(222)

Partially hydrogenated derivatives of lycopene are phytoene (224) and phytofluene (225). Both are widespread in nature and often accompany the red pigments in plant extracts. Phytoene possesses only three conjugated double bonds and is therefore colorless. Treatment of a phytoene solution with the oxidizing agent N-bromosuccinimide results in the appearance within 30 sec

TABLE II

Compounds	Formula	Conjugated double bonds
Lycopersene (223)		0
Phytoene (224)		3
Phytofluene (225)		5
ζ-Carotene (226)		7
Neurosporene (227)		9
Lycopene (228)		11
3,4-Dehydro-lycopene (229)		13
3,4,3',4'-Bis-dehydrolycopene (230)		15

of a strong fluorescence in ultraviolet light due to the formation of phytofluene with five conjugated double bonds. Within a minute the solution
turns dark red through the formation of the completed system of double
bonds of lycopene. Chromatographic separation of the oxidation mixture
establishes the series: phytoene — phytofluene — ζ-carotene (226) — neurosporene (227) — lycopene[121] (228). This series represents the addition of two
conjugated double bonds in each step, and was postulated by Porter and
Lincoln[128] as a possible biosynthesis of the pigments from non-colored precursors. This scheme of formation received further experimental support
through study of the production of carotenoids in *Neurospora crassa* by
Grob[129]. By exposing the mold to increasing amounts of light a series of
carotenoids of increasing unsaturation was isolated, indicating the possible
biosynthetic pathway: uncolored polyenes — phytofluene — ζ-carotene —
neurosporene — lycopene and monocyclic carotene. The primary coupling
product of the C_{20} precursor of this series, lycopersene, with 8 isolated double
bonds has recently been synthesized from two molecules of geranyl geraniol.
The presence in nature of this "C_{40} squalene" has been established[129]. The
series of increasing unsaturation has been completed by the synthesis of the
two compounds with 13 and 15 conjugated double bonds[121], (229) and (230).
3,4-Dehydrolycopene has been found to occur in micro-organisms and 3,4,3',
4'-bis-dehydrolycopene was identified in a spanish lemon variety.

Oxygen-containing acyclic carotenoids are usually substituted at the 3-
position as in lycoxanthin (220) and lycophyll (221). However, oxygen functional groups appear at other positions as for example in spirilloxanthin (222)
(rhodoviolascin) found in species of *Thio-* and *Athiorhodaceae*, which is substituted at the C-1 and C-1' position by methoxy groups[130].

(c) *Monocyclic and bicyclic carbon systems*

Ring formation of the cyclogeraniol type at the ends of the lycopene chain
leads to mono- and bicyclic carotenoids. The carotins represent various combinations of the end groups A, B, and C, as shown in Fig. 8, connected by
a chain of 10 conjugated double bonds.

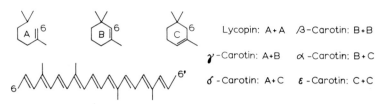

Lycopin: A + A β-Carotin: B + B

γ-Carotin: A + B α-Carotin: B + C

δ-Carotin: A + C ε-Carotin: C + C

Fig. 8. The building system of lycopin and carotins.

In most naturally occurring carotenoids the link between the rings and the acyclic middle section of the molecule is a single bond and has been designated as a "normal" (cyclohexenyl) structure. In some carotenoids this connection is made by a double bond, forming a cyclohexylidene group. This type of linkage is indicated by the prefix "retro". An example of such arrangement is found in rhodoxanthin (231), which is converted to the "normal" structure, dihydrorhodoxanthin (232), by hydrogenation with aluminum isopropyl-ate[121]. Transitions from "normal" to "retro" compounds have been achieved by direct dehydrogenation methods and with the aid of borontri-fluoride complexes. "Normal" physalien (233), zeaxanthin dipalmitate present in pods of *physalis*, is converted in this way to escholtzxanthin dipal-mitate (234) present in flower petals of the California poppy (*Escholtzia cali-fornica*).

| Rhodoxanthin | Dihydrorhodoxanthin |
| (231) | (232) |

Physalien	Escholtzxanthin dipalmitate
(Zeaxanthin dipalmitate)	(234)
(233)	

Widely distributed in nature are oxygen derivatives of the carotins substi-tuted at C-3 such as zeaxanthin and lutein, which are respectively 3,3'-dehydroxy β- and α-carotin. The oxidation of β-carotene with N-bromo-succinimide leads, however, to the introduction of keto groups at the C-4 position. Such oxidation products have been found in echinenone (4-keto-β-carotene), a pigment from sea urchins, and in canthaxanthin (235) (4,4'-diketo-β-carotene) the main pigment of the mushroom *Cantharellus cinnabarinus*. Oxidation with perphthalic acid leads to the formation of epoxides. This type of oxidation product is widespread in nature, for example, rubichrome (236) (5,8-epoxy-3-hydroxy-γ-carotene) and auroxanthin (5,8,5',8'-diepoxy-zea-xanthin). Cholnoky[131] suggested a role of the epoxides in the transmission of oxygen in leaves and ripening fruits. The epoxides with oxide bridge between C-5 and C-6 convert readily under influence of traces of acids to furanoid oxides with the oxide bridge between C-5 and C-8 as shown in the conversion of β-carotene epoxide (237) to the furanocarotenoid (238).

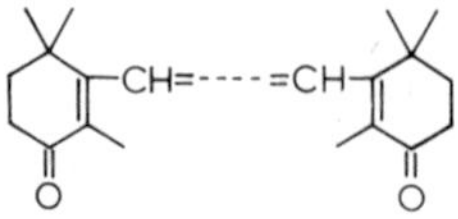

Canthaxanthin
(235)

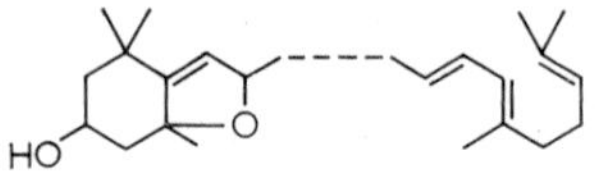

Rubichrome
(236)

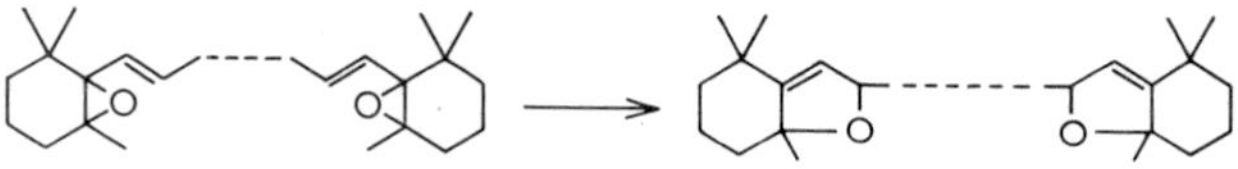

β–Carotene epoxide
(237)

β–Carotene furanoid oxide
(238)

Aromatization of the ring structure is found in carotenoids of the orange sponge renieratene (239) and isorenieratene[132] (240). These carotenoids show abnormal position of the ring methyl groups and indicate a methyl transfer as frequently seen in the previous series.

Oxidation to a carboxyl group of one of the gem-dimethyl groups is seen in torularhodin[133] (242).

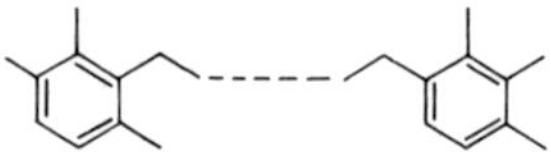

Renieratene
(239)

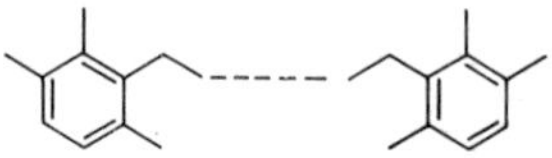

Iso-renieratene
(240)

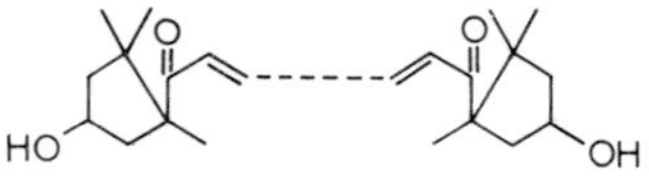

Capsorubin
(241)

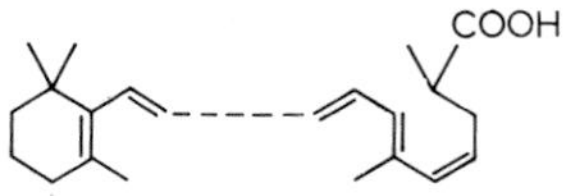

Torularhodin
(242)

Cyclopentane structures are found in the paprika ketones, capsanthin and capsorubin (241). The former has a cyclopentane ring on only one end of the molecule[134]. These ketones are probably formed through an oxidation of a carotene with epoxide formation followed by a pinacolic rearrangement.

(d) Naturally occurring degradation products

In the above carotenoid oxidation products the carbon skeletons consisting of 40 carbon atoms have been preserved. In other naturally occurring tetra-terpene derivatives there is evidence that further oxidation has resulted in a degradation with the formation of smaller molecules. Biologically the most important of these are vitamin A_1, neovitamin A_1 (cis-isomer of A_1), the vitamin A aldehydes retinene and neoretinene[135]. These compounds belong formally to the diterpenoid group and are considered to be formed by cleavage of the carotenoid molecule in the middle of the chain. Cleavage at different positions of the chain is seen in the pigment crocin from saffron, which is a digentiobiose ester of crocetin (243), containing 20 of the carbon atoms of the center part of the carotenoid structure. The remaining part of the precursor carotenoid is found in the glucoside of a monoterpene related to safranal, picrocrocin (244).

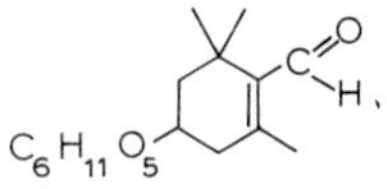

Picrocrocin
(244)

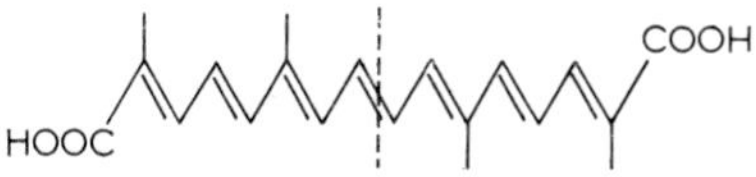

Crocetin
(243)

β—Citraurin
(246)

Azafrin
(247)

Bixin
(245)

A similar center fraction of a carotenoid molecule is found in bixin (245) (from annotto *Bixa orellana*), which is a monomethyl ester of a 24-carbon containing dicarboxylic acid. Other apparent degradation products are β-citraurin $(C_{30}H_{40}O_2)$ (246), a pigment of the orange, and azafrin (247), from azafran (*Escobidia scabrifolia*). The unsymmetrical structure and the presence of only one of the ionone type rings at the end of the long carbon chain with respectively 9 and 7 conjugated double bonds shows clearly their origin from a carotenoid precursor.

8. Mono- to polyterpenoid quinones and chromanes

The known tri- and tetraterpenoids are built of isopentane chains composed of a symmetrical arrangement of two farnesyl or two phytol chains. In recent years substances have been isolated which show a continuation of the head-to-tail building principle of geraniol, farnesol and phytol. The highest member can be looked upon as a pentaterpenoid with 10 isopentane units. These substances belong to the groups of terpenoid benzo- and naphthoquinones, chromanes and chromenes.

(a) Terpenoid quinones

The characteristic grouping of the quinones is present in the monoterpenoid thymoquinone (248), present in several species of *umbelliferae, labiatae* and *cupressaceae* and the sesquiterpenoid, perezone (249) from the roots of *Trixis pipitazhuae*. A doubling of an incomplete sesquiterpene structure, with the formation of a perinaphthoquinone, may be seen in pigments isolated from *aphid* species, as in erythroaphin (250). The diterpenoid orthoquinones cryptotanshinone (251) and tanshinone I (252) are found in the roots of *Salvia miltiorhiza*. Orthoquinones of triterpenoid extraction are probably the insecticide celastriol and the antibiotic pristimerin. Compounds of this type have been reviewed by Thomson[136], and their separation and analysis described by Hofmann-Ostenhof[137].

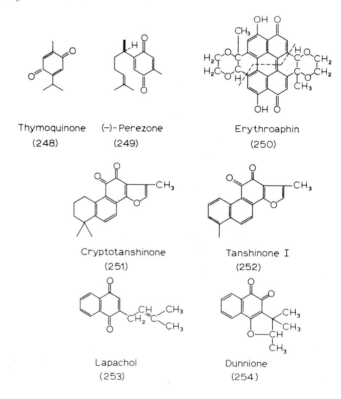

Thymoquinone	(−)-Perezone	Erythroaphin
(248)	(249)	(250)

Cryptotanshinone	Tanshinone I
(251)	(252)

Lapachol	Dunnione
(253)	(254)

A few naturally occurring substances have five-carbon branched units attached to the quinone structure. These are lapachol (253), dunnione (254) and the biologically important vitamins K_1 and K_2. Vitamin K_1 (255) has long been established as 2-methyl-3-phytyl-1,4-naphthoquinone.

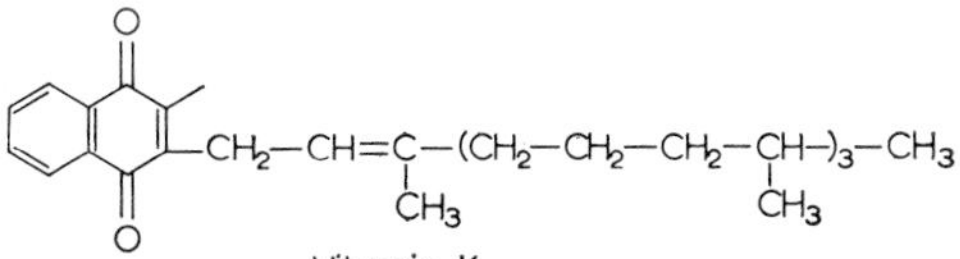

Vitamin K_1
(255)

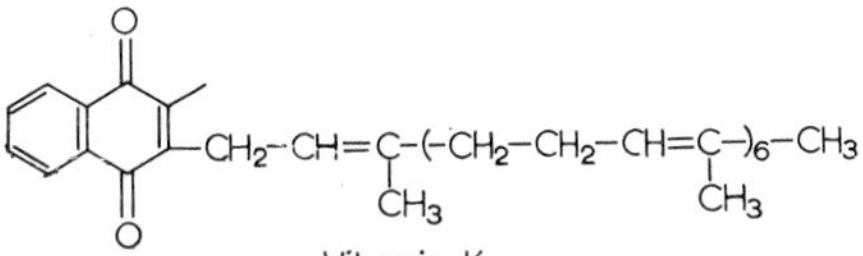

Vitamin K_2
(256)

The original vitamin K_2 (m.p. 54°), discovered by Doisy, is now formulated as 2-methyl-3-farnesylgeranylgeranyl-1,4-naphthoquinone[138] (256), with a C_{35} seven isopentane-unit side chain, and the structure has been proved by synthesis. A lower isoprenolog, m.p. 50°, with a C_{30} side chain was also found in putrified fish meal, the source of the original K_2. More recently, a vitamin K_2 possessing a solanesyl side chain, with 9 isopentane units, was isolated from *M. tuberculosis*, and the structure proven by synthesis[139]. Several other members of the series have been synthesized, varying the side chain from five to ten units. The role for vitamin K in electron transport and oxidative phosphorylation has been reviewed by Beyer[140], Brodie and Ballantine[141] and Green[142].

Another class of terpenoids with more than eight isopentane structural units has been discovered in the *ubiquinones* (257), which occur in liver and intestinal tissue. These substituted benzoquinones have a polyterpenoid side chain of 25 to 50 carbon atoms, several forms of which have been synthesized[143,144]. Reviews of the chemistry and importance of this group in elec-

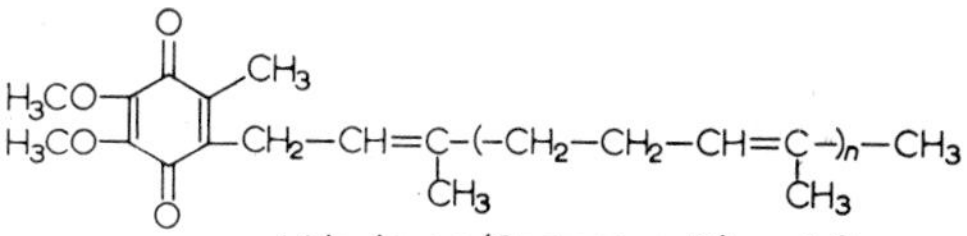

Ubiquinone (Coenzyme Q) n=4-9
(257)

tron transport have been published by Morton[145] and Green[142]. Coenzyme Q, one of the ubiquinones, has been shown to be essential in the reduction of cytochrome-*c* by succinate.

A similar compound, Kofler's quinone (Q254), has been found, differing from coenzyme Q in lacking its ring methyl group while the two methoxyl groups are replaced by methyl groups[143].

(b) Terpenoid chromanes

This group of biologically important compounds is based on a nucleus which has been best known in vitamin E (α-tocopherol) (258).

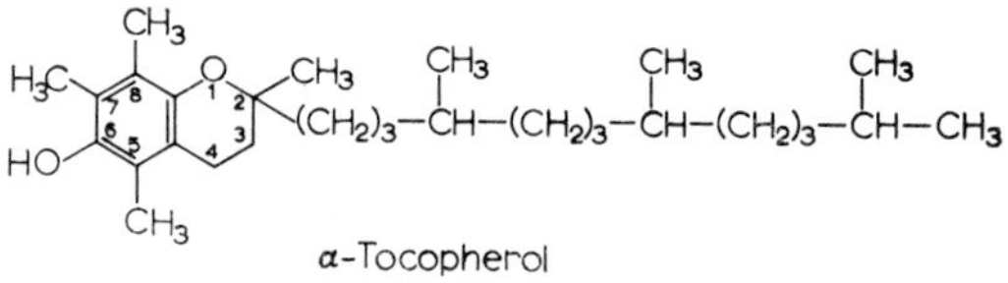

α-Tocopherol
(258)

This compound, which is apparently necessary for fertility of rats and other animals, also has antioxidant properties which are thought to be responsible for its physiological activity[146]. Seven tocopherols, derivatives of the parent substance *tocol*, 2-methyl-2-(trimethyltridecyl)-6-hydroxychromane, have been found in nature.

TABLE III

Tocopherol	Substituents
Alpha	5,7,8-trimethyltocol
Beta	5,8-dimethyltocol
Gamma	7,8-dimethyltocol
Delta	8-methyltocol
Eta	7-methyltocol
Zeta	5,7-dimethyltocol

If we consider the tocopherols derived from a substituted phenol by ring closure, forming the heterocyclic oxygen-containing ring, the chain length is that of four isoprenoid units.

A similarly built structure, solanochromene (259), was found in flue-cured tobacco leaves in amounts of 0.01−0.002% of the dry weight of the leaf by Rowland[147]. Also present were α-tocopherol and an alcohol, solanesol (260), with a 45-carbon isoprenoid chain[143].

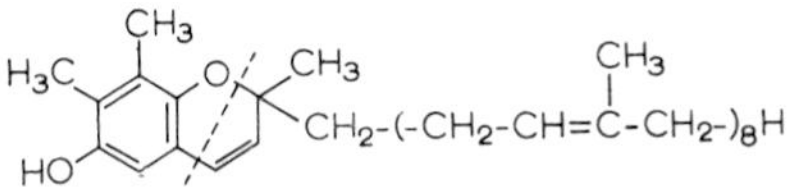

Solanochromene
(259)

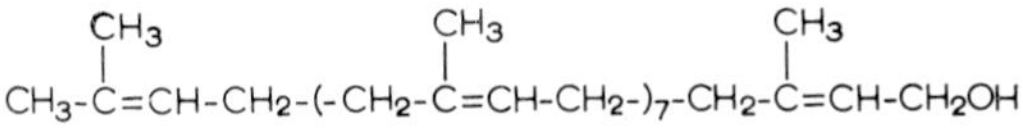

Solanesol
(260)

Solanochromene has an isoprene side chain of 9 units, counting from the benzene ring. Substituents in the benzene ring correspond to those in γ-tocopherol.

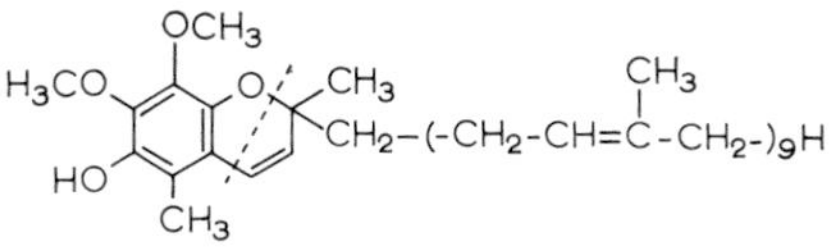

Ubichromenol
(261)

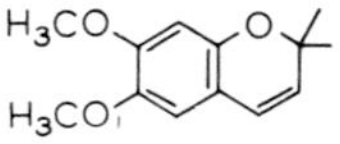

Ageratochromene
(262)

A recent addition to the polyterpene chromenes is Substance SC (ubichromenol) (261) isolated from human kidney[148]. The smallest member of the isoprenoid chromene series, ageratochromene (262), is found in the essential oils of some *Ageratum* species[149].

9. Polyterpenoids

The polyterpenoid class has customarily been confined to include the rubbers, since until recent years no other terpenoids between this class and the tetraterpenoids have been known. As mentioned earlier, true terpenoids with chain lengths of 45 to 50 carbon atoms have been found, but none approach the chain lengths of the rubber latex hydrocarbon terpenoids.

The chemistry of rubber has been reviewed recently in several references[150]. The polyterpenoids occur in latex of many families of *Dicotyledons*. Especially rich in latex are the families of *Moraceae*, *Asclepidaceae*, *Apocynaceae*, *Euphorbiceae*, *Papaveraceae* and *Compositae*. Rubber is produced by tropical and temperate zone plants of some 2000 species, but only a few of these have commercial significance. The rubber content may be as high as 20% of the dry weight of the plant, as in guayule, but is usually on the order of a few tenths of a percent. Rubber is absent in *monocotyledons, gymnosperms* and lower plants.

References p. 164

Great improvement has been made in yields per acre by proper agricultural methods, harvesting or tapping and through selection based on genetic studies[155]. Rubber is deposited mostly in stems and roots of the plants, and is often present as a suspension of particles. Latex particles vary in size and shape, their diameter ranging from 0.01–50 μ. The liquid serum, carrying the latex particles, is a complex mixture containing water- and ether-soluble substances, such as proteins, phospholipids, amino acids, glycerides, sugars, salts and triterpenes.

Other rubber types are gutta-percha from *Palaqium gutta* and balata from *Mimusops balata* (both *Sapotaceae*). Chicle, used as a base for chewing gum, comes from *Achras sapota*.

The terpenoid structure of rubber has been shown by chemical degradation, and size and shape have been determined by physical methods. Hevea rubber is an all-*cis* polyisoprene hydrocarbon chain (263). Gutta-percha is, on the contrary, all-*trans* (264).

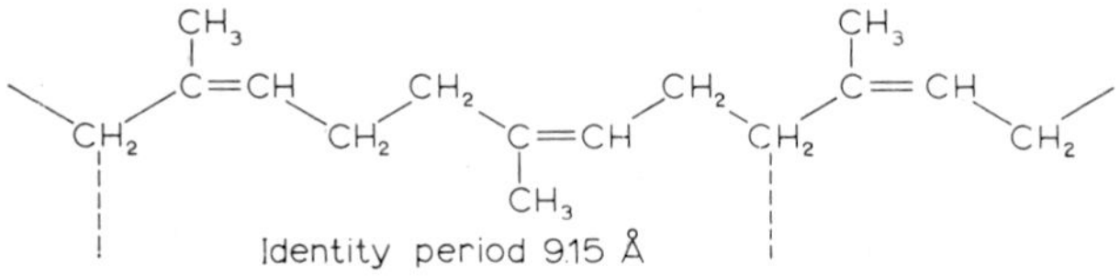

Identity period 9.15 Å

Hevea rubber *(cis)*
(263)

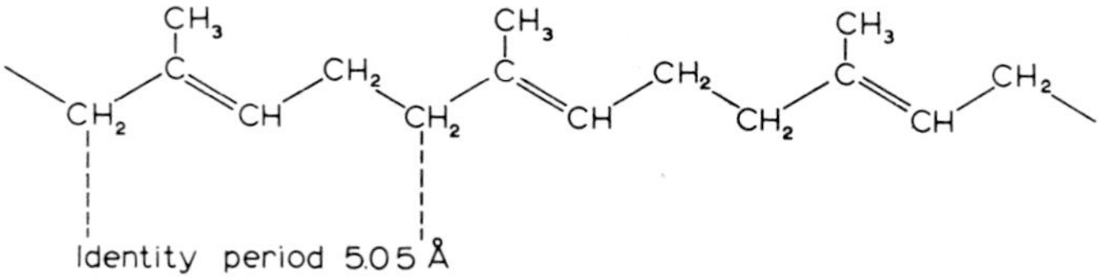

Identity period 5.05 Å

Gutta-percha *(trans)*
(264)

Mixed polyisoprene chains, containing *cis*- as well as *trans*-arrangements around the double bonds, do not seem to occur in nature. In the laboratory, treatment with iodine can partially isomerize the two forms.

Natural rubber gives only a diffuse X-ray pattern in the unstretched condition, but a well-defined crystalline pattern forms on stretching. The identity period of 9.15 Å for Hevea rubber corresponds to a *cis*-arrangement of the carbon chain with respect to the double bonds. Balata and gutta-percha are chemically similar to Hevea rubber, but they are physically much tougher and behave as non-elastic thermoplastic gums. As stated above, gutta-percha has an all-*trans* chain, with an identity period of 5.05 Å. It is crystalline at room temperature and becomes elastic only when the temperature is raised.

The observed identity periods for rubber are somewhat less than that calculated for a planar structure, indicating that the chains are coiled to form a three-dimensional structure. In the unstretched condition, there is a tendency toward random arrangement of the chains. On stretching, the chains become oriented. This behavior is responsible for the elastic properties of rubber. Storks[151] finds that the macromolecule is formed in concertina-like folds.

Rubber is soluble in benzene, petroleum ether, ether, carbon disulfide, etc., but insoluble in acetone, methyl alcohol and similar polar solvents. By solvent fractionation, it can be shown that rubber is made up of molecules of greatly varying size. The number of isopentane units in a solvent-fractionated rubber[152] ranges from about 440 to 5000. Only a small proportion is of low molecular weight.

The molecular weight of rubber in freshly-tapped Hevea latex, as determined by viscosity or osmotic measurements, ranges from several millions to less than one hundred thousand, with an approximate average of one million.

Benedict *et al.*[153] studied the molecular weight of guayule rubber in different parts of the plant. The highest molecular weight rubber is found in the roots, followed by the stem, the branches and the tips, in that order. The molecular weight ranged from 210,000 to 20,000, corresponding to a polymer of 3,000 to 300 isoprene units.

Enzyme preparations from the latex of rubber rapidly and specifically incorporate [2-^{14}C]-mevalonic acid into rubber, as reported by Park and Bonner[154].

Polymerization of isoprene has been accomplished by the action of stereospecific catalysts (finely divided lithium metal) at low temperatures. A *cis*-1,4-polyisoprene was obtained which had practically the same structure and molecular weight distribution as rubber[155].

REFERENCES

1 L. Ruzicka, *Experientia*, 9 (1953) 357.

2 E. Guenther, *The Essential Oils*, Vols. I–VI, Van Nostrand, New York, 1948–52.

3 J. L. Simonsen and L. N. Owen, *The Terpenes*, Cambridge University Press, Vol. I, 1947, *The Simpler Acyclic and Monocyclic Terpenes and their Derivatives*; Vol. II, 1949, *The Dicyclic Terpenes and their Derivatives*.
J. L. Simonsen and D. H. R. Barton, *ibid.*, Vol. III, 1952, *The Sesquiterpenes, Diterpenes and their Derivatives*.
J. L. Simonsen and W. C. J. Ross, *ibid.*, Vol. IV, 1957, *The Triterpenes and their Derivatives, Hydrocarbons, Alcohols, Hydroxyaldehydes, Ketones and Hydroxyketones*.
J. L. Simonsen and W. C. J. Ross, *ibid.*, Vol. V, 1957, *The Triterpenes and their Derivatives, Hydroxy-acids, Hydroxy-lactones, Hydroxy-aldehydo-acids, Hydroxy-keto-acids, and the Stereochemistry of the Triterpenes*.

4 *Encyclopedia of Plant Physiology*, Vol. X, *The Metabolism of Secondary Plant Products*, Springer, Berlin, 1958; O. Moritz, *Die Terpenoide*, p. 24–51; A. J. Haagen-Smit, *The Lower Terpenes*, p. 52–90; J. G. Kisser, *Die Ausscheidung von ätherischen Ölen und Harzen*, p. 91–131; T. W. Goodwin, *Carotenoids*, p. 186–222; B. Arreguin, *Rubber and Latex*, p. 223–248.

5 D. A. R. Barton, The Chemistry of the Diterpenoids, *Quart. Revs. (London)*, 3 (1949) 36.

6 P. de Mayo, *Mono- and Sesquiterpenoids*, 1959 and *The Higher Terpenoids*, 1959, Interscience, New York.

7 D. H. R. Barton and R. C. Cookson, The Principles of Conformational Analysis, *Quart. Revs. (London)*, 10 (1956) 44.

8 W. Hückel and M. Hanack, *Ann.*, 616 (1958) 18.

9 A. J. Birch, *Ann. Repts. on Progr. Chem. (London)*, 47 (1950) 191.

10 W. Klyne, *Progress in Stereochemistry*, Vol. I, Butterworth, London, 1954; W. Klyne, Optical Rotatory Dispersions and the Study of Organic Structures, *Advances in Organic Chem.*, 1 (1960) 239; C. Djerassi, *Optical Rotatory Dispersion, Applications to Organic Chemistry*, McGraw-Hill, New York, 1960.

11 L. Ruzicka in Sir Alexander Todd (Ed.), *Chemie der Terpenverbindungen, Perspectives in Organic Chemistry*, Interscience, New York, 1956.

12 *Nomenclature for Terpene Hydrocarbons, Advances in Chemistry Series*, No. 14, March, 1955, American Chemical Society.

13 A. J. Birch, *Chem. Weekblad*, 56 (1960) 597.

14 N. J. Leonard, *Senecio Alkaloids, The Alkaloids: Chemistry and Physiology*, Vol. VI; R. H. F. Manske (Ed.), Academic Press, New York, 1960, pp. 37–122.

15 A. R. H. Cole, Infra-red Spectra of Natural Products, *Progr. in Chem. Org. Nat. Prods.*, 13 (1956) 1.

16 H. Schinz and J. P. Bourquin, *Helv. Chim. Acta*, 25 (1942) 1599; Y. R. Naves, *Compt. rend.*, 249 (1959) 562.

17 Tetsuo Nozol, Natural Tropolones and some related Troponoids, *Progr. in Chem. Org. Nat. Prods.*, 13 (1956) 232.

18 Y. R. Naves and P. Ochsner, *Helv. Chim. Acta*, 43 (1960) 406.

19 F. Korte, H. Barkemeyer and I. Korte, *Progr. in Chem. Org. Nat. Prods.*, 17 (1959) 124.

20 K. Wiesner, Z. Valenta, B. S. Hurlbert, F. Bickelhaupt and L. R. Fowler, *J. Am. Chem. Soc.*, 80 (1958) 1521; G. Singh, G. V. Nair, K. P. Aggarwal and S. S. Saksena, *J. Sci. Ind. Research India*, 17 (1958) B333.

21 S. M. McElvain and E. J. Eisenbraun, *J. Org. Chem.*, 22 (1957) 976.

22 G. W. K. Cavill, The Cyclopentanoid Monoterpenes, *Rev. Pure and Appl. Chem.*, 10 (1960) 169.

23 E. E. van Tamelen, J. McNary and F. A. Lornitzo, *J. Am. Chem. Soc.*, 79 (1957) 1231.

24 H. Erdtmann, *Progr. in Org. Chem.*, 1 (1952) 22.

25 A. Anderson and E. C. Sherrard, *J. Am. Chem. Soc.*, 55 (1933) 3813.

26 M. Kosake and H. Nonake, *Ann.*, 607 (1957) 153.

27 D. H. R. Barton and P. de Mayo, *Quart. Rev. (London)*, 18 (1957) 68.

28 A. J. Haagen-Smit, Sesquiterpenes and Diterpenes, *Progr. in Chem. Org. Nat. Prods.*, 12 (1955) 1; F. Sorm, *Record Chem. Progr.*, 21 (1960) 73.

29 M. Gordon, *Chem. Rev.*, 50 (1952) 127.

30 W. Treibs, W. Kirckhof and W. Ziegenbein, *Fortschritte der Chem. Forsch.*, 3 (1954) 334.

31 K. Hafner, *Angew. Chem.*, 70 (1958) 419.

32 P. de Mayo, *Perfumery Essent. Oil Record*, 18 (1957) 68.

33 A. J. Birch, R. Massy-Westropp and S. E. Wright, *Australian J. Chem.*, 6 (1953) 385.

34 T. Kubota and T. Matsura, *Chem. & Ind. (London)*, (1957) 491.

35 A. Quilico, F. Piozzi and M. Pavan, *Tetrahedron*, 1 (1957) 177; A. Quilico, P. Grünauger and F. Piozzi, *ibid.*, 1 (1957) 186.

36 A. Eschenmoser, D. Felix, M. Gut, Y. Meier and P. Studtler, *Ciba Foundation Symposium on the Biosynthesis of Terpenes and Sterols*, Little-Brown and Co., Boston, p. 217; M. Tsutsui and E. A. Ashworth Tsutsui, Diterpenoids, *Chem. Rev.*, 59 (1959) 1030; W. H. Schuller and R. V. Lawrence, *J. Am. Chem. Soc.*, 83 (1961) 2563.

37 G. H. Gamboni, H. Schinz and A. Eschenmoser, *Helv. Chim. Acta*, 37 (1954) 964; L. Re and H. Schinz, *ibid.*, 41 (1958) 1717.

38 M. Suchy, M. Horak, V. Herout and F. Sorm, *Chem. & Ind. (London)*, (1957) 894.

39 D. H. R. Barton and P. de Mayo, *J. Chem. Soc. (London)*, (1957) 150.

40 F. Sorm, M. Streibl, V. Jarolim, L. Novatny, L. Dolejs abd V. Herout, *Collection Czech. Chem. Communs.*, 19 (1954) 570.

41 Sukh Dev, *Tetrahedron Letters*, 7 (1959) 12.

42 V. Herout and M. Suchy, *Collection Czech. Chem. Communs.*, 23 (1958) 2175.

43 H. Erdtman and J. Gripenberg, *Nature*, 161 (1948) 719; R. B. Campbell and J. M. Robertson, *Chem. & Ind. (London)*, (1953) 1266.

44 V. Herout and V. Sykora, *Tetrahedron*, 4 (1958) 246; V. Sykora, V. Herout and F. Sorm, *Collection Czech. Chem. Communs.*, 23 (1958) 2181; O. Motl, V. Sykora, V. Herout and F. Sorm, *ibid.*, 23 (1958) 1297.

45 M. D. Soffer, M. Brey and J. Fournier, *Chem. & Ind. (London)*, (1958) 19.

46 L. Ruzicka, J. Meyer and M. Mingazzini, *Helv. Chim. Acta*, 5 (1922) 345.

47 B. Riniker, J. Kalvoda, D. Arigoni, A. Furst, O. Jeger, A. M. Gold and R. B. Woodward, *J. Am. Chem. Soc.*, 76 (1954) 313.

48 V. Benesova, V. Sykora, V. Herout and F. Sorm, *Chem. & Ind. (London)*, (1958) 363, 1359.

49 O. Motl, V. Herout and F. Sorm, *Collection Czech. Chem. Communs.*, 22 (1957) 785.

50 T. Nataksuka and Y. Hirose, *Bull. Agr. Chem. Soc. Japan*, 20 (1956) 215.

51 W. Cocker and T. B. U. McMurry, *Proc. Chem. Soc.* (1958) 147; H. Bruderer, D. Arigoni and O. Jeger, *Helv. Chim. Acta*, 39 (1956) 858.

52 M. Sumi, *J. Am. Chem. Soc.*, 80 (1958) 4869.

53 K. Tsuda, K. Tomabe, I. Iwai and K. Funakoshi, *J. Am. Chem. Soc.*, 79 (1957) 1009, 5721.

54 D. H. R. Barton, *Helv. Chim. Acta*, 42 (1959) 2604.

55 C. Djerassi, R. Riniker and B. Riniker, *J. Am. Chem. Soc.*, 78 (1956) 6362.

56 C. Djerassi and S. Burstein, *J. Am. Chem. Soc.*, 80 (1958) 2593; M. G. Rossman and W. N. Lipscomb, *Tetrahedron*, 4 (1958) 275; P. Crabbe, S. Burstein and C. Djerassi, *Bull. Soc. Chim. Belges*, 67 (1958) 632.

57 C. J. W. Brooks and K. H. Overton, *Proc. Chem. Soc.*, (1957) 322.

58 L. Caglioti, H. Naef, D. Arigoni and O. Jeger, *Helv. Chim. Acta*, 41 (1958) 2278.

59 E. Stahl, *Ber.*, 87 (1954) 1626.

60 D. H. R. Barton and C. R. Narayanen, *J. Chem. Soc. (London)*, (1958) 963; L. Dolejs, M. Soucek, M. Horak, V. Herout and F. Sorm, *Chem. & Ind. (London)*, (1958) 530; *Collection Czech. Chem. Communs.*, 23 (1958) 2195.

61 H. Herout, M. Holub, L. Novotny, F. Sorm and V. Sykora, *Chem. & Ind. (London)*, (1960) 662.

[62] L. DOLEJS, V. HEROUT AND F. SORM, *Collection Czech. Chem. Communs.*, 23 (1958) 504; R. G. DEUEL AND T. A. GEISSMAN, *J. Am. Chem. Soc.*, 79 (1957) 3778.

[63] T. KARIYONE AND T. OKUDA, *Chem. Abstr.*, 48 (1954) 9971.

[64] D. E. HATHAWAY, *J. Chem. Soc. (London)*, (1957) 4953; H. CONROY, *J. Am. Chem. Soc.*, 79 (1957) 5550.

[65] V. SYKORA, V. HEROUT, J. PLIVA AND F. SORM, *Chem. & Ind. (London)*, (1956) 1231.

[66] O. GÜNTHER, H. FARNOW, P. WOLFGANG AND G. SCHADE, *Ann.*, 625 (1959) 206.

[67] G. BÜCHI AND D. M. WHITE, *J. Am. Chem. Soc.*, 79 (1957) 750.

[68] A. VESTERBERG, *Ber.*, 36 (1903) 4200.

[69] L. RUZICKA AND FR. BALAS, *Helv. Chim. Acta*, 6 (1923) 677.

[70] W. KLYNE, *Chem. & Ind. (London)*, (1954) 725.

[71] F. G. FISCHER AND W. RÜDIGER, *Ann.*, 627 (1959) 35.

[72] R. LUKES AND A. ZABACOVA, *Collection Czech. Chem. Communs.*, 22 (1957) 1649.

[73] J. W. K. BURRELL, L. M. JACKMAN AND B. C. L. WEEDON, *Proc. Chem. Soc. (London)*, (1959) 263.

[74] R. L. ROWLAND, *J. Am. Chem. Soc.*, 79 (1957) 5007.

[75] F. SORM, M. SUCHY AND V. HEROUT, *Collection Czech. Chem. Communs.*, 16 (1951) 278.

[76] R. A. MORTON AND G. A. J. PITT, *Progr. in Chem. Org. Nat. Prods.*, 14 (1957) 244; K. EITER, E. TRUSCHEIT AND H. OEDIGER, Neuere Ergebnisse in der Vitamin-A-Reihe, *Z. anorg. Chem.*, 72 (1960) 948.

[77] J. A. BARLTROP AND A. C. DAY, *Chem. & Ind. (London)*, (1958) 439.

[78] F. E. KING AND G. JONES, *J. Chem. Soc. (London)*, (1955) 658.

[79] G. OHLOFF, *Helv. Chim. Acta*, 41 (1958) 845; *Ann.*, 617 (1958) 134.

[80] G. BÜCHI, *Croat. Chim. Acta*, 29 (1957) 162.

[81] E. McC. ROBERTS AND R. V. LAWRENCE, *U.S. Dept. of Agric.*, Naval Stores Station, Olustee, Fla.

[82] D. H. R. BARTON AND D. ELAD, *J. Chem. Soc. (London)*, (1956) 2085, 2090; M. P. CAVA AND E. J. SOBOCZENSKI, *J. Am. Chem. Soc.*, 78 (1956) 5317.

[83] E. WENKERT, *Chem. & Ind. (London)*, (1955) 282.

[84] E. WENKERT AND G. W. CHAMBERLIN, *J. Am. Chem. Soc.*, 80 (1958) 2912.

[85] O. JEGER, O. DÜRST AND G. BÜCHI, *Helv. Chim. Acta*, 30 (1947) 1853.

[86] F. E. KING, T. J. KING AND J. G. TOPLIS, *J. Chem. Soc. (London)*, (1957) 573; P. N. RAO AND K. RAMAN, *Tetrahedron*, 4 (1958) 294.

[87] C. W. BRAND AND B. R. THOMAS, *New Zealand J. Sci. Technol.*, B33 (1951) 30.

[88] J. A. BARLTROP AND N. A. J. ROGERS, *Chem. & Ind. (London)*, (1957) 397.

[89] A. HARRIS, A. ROBERTSON AND W. B. WHALLEY, *J. Chem. Soc. (London)*, (1958) 1799; D. ARIGONI, *Ciba Foundation Symposium* (see ref. 36).

[90] B. E. CROSS, J. F. GROVE, J. MCMILLAN, J. S. MOFFAT, T. P. C. MULHOLLAND, J. C. SEATON AND N. SHEPPARD, *Proc. Chem. Soc. (London)*, (1959) 302; A. J. BIRCH AND HERSCHEL SMITH, *Ciba Foundation Symposium* (see ref. 36); P. W. BRIAN, J. F. GROVE AND J. MACMILLAN, *Fortschr. Chem. org. Naturstoffe*, 18 (1960) 350.

[91] K. WIESNER AND Z. VALENTA, *Fortschr. Chem. org. Naturstoffe*, 16 (1958) 26.

[92] K. WIESNER, S. ITO AND Z. VALENTA, *Experientia*, 14 (1958) 167.

[93] D. DVORNIK AND O. E. EDWARDS, *Chem. & Ind. (London)*, (1958) 623.

[94] D. H. R. BARTON, *The Chemistry of the Triterpenoids, Progress in Organic Chemistry*, Vol. II, Academic Press, New York, 1953, p. 67.

[95] M. STEINER AND H. HALTZEM in K. PAECH AND M. V. TRACEY (Eds.), *Moderne Methoden der Pflanzenanalyse*, Vol. III, Springer, Berlin, 1955, p. 58.

[96] L. RUZICKA, H. W. HUYSER, M. PFEIFFER AND C. F. SEIDEL, *Ann.*, 471 (1929) 21.

[97] L. RUZICKA, H. SCHELLENBERG AND M. W. GOLDBERG, *Helv. Chim. Acta*, 20 (1937) 791, 1155.

[98] K. BLOCH, Biogenesis and Transformations of Squalene, *Ciba Foundation Symposium* (see ref. 36).

[99] P. KARRER AND A. HELFENSTEIN, *Helv. Chim. Acta*, 14 (1931) 78; W. G. DAUBEN AND H. L. BRADLOW, *J. Am. Chem. Soc.*, 74 (1952) 5204; *Helv. Chim. Acta*, 36 (1953) 717.

100 S. Trippett, *Chem. & Ind. (London)*, (1956) 80; D. W. Dicker and M. C. Whiting, *Chem. & Ind. (London)*, (1956) 351.
101 N. Nicolaides and F. Laves, *J. Am. Chem. Soc.*, 76 (1954) 2596.
102 T. T. Tchen and K. Bloch, *J. Am. Chem. Soc.*, 78 (1956) 1516.
103 L. Ruzicka and F. Lardon, *Helv. Chim. Acta*, 29 (1946) 913.
104 E. Lederer, F. Marx, D. Mercier and G. Perat, *Helv. Chim. Acta*, 29 (1946) 1354.
105 D. H. R. Barton and K. H. Overton, *J. Chem. Soc. (London)*, (1955) 2639.
106 W. G. Dauben, Y. Ban and J. H. Richards, *J. Am. Chem. Soc.*, 79 (1957) 968.
107 R. B. Woodward, A. A. Patchett, D. H. R. Barton, D. A. J. Ives and R. B. Kelly, *J. Am. Chem. Soc.*, 76 (1954) 2852.
108 D. H. R. Barton, J. E. Page and E. W. Warnhoff, *J. Chem. Soc. (London)*, (1954) 2715; J. M. Beaton, J. D. Easton, M. M. MacArthur, F. S. Spring and R. Stevenson, *J. Chem. Soc. (London)*, (1955) 3992.
109 A. Zurcher, O. Jeger and L. Ruzicka, *Helv. Chim. Acta*, 37 (1954) 2145.
110 D. Arigoni, D. H. R. Barton, R. Bernasconi, C. Djerassi, J. S. Mills and R. Wolff, *Proc. Chem. Soc. (London)*, (1959) 306; D. Arigoni, D. H. R. Barton, E. J. Corey and O. Jeger, *Experientia*, 16 (1960) 41; S. Arnott, A. W. Davie, J. M. Robertson, G. A. Sim and D. G. Watson, *Experientia*, 16 (1960) 49.
111 D. H. R. Barton, *Helv. Chim. Acta*, 42 (1959) 2604.
112 T. G. Halsall, E. R. H. Jones and R. E. H. Swayne, *J. Chem. Soc. (London)*, (1954) 1902, 1905; T. G. Halsall, E. R. H. Jones and G. D. Meakins, *ibid.*, (1952) 2862; T. R. Ames, T. G. Halsall and E. R. H. Jones, *ibid.*, (1951) 450.
113 J. Fridrichsons and A. McL. Mathieson, *J. Chem. Soc. (London)*, (1953) 2159.
114 W. Klyne, *Chem. & Ind. (London)*, (1952) 172.
115 G. Stork and A. W. Burgstahler, *J. Am. Chem. Soc.*, 77 (1955) 5068.
116 T. W. Goodwin, The Biosynthesis and Function of the Carotenoid Pigments, *Adv. Enzym.*, 21 (1959) 295; T. W. Goodwin, Carotenoids, *Encyclopedia of Plant Physiology*, Vol. X, Springer, Berlin, 1958, p. 186; T. W. Goodwin, Carotenoids, *Ann. Rev. Biochem.*, 24 (1955) 497; T. W. Goodwin, *The Comparative Biochemistry of the Carotenoids*, Chapman and Hall, London, 1952.
117 P. Karrer and E. Jucker, *Carotenoids*, Elsevier, Amsterdam, 1950; A. Winterstein, Neuere Ergebnisse der Carotenoid Forschung, *Angew. Chem.*, 72 (1960) 902.
118 K. Paech and M. V. Tracey (Eds.), *Handbook of Plant Analysis*, Vol. III, Springer, Berlin, 1955.
119 L. Zechmeister and L. v. Cholnoky, *Die chromatographische Adsorptionsanalyse*, Springer, Berlin, 1938.
120 H. H. Strain, *Chromatographic Adsorption Analysis*, Interscience, New York, 1945.
121 L. Zechmeister, Some *in vitro* Conversions of Naturally Occurring Carotenoids, *Fortschr. Chem. org. Naturstoffe*, 15 (1958) 31; L. Zechmeister, Some Stereochemical Aspects of Polyenes, *Experientia*, 10 (1954) 1.
122 O. Isler and P. Zeller, *Vitamins and Hormones*, 15 (1957) 31; O. Isler and M. Montavon, *Chimia (Switz.)*, 12 (1958) 1.
123 R. Willstätter and W. Meig, *Ann.*, 355 (1907) 1.
124 L. Zechmeister and L. v. Cholnoky, *Ber.*, 61 (1928) 1534.
125 E. F. Magoon and L. Zechmeister, *Arch. Biochem.*, 69 (1957) 535.
126 L. Zechmeister and E. F. Magoon, *Chem. & Ind. (London)*, (1957) 431; L. Zechmeister, *Cis–trans* Isomeric Carotenoid Pigments, *Fortschr. Chem. der Naturstoffe*, 18 (1960) 223.
127 T. W. Goodwin, Carotenoids, *Ann. Rev. Biochem.*, 24 (1955) 497.
128 J. W. Porter and R. E. Lincoln, *Arch. Biochem.*, 27 (1950) 390.
129 E. C. Grob, *Chimia (Switz.)*, 12 (1958) 86; P. Karrer and H. Kramer, *Helv. Chim. Acta*, 27 (1944) 1301; L. F. Krzeminsky and F. W. Quakenbush, *Arch. Biochem. Biophysics*, 88 (1960) 64.
130 M. S. Barber, L. M. Jackman and B. C. L. Weedon, *Proc. Chem. Soc. (London)*, (1959) 96.
131 L. v. Cholnoky, C. Gyorgyfy, E. Nagy and M. Panczel, *Nature*, 178 (1956) 410.
132 M. Yamaguchi, *Bull. Chem. Soc. Japan*, 31 (1958) 51, 739.

133 O. Rüegg, W. Guex, M. Montavon, U. Schwieter, G. Saucy and O. Isler, *Chimia (Switz.)*, 12 (1958) 327.

134 M. S. Barber, L. M. Jackman, C. K. Warren and B. C. L. Weedon, *Proc. Chem. Soc. (London)*, (1960) 19.

135 I. Heilbron and B. C. L. Weedon, *Bull. soc. chim. France*, (1958) 83.

136 R. H. Thomson, *Naturally Occurring Quinones*, Butterworth, London, 1957.

137 O. Hofmann-Ostenhof in K. Paech and M. V. Tracey (Eds.), Ein- und zwei-Kernige Chinone, *Moderne Methoden der Pflanzenanalyse*, Vol. III, Springer, Berlin, 1955, p. 359.

138 O. Isler, R. Rüegg, L. H. Chopard-dit-Jean and A. Winterstein, *Helv. Chim. Acta*, 41 (1958) 786.

139 H. Noll, R. Rüegg, U. Gloor, G. Ryser and O. Isler, *Helv. Chim. Acta*, 43 (1960) 433.

140 R. E. Beyer, *J. Biol. Chem.*, 234 (1959) 688.

141 A. F. Brodie and J. Ballantine, *J. Biol. Chem.*, 235 (1960) 226.

142 D. E. Green, *Adv. Enzymology*, 21 (1959) 73.

143 C. H. Shunk, R. E. Frickorn, E. L. Wong and K. Folkers, *J. Am. Chem. Soc.*, 81 (1959) 5000.

144 R. Rüegg, U. Gloor, R. N. Groel, O. Wiss and O. Isler, *Helv. Chim. Acta*, 42 (1959) 2616.

145 R. A. Morton, *Nature*, 182 (1958) 1764.

146 A. White, P. Handler, E. L. Smith, DeWitt Stetten, *Principles of Biochemistry*, McGraw-Hill, New York, 1959.

147 R. L. Rowland, P. H. Latimer and J. A. Giles, *J. Am. Chem. Soc.*, 78 (1956) 4680; R. L. Rowland, *J. Am. Chem. Soc.*, 80 (1958) 6130.

148 D. L. Laidman, R. A. Morton, J. Y. F. Paterson and J. F. Pennock, *Biochemical J.*, 74 (1960) 541.

149 A. R. Alertsen, *Acta Chem. Scand.*, 9 (1955) 1725.

150 B. Arreguin, Rubber and Latex, *Handbuch der Pflanzenphysiologie*, Vol. X, Springer, Berlin, 1958; H. M. Benedict in K. Paech and M. V. Tracey (Eds.), The Occurrence of Rubber in Plants, *Moderne Methoden der Pflanzenanalyse*, Vol. III, Springer, Berlin, 1955, p. 312; Harry L. Fisher, *Chemistry of Natural and Synthetic Rubbers*, Reinhold, New York, 1957.

151 K. H. Storks, *Bell Labs. Record*, 21 (1943) 390.

152 G. F. Bloomfield and E. H. Farmer, *J. Rubber Inst. Trans.*, 16 (1940) 69.

153 H. M. Benedict, P. M. Brooks and R. F. Puckett, *Plant Physiol.*, 25 (1950) 120.

154 R. B. Park and J. Bonner, *J. Biol. Chem.*, 233 (1958) 340.

155 F. W. Steveley et al., *Ind. Eng. Chem.*, 48 (1956) 778; S. E. Horne, J. P. Kiehl, J. J. Shipman, V. L. Folt, C. F. Gibbs, E. A. Willsen, E. B. Newton and M. A. Reinhart, *Ind. Eng. Chem.*, 48 (1956) 784.

Chapter VI

Vitamin A

J. G. BAXTER

Laboratories of Distillation Products Industries,
Division of Eastman Kodak Company, Rochester, N.Y. (U.S.A.)*

1. Introduction

Vitamin A (retinol—ref. 1—, vitamin A alcohol, vitamin A_1, axerophthol) (I) is an essential nutritional factor for man and most animals. Fish liver oils are the richest, common, natural source of this factor. Retinol plays an integral part in the mechanism by which we see in dim light. It is necessary to the maintenance of healthy epithelial tissue and a deficiency causes an abnormality in the exterior surface of the eye known as xerophthalmia.

A number of reviews on the chemistry of retinol have appeared within the last ten years[2–8] and this has made it possible to give chief attention in the present review to basic chemistry and the more recent developments. Specific references are given in this text only to certain papers, but names of senior authors and dates of publication are cited on a number of others.

Studies on the biochemistry of retinol date back at least as far as 1913 (Osborne and Mendel; McCollum and Davis). However, rapid progress in the chemistry of retinol began with the preparation of rich concentrates from the unsaponifiable matter of fish liver oils and establishment of its structure (Karrer, 1931).

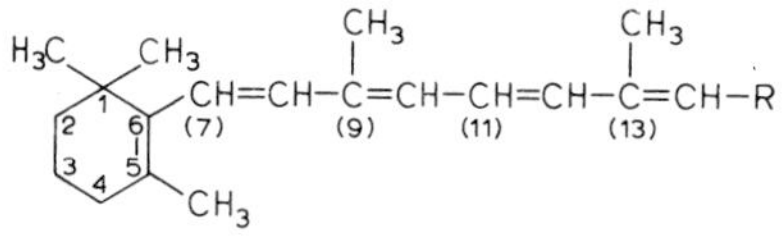

(I) Retinol   (R= CH_2OH)

The crystalline vitamin was first prepared as the β-naphthoate and anthraquinonecarboxylate esters (Hamano, 1935; Mead, 1939). The free vitamin

---

* Communication No. 271.

References p. 186

(in the form we now recognize to be the all-*trans* isomer) was crystallized first as the addition compound with methanol (m.p. 8°, Holmes, 1937) and later in solvent-free form (m.p. 64°, Baxter, 1942). The crystalline acetate, palmitate, and acid succinate esters were also prepared. The work at these laboratories was greatly facilitated by the development of the molecular still (Hickman, 1937).

Closely related to retinol is vitamin A aldehyde (retinal —ref. 1—, retinene) (I, R = CHO). The two compounds are readily interconverted in the body and the all-*trans* isomers have biopotencies within 10% of each other.

Retinol occurs in fish liver oils almost exclusively as an ester of the higher fatty acids (Bacharach, 1928). One of these fatty acids has been established to be palmitic (Tischer, 1938). In blood plasma much of the vitamin A is present as retinol, loosely attached to protein. Much still remains to be learned about the absorption, transport and storage of the vitamin.

Retinol concentrations are expressed in U.S.P. (United States Pharmacopeia) or International Units per gram. The two units are currently the same and equivalent to the amount of all-*trans* vitamin A (retinyl) acetate (0.344 μg) having the biological activity of 0.3 μg of all-*trans* retinol. The U.S.P. vitamin A reference solution contains all-*trans* retinyl acetate dissolved in vegetable oil at a concentration of 100,000 U.S.P. units/g.

While the bioassay, either by the rat growth or liver storage methods, is still the basic way of measuring vitamin A activity, its use is largely confined to research; relatively concentrated preparations are usually assayed by the U.S.P. physicochemical procedure. In this method, the retinol concentration is measured by determining the relative intensity of absorption at 325 mμ,

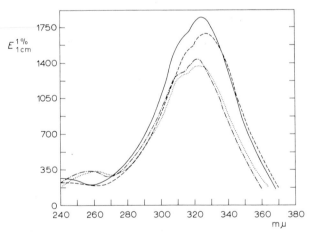

Fig. 1. Ultraviolet absorption spectra of geometric isomers of retinol: all-*trans* (———); 13-*cis* (------); 9-*cis* (–.—.–.–); 9,13-di-*cis* (.........).

the ultraviolet maximum (Fig. 1). Extraneous absorption is corrected for by a formula (Morton, 1946).

Low levels of vitamin A, as in animal feeds, are customarily assayed by measuring the relative intensity of the blue color (absorption maximum 620 mμ) formed by treatment with antimony trichloride. This reaction was discovered by Carr and Price (1926).

Most of the high potency concentrates of retinol now used consist of the palmitate or acetate esters and are made by chemical synthesis. For the fortification of animal feeds, both synthetic vitamin A and vitamin A from fish liver oils are used. For many purposes, extra protection against oxidative deterioration is desirable and this is achieved by use of "dry" vitamin A made by incorporating the acetate or palmitate esters in gelatin or other solid protective coating. Vitamin A is fat-soluble, but may be dispersed in water with emulsifying agents. Such aqueous preparations, usually containing other vitamins as well, find extensive use in the U.S.A., particularly in infant nutrition.

2. Retinol

(a) Geometric isomers

Retinol contains five double bonds, three of which (9, 11, 13; Formula I) have been shown to be capable of serving as centers for the formation of six geometrical isomers. The all-*trans* isomer was the first to be prepared in a crystalline form (m.p. 64°) and, since no other isomers were known, was designated as "vitamin A". The isolation in crystalline form of the 13-*cis* isomer, or neovitamin A, from shark and other fish liver oils (Robeson, 1947) indicated that *cis* isomers occur naturally.

The 9-*cis* isomer was prepared synthetically from *cis*-"C$_{18}$ ketone" (Graham, 1949).

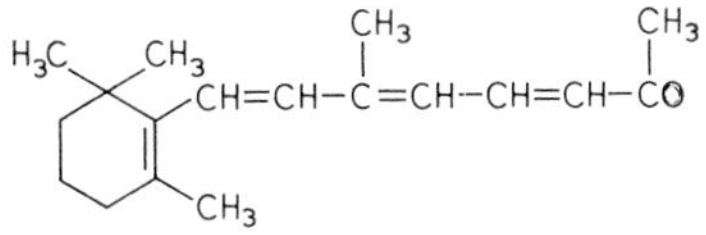

C$_{18}$ Ketone

This and the 9,13-di-*cis* isomer were also synthesized from *cis*-ethyl-β-ionylideneacetate (Fig. 2).

11-*Cis* or "neo-b" retinol was identified in the eyes of lobsters and in other marine crustacea (Wald, 1955; Plack, 1956). This and the 11,13-di-*cis* isomer were synthesized (Oroshnik, 1956). Thus six geometric isomers of retinol are

References p. 186

TABLE I

PROPERTIES OF ISOMERS OF RETINOL, RETINAL AND RETINOIC ACIDS (SOLVENT: ETHANOL)

Trivial name	Configuration	Retinols				Retinals				Retinoic acids		
		m.p.	λmax	$E_{1\ cm}^{1\ 0/0}$	Relative biopotency[a]	m.p.	λmax	$E_{1\ cm}^{1\ 0/0}$	Relative biopotency[b]	m.p.	λmax	$E_{1\ cm}^{1\ 0/0}$
all-*trans*	all-*trans*	64°	325	1845	100	57°,65°	381	1530	91	180°	350	1510
neo-a	13-*cis*	60°	328	1690	75	77°	375	1255	93	175°	354	1330
iso-a	9-*cis*	83°	323	1480	22	64°	373	1290	19	191°	345	1230
iso-b	9,13-di-*cis*	59°	324	1390	24	49°,85°	368	1150	17	136°	346	1150
neo-b	11-*cis*	oil	322	945	23	64°	376	860	48	—	—	—
neo-c	11,13-di-*cis*	oil	311	910	15	oil	373	700	—	—	—	—

[a] As acetate ester, compared with U.S.P. reference standard.
[b] Compared with U.S.P. reference standard.

now known and these few words summarize work which has extended over a period of 15 years.

The geometric isomers of retinol give equal intensity in the blue color formed by reaction with antimony trichloride, but differ in most other properties. They have different ultraviolet absorption spectra (Fig. 1) and different extinction coefficients at the absorption maximum (Table I). The *cis* isomers, other than 13-*cis*, absorb at shorter wave lengths than the all-*trans* isomer and have lower extinction coefficients.

The *cis* isomers also have less biological potency (Table I). All-*trans* retinol is the most active, 13-*cis* retinol has about 75% activity relative to the U.S.P. reference solution; the other *cis*-isomers have less than 25% relative activity (Ames, 1955).

(b) Occurrence and assay

Commercial synthetic vitamin A largely consists of the palmitate or acetate esters of the all-*trans* isomer, together with some of the corresponding esters of 13-*cis* retinol. Its biopotency in units per gram is properly estimated by the U.S.P. physicochemical procedure which corrects for the 13-*cis* retinol present.

Fish liver oils were found to contain all-*trans* and 13-*cis* retinol in a ratio which was estimated to be about 65:35 (Robeson, 1947). More recent evidence indicates that samples of cod, shark, and rat liver oils also contain the 9-*cis* and 9,13-di-*cis* isomers. Together, these isomers amounted to 15–25% of the retinol present in the oils assayed (Brown, 1960). It is not known at present whether these *cis* isomers are formed *in vivo*, or during processing of the livers for oil, or in both ways.

The 9-*cis* and 9,13-di-*cis* isomers have been found elsewhere. During studies on aqueous dispersions containing all-*trans* vitamin A palmitate, an emulsifying agent, ascorbic acid and thiamine nitrate, it was found that the all-*trans* isomer isomerized during six months storage at room temperature to mixtures containing the 13-*cis*, 9-*cis*, and 9,13-di-*cis* isomers (Lehman, 1960). At equilibrium, the proportions of isomers were about 55% all-*trans*, 20% 13-*cis*, and 25% combined 9-*cis* and 9,13-di-*cis* isomers. Formation of these *cis* isomers caused a loss of biological activity which was not correctly estimated by the current U.S.P. procedure and demonstrated the need for physicochemical methods for estimating the biopotency of natural and synthetic vitamin A sources containing the four isomers. Some progress in developing such assay methods has been made.

One such method involves the "maleic value". Maleic anhydride forms a condensation product of the Diels – Alder type with retinol or retinol ester isomers in which both the 13- and 11-double bonds are *trans* (Robeson, 1947).

References p. 186

This includes all-*trans* and 9-*cis* vitamin A. The 13-*cis* and 9,13-di-*cis* isomers do not react. Hence, the proportion of these isomers in the total retinol can be estimated by reaction with maleic anhydride (in benzene) and determination of the amount of unreacted retinol by assay with antimony trichloride. This procedure has been extended by developing an equation which estimates the biopotency of mixtures containing *cis* isomers, relative to that of the U.S.P. reference solution, from the maleic value (Ames, 1960).

Progress has also been made in determining the 9-*cis* and 9,13-di-*cis* isomer content of mixed retinol isomer preparations by reaction of the retinals with the retinal protein, opsin, or by infrared analysis of the retinals (Brown, 1960).

The 11-*cis* isomer of retinol has so far not presented assay problems since it has been found only in the eye. It was once thought to be present in a concentrate from fish liver oil (Hubbard, 1952) but the isomer present was later found to be the 9-*cis* form. The 11,13-di-*cis* isomer has also not presented assay problems yet, because it has not been found naturally but is formed by chemical synthesis.

(c) *Stability*

The stability of the retinol isomers is greater than might be expected. The all-*trans*, 13-*cis*, 9-*cis*, and 9,13-di-*cis* isomers can be preserved as crystals, stored at 0°, for at least a year, although interconversion does occur in solution, especially in the presence of isomerizing agents, such as acids or iodine.

The existence of these four isomers was explained on theoretical grounds, following the earlier investigation of the stereochemistry of the carotenes (Pauling, 1939; Zechmeister, 1944). It was concluded that *cis* configurations about the 9- and 13-double bonds of vitamin A should be possible and stable since their formation would serve to relieve the minor degree of strain present in the all-*trans* configuration. These double bonds were hence characterized as "stereochemically effective" double bonds.

It appeared from theoretical considerations that the 7- and 11-double bonds were highly strained in the *cis* configuration. These bonds were hence regarded as "stereochemically ineffective", and it appeared improbable that compounds containing such bonds could exist.

Actually 11-*cis* vitamin A proved to be relatively stable as crystals, stored at low temperature. The 11,13-di-*cis* vitamin A isomer proved to exist, but has been reported to be unstable, isomerizing slowly, even at —15° in the dark. This and other experimental evidence has necessitated a reappraisal of the theory and it is now considered (Pauling, 1949) that what is prohibited is the formation of a *cis* configuration at the 7- or 11-positions by chemical or thermal isomerization of the corresponding *trans* isomers. This agrees with our present knowledge.

3. Retinal

Each of the six isomeric forms of retinal has been prepared by oxidation of the corresponding retinol with manganese dioxide (Table I). Trivial names are often used for these retinal isomers and these are listed in the table.

The biological potencies of the all-*trans*, 9-*cis* and 9,13-di-*cis* retinals were found to be within 10% of the potencies of the corresponding retinol isomers. The 13- and 11-isomers were substantially more potent as retinals. These findings indicate ready interconversion of the alcohol and aldehyde forms in the body, plus isomerization of 13-*cis* and 11-*cis* retinals to isomers of higher potency, probably all-*trans*, during metabolism (Ames, 1955).

11-*Cis* retinal is a "hindered" isomer and was prepared in crystalline form after irradiating the all-*trans* isomer with light (Hubbard, 1952). The studies of Wald, Morton, and other investigators have shown that this isomer is a component of visual purple or rhodopsin, the light sensitive pigment in the rods of vertebrate retinas which is involved in the mechanism of vision in dim light. The body oxidizes and isomerizes retinol to 11-*cis* retinal which then combines with opsin to form rhodopsin ($\lambda_{max} = 500$ mμ). Lack of retinol retards rhodopsin formation and results in defective night vision or night blindness. The visual process involves a cycle in which all-*trans* vitamin A is converted to 11-*cis* retinal; this reacts with opsin to form rhodopsin; bleaching by exposure to light then reforms all-*trans* retinal and all-*trans* retinal. The study by which the mechanism of this and other parts of the visual process were elucidated by Wald, Morton and others is a fascinating one.

9-*Cis* retinal combines with opsin to form the pigment isorhodopsin ($\lambda_{max} = 487$ mμ). The ease with which the 9,13-di-*cis* isomer isomerizes to 9-*cis* retinal causes it to also form isorhodopsin on treatment with opsin but the reaction time is longer. Application of these facts made it possible to estimate the 9-*cis* and 9,13-di-*cis* isomer contents of fish liver oils (Brown, 1960). As far as is known, isorhodopsin is not involved in the visual process.

Until relatively recently, the retinals were found naturally only in the retina. Retinal has now been found in the ripe eggs of herring and in hen's eggs (Plack, 1960). The aldehyde form may thus be a more widely occurring natural form of vitamin A than had been thought earlier.

4. Vitamin A acid (retinoic acid)[1]

Retinoic acid (I, R=COOH) is prepared by oxidation of retinal or by chemical synthesis. Four of the geometric isomers have been prepared by synthesis and their properties are listed in Table I.

Retinoic acid has interesting physiological properties. Van Dorp and Arens first reported the synthesis of the all-*trans* acid in pure form in 1946. According to growth bioassays, it had one-tenth the activity of retinol when administered orally in oil. It was found to have full potency when the sodium salt was buffered to pH 10 in aqueous solution and given orally. We have not been able to confirm this high degree of activity for the sodium salt in our laboratory, probably because we found that the sodium salt deteriorated rapidly in water solution.

The growth promoting activity of the all-*trans* acid in rats was confirmed (Dowling, 1959), but the rats lost weight as soon as supplementation of the diet ceased, indicating that liver storage of retinol did not occur. The rats also became night blind, indicating that they were not able to utilize retinoic acid to form rhodopsin. This interesting selective action of retinoic acid suggests that studies on its metabolism may provide more information on the mechanism by which vitamin A exerts its physiological action.

5. Retinol synthesis

A number of methods for the synthesis of retinol have been devised since the first one was reported by Kuhn and Morris in 1937. β-Ionone, made from citral, has been the usual starting material. Some seven procedures were described in a review[7] covering the literature through 1950.

Two syntheses are described here: (*1*) via esters of β-methyl glutaconic acid (Robeson[9]) because this synthesis is flexible and served to prepare the four unhindered retinol isomers, (*2*) via vinyl-β-ionol (Pommer and Sarnecki[10]) because this procedure illustrates the application of the Wittig reaction to retinol synthesis.

The synthesis employing methyl-β-methyl glutaconate proceeds according to the following equations (Fig. 2).

β-Ionone was converted to the individual *cis*- and *trans*-methyl β-ionylideneacetates (isomerism about double bond starred, Fig. 2), via the corresponding β-ionylideneacetic acids. The individual *cis* and *trans* isomers of the acids were obtained by fractional crystallization of the mixed acids prepared by saponifying ethyl β-ionylideneacetate. This served to fix the configuration at carbon atom 9 of retinol, in *cis* and *trans* positions.

Cis- and *trans*-β-ionylidene-ethanols were prepared by reduction of the corresponding methyl β-ionylideneacetates with lithium aluminum hydride. *Cis*- and *trans*-β-ionylideneacetaldehydes were prepared by oxidation of the β-ionylidene-ethanols with manganese dioxide.

When *trans*-β-ionylideneacetaldehyde was condensed with methyl β-meth-

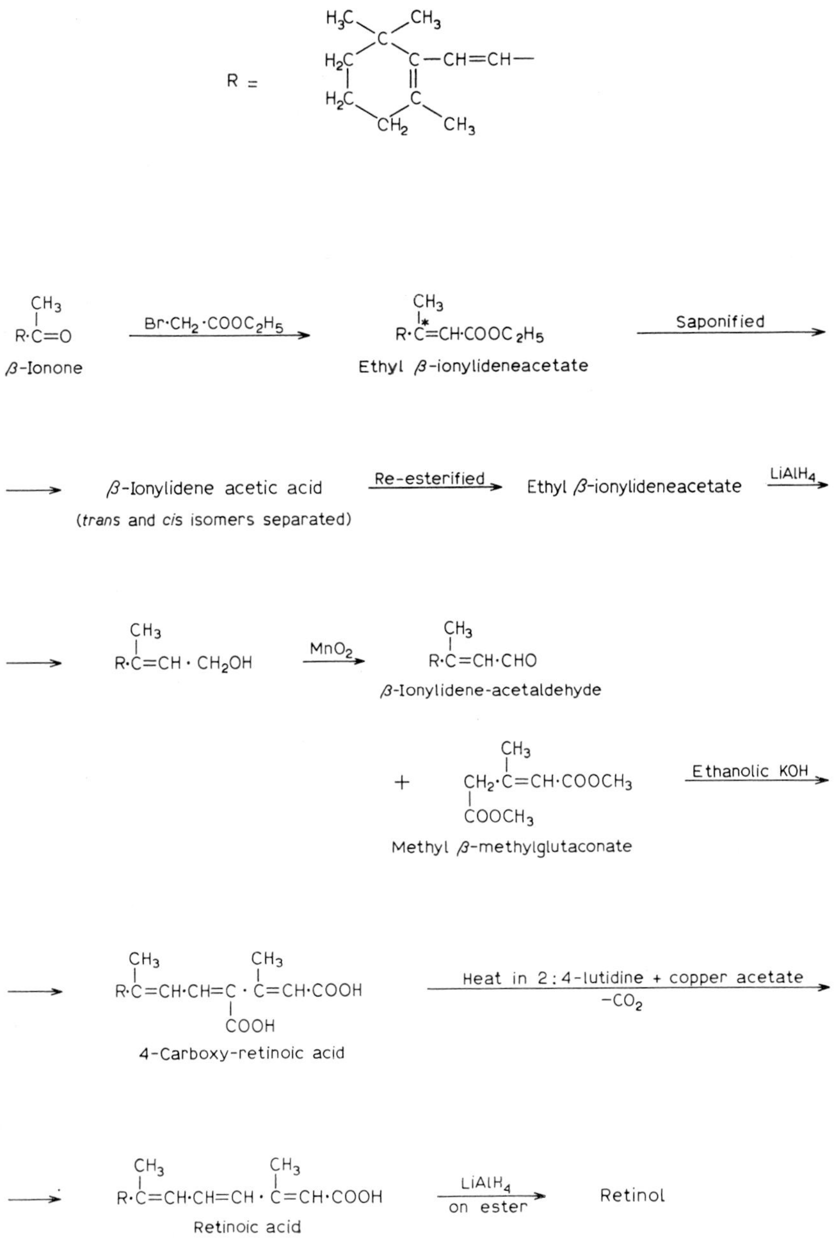

$$R = \quad \text{[structure: } H_3C,\ CH_3,\ C,\ H_2C,\ C-CH=CH-,\ H_2C,\ C,\ CH_2,\ CH_3 \text{]}$$

$$\begin{array}{c} CH_3 \\ | \\ R{\cdot}C{=}O \end{array} \xrightarrow{Br{\cdot}CH_2{\cdot}COOC_2H_5} \begin{array}{c} CH_3 \\ |_* \\ R{\cdot}C{=}CH{\cdot}COOC_2H_5 \end{array} \xrightarrow{\text{Saponified}}$$

β-Ionone   Ethyl β-ionylideneacetate

$$\longrightarrow \quad \beta\text{-Ionylidene acetic acid} \xrightarrow{\text{Re-esterified}} \text{Ethyl } \beta\text{-ionylideneacetate} \xrightarrow{LiAlH_4}$$

(*trans* and *cis* isomers separated)

$$\longrightarrow \begin{array}{c} CH_3 \\ | \\ R{\cdot}C{=}CH{\cdot}CH_2OH \end{array} \xrightarrow{MnO_2} \begin{array}{c} CH_3 \\ | \\ R{\cdot}C{=}CH{\cdot}CHO \end{array}$$

β-Ionylidene-acetaldehyde

$$+ \quad \begin{array}{c} CH_3 \\ | \\ CH_2{\cdot}C{=}CH{\cdot}COOCH_3 \\ | \\ COOCH_3 \end{array} \xrightarrow{\text{Ethanolic KOH}}$$

Methyl β-methylglutaconate

$$\longrightarrow \begin{array}{c} CH_3 \qquad\qquad CH_3 \\ | \qquad\qquad\quad | \\ R{\cdot}C{=}CH{\cdot}CH{=}C{\cdot}C{=}CH{\cdot}COOH \\ | \\ COOH \end{array} \xrightarrow[-CO_2]{\text{Heat in 2:4-lutidine + copper acetate}}$$

4-Carboxy-retinoic acid

$$\longrightarrow \begin{array}{c} CH_3 \qquad\qquad CH_3 \\ | \qquad\qquad\quad | \\ R{\cdot}C{=}CH{\cdot}CH{=}CH{\cdot}C{=}CH{\cdot}COOH \end{array} \xrightarrow[\text{on ester}]{LiAlH_4} \text{Retinol}$$

Retinoic acid

Fig. 2. Synthesis of four retinol geometric isomers[9].

ylglutaconate under strongly alkaline conditions, there resulted almost exclusively and in excellent yield a 4-carboxy-retinoic acid which for convenience was called C-diacid (configuration now considered to be: 9-*trans*, 11-*trans*, 13-*cis*). For the diacid prepared in similarly good yield from *cis*-β-ionylideneacetaldehyde, the prefix D- was used (configuration: 9-*cis*, 11-*trans*, 13-*cis*).

Decarboxylation of C-diacid gave almost exclusively 13-*cis* or neovitamin A acid. When its methyl ester was reduced with lithium aluminum hydride, at low temperatures (—50°), a retinol isomer was obtained which had identical properties with those of natural 13-*cis* retinol.

The conversion of 13-*cis* retinoic acid to the all-*trans* acid was accom-

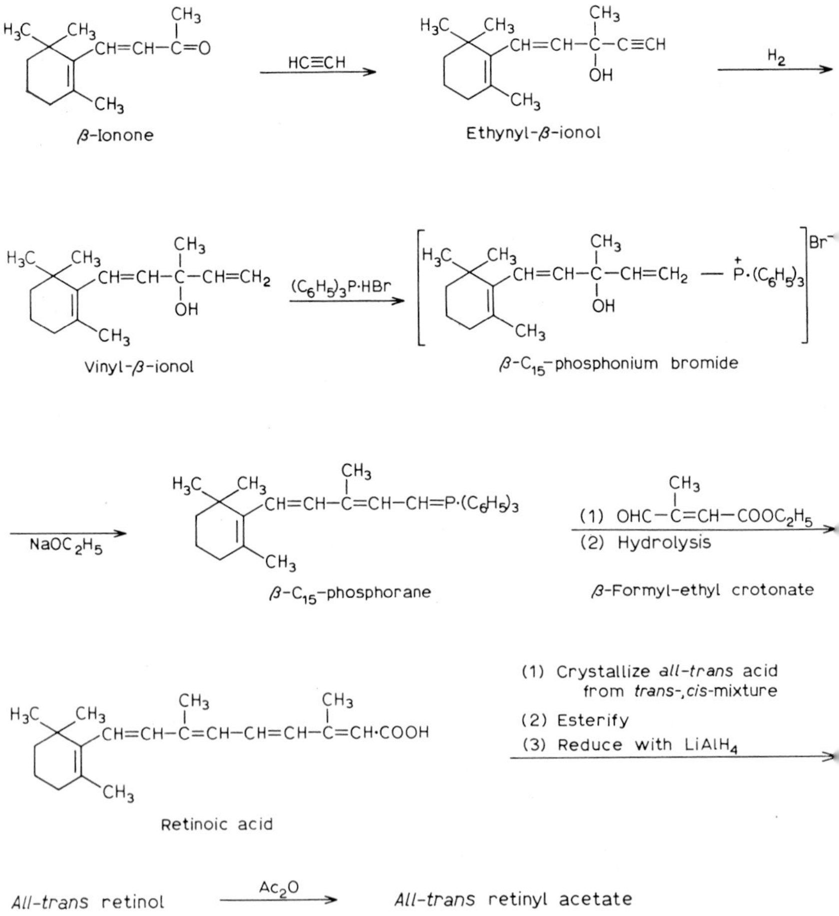

Fig. 3. Synthesis of retinol (Pommer and Sarnecki).

plished by isomerization with iodine. All-*trans* retinol with the properties of the natural vitamin was prepared by reduction of the methyl ester of the *trans*-acid, with lithium aluminum hydride.

Decarboxylation of D-diacid gave almost exclusively a retinoic acid having a lower melting point ($135-136°$) than any retinoic acid previously described. This was identified as 9,13-di-*cis* retinoic acid. By isomerization of this acid with iodine, an isomerate was obtained from which another acid was obtained by crystallization (m.p. $189-190°$). This was 9-*cis* retinoic acid. The retinol isomers obtained by reduction with lithium aluminum hydride of the methyl esters of this pair of retinoic acids were purified by crystallization from ethyl formate. Properties are given in Table I.

The condensation of β-ionylideneacetaldehyde with ethyl senecioate has also been employed to synthesize all-*trans* retinol and other geometric isomers (Matsui, 1958).

The Pommer and Sarnecki procedure is one of a number employing the Wittig reaction and described in the patent literature. It proceeds according to the following steps (see Fig. 3).

β-Ionone is reacted with acetylene to give ethynyl-β-ionol which is selectively reduced to vinyl-β-ionol. Phosphonium halides are prepared from this by reaction with triphenylphosphonium halides. Treatment with base gives the β-C_{15}-phosphorane which is condensed with β-formyl-crotonic acid esters. By saponification of the reaction product, retinoic acid is obtained as a mixture of the all-*trans* and 13-*cis* isomers. Crystallization gives pure all-*trans* acid. By esterification of the acid and reduction with lithium aluminum hydride, pure all-*trans* retinol is obtained which is then converted to its esters.

Radioactive retinol

The chemical synthesis of retinol has made it possible to incorporate carbon-14 labelled atoms in the molecule. All-*trans*, 9-*cis* and 13-*cis* [2-^{14}C]vitamin A have been prepared at a specific activity of 1.07 mC/mmole via interaction of "C_{18} ketone" and methylbromo-[2-^{14}C]acetate (Garbers, 1956). All-*trans*-[2-^{14}C]retinol was prepared earlier by this same procedure (Wolf, 1954) and fed to rats to determine the distribution during metabolism. One interesting metabolite was water soluble and was isolated from the urine. A tritium labelled retinol has also been described (Wolf, 1958).

The success that has been achieved in synthesizing retinol would have seemed barely credible 15 years ago. Supplies are now being made in many parts of the world and offer promise of improving the nutritional status of mankind, particularly among the great and undernourished populations of Asia and Africa.

References p. 186

TABLE II

PROPERTIES OF SOME COMPOUNDS RELATED TO RETINOL

Compound	m.p.	λ max. and $E_{1\,cm}^{1\%}$	Solvent	λmax and $E_{1\,cm}^{1\%}$ of $SbCl_3$ blue complex	Relative biopotency (Retinol = 1)
Vitamin A$_2$					
3-Dehydroretinol	—	E(287,351 mμ) = 820,1460	Ethanol	E(693 mμ) = 4100	0.4
3-Dehydroretinal	61°,77°	E(385 mμ) = 1460	Cyclohexane	E(705 mμ) = 3720	—
α-Vitamin A					
Alcohol	—	E(298,311,325 mμ) = 1220,1650,1500	Ethanol	λmax = 561 mμ	—
Aldehyde	86°	E(250,368 mμ) = 284,1720	Ethanol	E(561 mμ) = 4420	less than 0.02
Ethers					
Methyl ether	35°	E(328 mμ) = 1800	Ethanol	E(620 mμ) = 4400	0.6–1.0
Phenyl ether	92°	E(327 mμ) = 1470	Ethanol	—	ca. 0.05
Hydrocarbons					
Vitamin A hydrocarbon	72°	E(323 mμ) = 1800	Ethanol	—	0.25
Desmethyl vitamin A hydrocarbon	62°	E(319 mμ) = 1815	Ethanol	—	less than 0.0001
Axerophthene	—	E(331,346,364 mμ) = 1080,1260,952	Ethanol	E(474, 577 mμ)	0.1
Anhydrovitamin A	77°	E(351,371,392 mμ) = 2540,3680,3200	Ethanol	E(620 mμ) = 5500	0.005
Isoanhydrovitamin A	—	E(330,350,370 mμ) = —,1320,—	Ethanol	E(620 mμ) = 3200	ca. 0.005
Alcohols					
Rehydrovitamin A	—	E(330,351,369 mμ) = —,10.2,—(conc.)	Ethanol	612 mμ	0.1
Subvitamin A	—	E(290 mμ) = 150 (conc.)	Ethanol	E(617 mμ) = 310	0
Kitol	90°	E(290 mμ) = 707	Ethanol	E(428,505,580 mμ) = 228,162,104 (conc.)	ca. 0.005

6. Substances related to retinol

(a) Vitamin A_2

The discovery of vitamin A_2, which accompanies vitamin A in the liver oils of fresh-water fish (Lederer, 1937; Gilliam, 1938) stimulated research which resulted in its isolation from fish liver oil in essentially pure form (Shantz, 1948). A crystallized product has not yet been described. Some of its physical properties are given in Table II; its biological activity was 40% of that of retinol in the growth test.

Vitamin A_2 aldehyde (retinene₂) has been prepared as crystals (Salah, 1948).

The role of vitamin A_2 and its aldehyde in the retinas of fresh-water fish has been investigated, a modified visual purple known as porphyropsin (λ_{max} 520 mμ) being formed. The vitamin A deficient rat is able to utilize vitamin A_2 to form porphyropsin in the retina. Thus the metabolism of vitamin A and vitamin A_2 is similar in these respects.

After many hypotheses on the structure of vitamin A_2 were examined, vitamin A_2 was found by synthesis to be 3-dehydroretinol (Farrar, 1952).

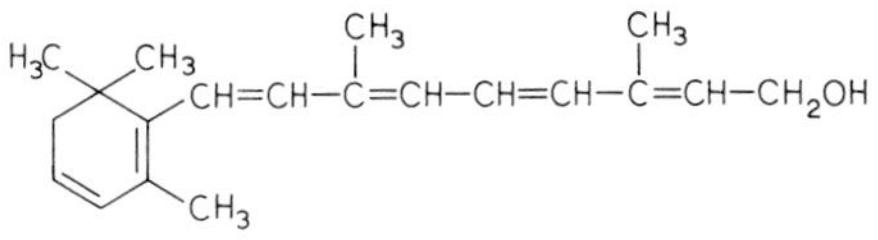

Vitamin A_2 (3–dehydroretinol)

In the synthesis, a double bond was introduced into the β-ionone ring of the methyl ester of retinoic acid by bromination with N-bromosuccinimide followed by dehydrobromination with 4-phenylmorpholine. Treatment with lithium aluminum hydride then gave a product which agreed closely in its properties with the natural vitamin.

3-Dehydroretinol is now comparatively readily prepared since it was found (Henbest, 1955) that retinal can likewise be brominated with N-bromosuccinimide and debrominated to 3-dehydroretinal. By reduction with lithium aluminum hydride, 3-dehydroretinol was formed in 60% yield.

(b) α-Vitamin A

All-*trans* α-vitamin A aldehyde (α-retinal) and all-*trans* α-retinol (Table II) with the formula:

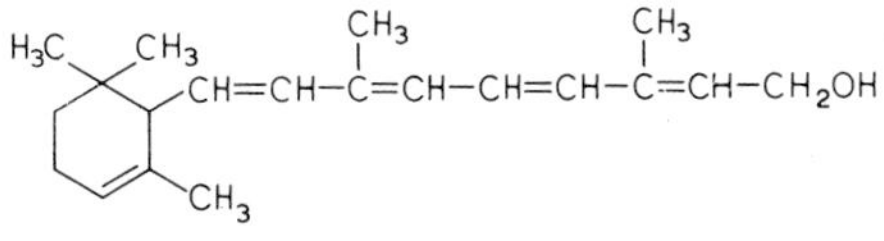

α-Vitamin A (α-retinol)

have been prepared from α-ionone via the β-methylglutaconic acid ester route previously described. α-Retinal has the interesting property that it is reduced, absorbed, transported, and stored in the rat liver like vitamin A but showed no growth promoting activity at the highest level tested (50,000 units/g) (Ames, 1955). This interesting compound deserves further study.

(c) Retinol ethers

A report on the synthesis of purified retinol methyl ether (I, R = CH_2OCH_3) appeared prior to reports on the synthesis of retinol itself (Isler, 1946). The phenyl ether was subsequently prepared (properties, Table II). So far as is known the ethers do not occur naturally and have not been employed extensively as a source of vitamin A, even though they have biological activity.

The methyl ether was reported to have a potency of 2.7 million units/g and to be as active on a molar basis as retinol (Isler, 1949). The phenyl ether had only one-tenth of the biological potency of the methyl ether, presumably reflecting the greater difficulty of hydrolysis in the body. Bioassays on the methyl ether in our laboratories, by the rat liver storage method, have indicated a potency which was only about two-thirds that of all-*trans* retinyl acetate on a molar basis.

The methyl ether from natural retinol has also been prepared (Cawley, 1943; Hanze, 1948).

(d) Vitamin A hydrocarbon

This substance (I, R = CH_3) has not yet been named by the new "retin" system[1]. It is different from a substance called axerophthene, now known to have a "retro" structure with absorption peaks at 331, 346, and 364 mμ and prepared via interaction of C_{18} ketone with ethyl magnesium bromide.

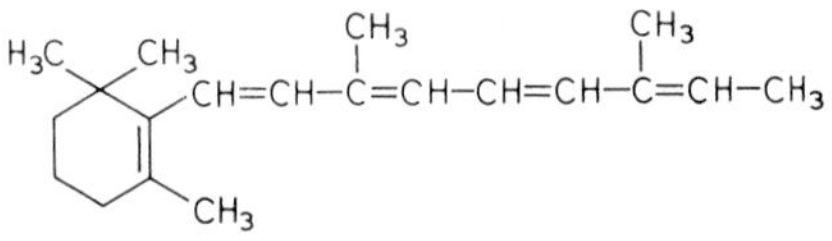

Vitamin A hydrocarbon

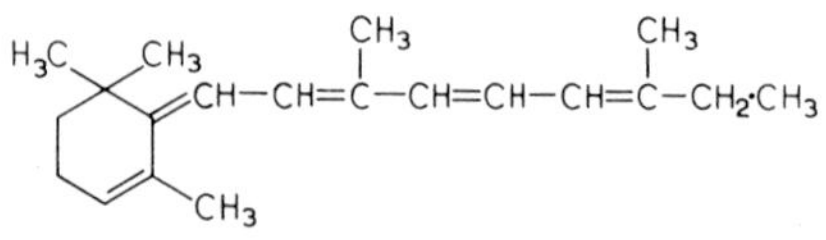

Axeropthene

Authentic vitamin A hydrocarbon was prepared by Oroshnik (1953) and later by Robeson. The latter described a convenient synthesis from retinal by a Reformatsky reaction with ethyl α-bromopropionate[11]. A β-hydroxy ester was formed which was hydrolyzed to the acid.

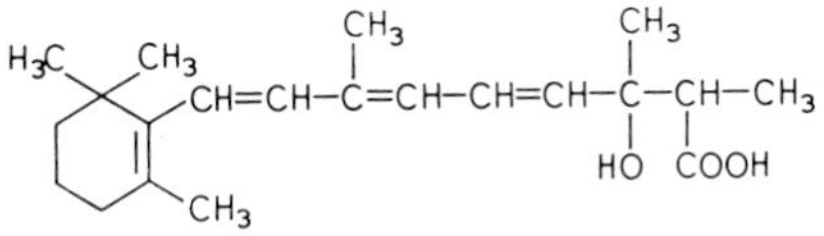

Treatment of this acid with acetic anhydride caused dehydration and decarboxylation to give vitamin A hydrocarbon (yellow crystals, properties, Table II). The ultraviolet absorption spectrum of vitamin A hydrocarbon has a single maximum with $E_1^{1\%}{}_{cm}(323\ m\mu) = 1800$. Its biological potency by the rat liver storage method was about 25% of that of retinol[11].

Vitamin A hydrocarbon is of physiological interest because it has good biological activity without containing the oxygenated terminal group, so often characteristic of biologically active derivatives of vitamin A. It deserves further study.

Desmethyl vitamin A hydrocarbon has also been described[11].

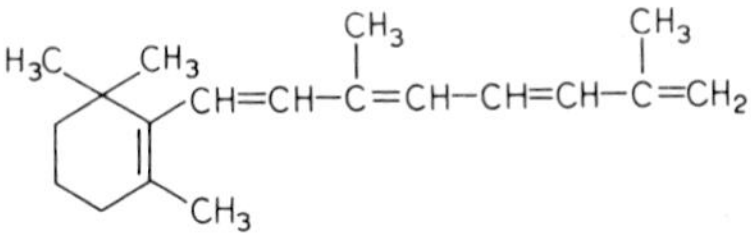

Desmethyl vitamin A hydrocarbon

It had little or no activity in the U.S.P. growth assay method for vitamin A.

(e) Anhydrovitamin A

Treatment of retinol with mineral acid forms a hydrocarbon which was studied (Edisbury, 1932) and later crystallized and called anhydrovitamin A (Shantz, 1943). Formation of anhydrovitamin A must be guarded against in all operations involving retinol where acidic conditions are present. Anhydrovitamin A was found to have a "retro" structure (Meunier, 1943).

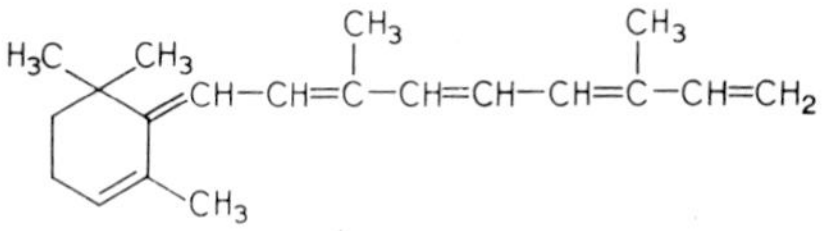

Anhydrovitamin A

The formation of anhydrovitamin A from retinol can be explained on the basis of an initial removal of an hydroxyl group with its bonding electrons to give an allylic carbonium ion. This loses a proton to the medium yielding anhydrovitamin A which has a relatively stable, unstrained molecular structure. Anhydrovitamin A has a small amount of vitamin A activity; its properties are given in Table II.

A pure preparation of anhydrovitamin A_2 has not yet been reported. The compound formed by treating vitamin A_2 in ethanolic hydrochloric acid, and once designated as anhydrovitamin A_2, has been shown to be 4-ethoxy-anhydrovitamin A (Henbest, 1955).

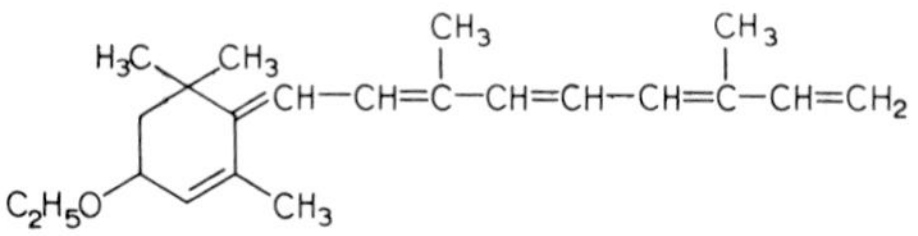

4-Ethoxyanhydrovitamin A

(f) Kitol

Kitol (Table II) is a dihydric alcohol occurring in esterified form in whale, dog fish, and shark liver oils (Embree, 1943). It has been prepared in pure crystalline form (Clough, 1947), but has not been synthesized, nor has its structure been determined.

Kitol is a bimolecular form of retinol which has no biological potency but pyrolyzes at temperatures above 200° to yield retinol. From 0.75 to 1.0 mole of retinol form from each mole of kitol ester pyrolyzed.

(g) Isoanhydrovitamin A, rehydrovitamin A, subvitamin A

These are substances related to vitamin A which have little or no vitamin A activity. Their chemistry has been previously reviewed[7]; their properties are given in Table II.

(h) Modified retinol structures

A number of these have been prepared by Heilbron and coworkers and the chemistry has been reviewed by Heilbron and Weedon[3]. The biopotencies found for these substances were small and served to demonstrate principally the important part played by methyl groups and the conjugated double bond system in determining the biological activity of vitamin A.

7. Conclusion

It will be evident from this review that high biological activity is characteristic only of retinol, its esters, and the methyl ether, all of which are transformed to the vitamin in the body. It does not appear, however, that conversion to retinol is essential to biological activity, as witness the activity of retinoic acid. It would appear at present, that the rat growth assay is not specific for retinol and that other substances having this skeleton can be utilized to a degree which depends upon their structure and their ability to be absorbed and carried to the proper body tissues.

References p. 186

REFERENCES

1 Rules for Nomenclature of Vitamins, *J. Am. Chem. Soc.*, 82 (1960) 5581.
2 A. F. WAGNER AND K. FOLKERS in A. BURGER (Ed.), *Medicinal Chemistry*, 2nd ed., Interscience, New York, 1960, p. 200.
3 I. HEILBRON AND B. C. L. WEEDON, *Bull. soc. chim. France*, (1958) 83.
4 S. R. AMES, *Ann. Rev. Biochem.*, 27 (1958) 371.
5 T. MOORE, *Vitamin A*, Elsevier, Amsterdam, 1957.
6 R. A. MORTON AND G. A. J. PITT, *Fortschr. Chem. org. Naturstoffe*, 14 (1957) 245.
7 J. G. BAXTER, *Fortschr. Chem. org. Naturstoffe*, 9 (1952) 42.
8 H. J. DEUEL, *The Lipids*, Vol. 1, Interscience, New York, 1951, 667.
9 C. D. ROBESON, J. D. CAWLEY, L. WEISLER, M. H. STERN, C. C. EDDINGER AND A. J. CHECHAK, *J. Am. Chem. Soc.*, 77 (1955) 4111.
10 H. POMMER AND W. SARNECKI, *German patent 1,046,612*, 18 December 1958; *1,059,900*, 25 June 1959.
11 C. D. ROBESON, *U.S. Patent 2,835,713*, 20 May 1958.

Chapter VII

Vitamins E

ROBERT S. HARRIS

Massachusetts Institute of Technology, Cambridge, Mass. (U.S.A.)

The first studies of the chemical nature of vitamin E indicated that it is to be found in the nonsaponifiable fractions of lipids[1], that it is destroyed by bromination (but not by hydrogenation) and that it is decomposed during vacuum distillation. It was observed also that diets containing either rancid lipids or lipids treated with ethereal ferric chloride would accelerate the development of sterility in experimental animals[2]. Concentrates made from the oil of lettuce were found to have high antioxidant power, and high vitamin E activity[3,4]; these were called "inhibitols" because they contained *ortho*- and *para*-hydroxyl groups[5].

Though it was shown later that vitamin E and the antioxidant were identical, the biological and antioxidant properties did not run in parallel in different preparations. This was because there were several vitamin E active substances with unequal activity and antioxygenic action[6]. The several vitamins E have been shown to be the major antioxidants of natural oils.

Potent concentrates, prepared from wheat germ oil by adsorption on aluminum oxide, showed an adsorption[7] maximum at 2940 Å and minimum at 2670 Å. When treated with ultraviolet radiations this band persisted in proportion to the vitamin E activity.

Pure vitamin E was isolated first by the Evans group[8] from the nonsaponifiable fraction of wheat germ oil and in the form of three solid aleophanates which varied in biological potency. α-Tocopherol was the most potent, β-tocopherol was less potent, and γ-tocopherol had no potency at all. It is probable that β-tocopherol was the substance isolated from wheat germ oil also by Todd *et. al.*[9], by Karrer *et al.*[10] and by John[11].

The chemical identification of α-tocopherol was begun by Fernholz[12] who isolated tetramethylhydroquinone from its thermal decomposition products. This substance was also produced by dehydrogenation with selenium[13]. The accumulated evidence proved that tocopherol has a chromanol nucleus and a side chain of isoprene residues.

References p. 191

On thermal decomposition, tocopherol produced an unsaturated aliphatic hydrocarbon as well as durohydroquinone. Mild oxidation of this hydrocarbon produced a lactone ($C_{21}H_{40}O_2$) the free hydroxy-acid of which was so easily relactonized that a tertiary hydroxyl had to be postulated. More rigorous oxidation yielded dimethylmaleic anhydride, an acid ($C_{16}H_{32}O_2$), a ketone ($C_{18}H_{36}O$), diacetyl and acetone. The formation of a C_{16} acid placed a limitation on the number of possible structures for the lactone. Fernholz[14] reasoned that α-tocopherol was a substituted 6-hydroxychroman, with a lengthy aliphatic side chain attached to the pyran ring. The presence of a chroman nucleus was soon confirmed[15,16].

Karrer et al.[17] produced a nearly quantitative condensation of trimethyl-hydroquinone with phytyl bromide. Though it had no optical activity, this product had the same physical, chemical and physiological properties[18] as vitamin E. Thus, a complex organic compound was synthesized before its chemical composition was known.

Though 15 years elapsed between the recognition of vitamin E activity and the synthesis of a physiologically active tocopherol, the last two years of this period witnessed fevered activity in several laboratories. The Karrer synthesis with phytyl bromide was repeated without a catalyst[19] and by the use of dienes[20], and of allyl and crotyl compounds and butadiene[21]. Farnesol[22], and citral[23] were used for the synthesis of the phytol chain. The presence of a chroman nucleus was proven further by permanganate oxidation[24] which produced the same lactone, by the use of carbinols in synthesis[25] and by quantitative conversion of tocopherol into the diacetate[26].

John[11] and Karrer et al.[27] proposed that β-tocopherol has the same structure as α-tocopherol, less one methyl group, and John[28] concluded that the methyl groups are in the 5,8 positions. The general structure was confirmed by obtaining the same lactone from both β- and γ-tocopherol[29]. Both had been synthesized from dimethylhydroquinones and phytyl bromide[30], and the products had vitamin E activity comparable to the respective tocopherols. The structure of γ-tocopherol was confirmed by degradation studies[31].

The suggestion by Karrer and Fritzsche[32] that the unsubstituted tocopherol be called tocol has been adopted generally.

The properties of the various tocopherols are as follows:

α-Tocopherol

Crystallized from natural sources: m.p. $+2.5°$ to $+3.5°$.

dl-Form: slightly viscous, pale yellow oil; $d_4^{25} = 0.950$; b.p.$_{0.1} = 200-220°$; $n_D^{25} = 1.5045$; absorption max. 294 mμ; absorption min. 267 mμ; ($E_{1cm}^{1\%} = 71-76$); insoluble in water; freely soluble in acetone, alcohol, chloroform, ether, lipids, lipid solvents; very stable to heat and alkalies; slowly oxidized by atmospheric oxygen, rapidly oxidized by silver and ferric salts; darkens gradually when exposed to light; not precipitated with digitonin. Mol. wt. 430.69.

d-α-Tocopherol: optically active $[\alpha]_{5461}^{25}$ —3.0° (benzene); $[\alpha]_{5461}^{25}$ +0.32° (alcohol).

l-α-Tocopherol: $[\alpha]_{5461}^{25}$ —3.0° (benzene).

β-Tocopherol

Pale-yellow, viscous oil; b.p.$_{0.1}$ = 200–210°; $[\alpha]_D^{20}$ + 6.37°; absorption max. 297 mμ; $E_{1cm}^{1\%}$ = 86.4, insoluble in water, freely soluble in acetone, alcohol, chloroform, ether, lipids, lipid solvents; stable to heat and alkalies; oxidizes slowly in air, rapidly with ferric and silver salts; gradually darkens under light; not precipitated with digitonin. Mol. wt. 416.66.

γ-Tocopherol

Pale-yellow, viscous oil; crystallizes at —30°; b.p.$_{0.1}$ = 200–210°; $[\alpha]_D^{20}$ —2.4° (alcohol); absorption max. 298 mμ; $E_{1cm}^{1\%}$ = 92.8; insoluble in water, easily soluble in acetone, alcohol, chloroform, ether, lipids, lipid solvents; very stable to heat and alkalies; slowly oxidized by air; rapidly oxidized by ferric and silver salts; darkens slowly under light; unsaponifiable. Mol. wt. 416.66.

δ-Tocopherol

Pale-yellow, viscous oil; $[\alpha]_{5461}^{25}$ +3.4° (15.5 g in 100 ml absolute alcohol); $[\alpha]_{5461}^{25}$ + 1.1° (10.9 g in 100 ml benzene); absorption max. 298 mμ; $E_{1cm}^{1\%}$ = 91.2; insoluble in water; easily soluble in acetone, alcohol, chloroform, ether, lipids, lipid solvents. Mol. wt. 402.67.

The term "vitamin E" is now considered synonymous with "tocopherol", and refers to a group of mono-, di- and tri-methyl tocols which represent all 7 possible methyl derivatives of the phenolic ring with a 6-hydroxychroman nucleus. Although all 7 tocopherols have been reported to be present in biological materials, α-tocopherol is considered to be the prototype of vitamin E since it comprises most of the tocopherols in animal tissues and is reputed to have highest biological activity. A number of tocopherol derivatives (oxidation products, esters) occur in nature and show biological activity, but essentially all of them are of low potency.

Boyer[33] isolated a biologically active epoxide, designated as D-α-tocopheroxide, which is readily reduced to D-α-tocopherol by ascorbic acid, or is changed to D-α-tocopherylquinone by exposure to weak acid. Tocopheroxide is a hemiacetal of α-tocopherylquinone (tocopherethoxide), but is not likely to be present in nature[34].

More detailed information on the chemistry of vitamin E and related substances may be obtained from a review by Mattill[35].

TABLE I

FORMULAE OF THE PRINCIPAL VITAMINS E

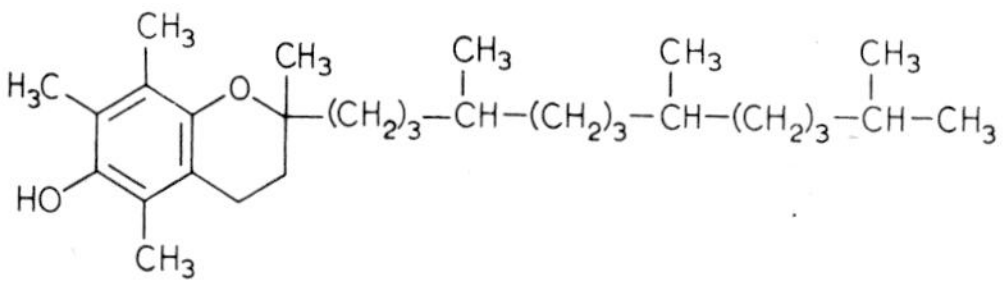

α-Tocopherol, $C_{29}H_{50}O_2$, 2,5,7,8-tetramethyl-2(4',8',12'-trimethyltridecyl)-6-chromanol; or 5,7,8-trimethyl tocol.

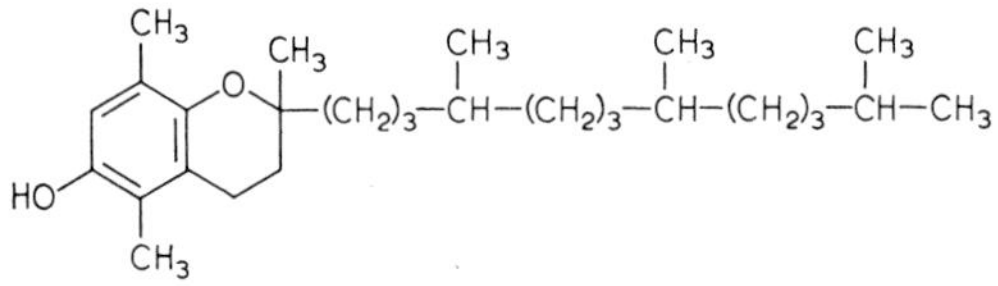

β-Tocopherol, $C_{28}H_{48}O_2$, 2,5,8-trimethyl-2(4',8',12'-trimethyltridecyl)-6-chromanol; or 5,8-dimethyl tocol.

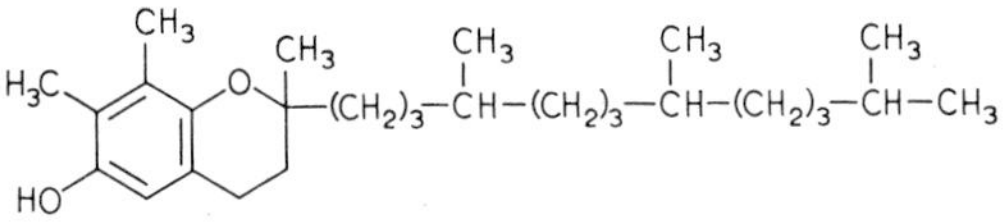

γ-Tocopherol, $C_{28}H_{48}O_2$, 2,7,8-trimethyl-2(4',8',12'-trimethyltridecyl)-6-chromanol; or 7,8-dimethyl tocol.

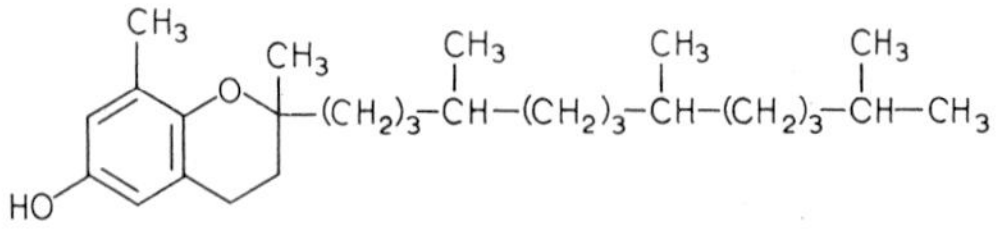

δ-Tocopherol, $C_{27}H_{46}O_2$, 2,8-dimethyl-2(4',8',12'-trimethyltridecyl)-6-chromanol; or 8-methyl tocol.

REFERENCES

1 H. M. EVANS AND G. O. BURR, *Mem. Univ. Calif.*, 8 (1927) 176.
2 L. T. ANDEREGG AND V. E. NELSON, *Ind. Eng. Chem.*, 18 (1926) 620.
3 H. S. OLCOTT AND H. A. MATTILL, *J. Biol. Chem.*, 93 (1931) 59.
4 H. S. OLCOTT AND H. A. MATTILL, *J. Am. Chem. Soc.*, 58 (1936) 1627.
5 H. A. MATTILL, *J. Am. Med. Assoc.*, 89 (1927) 1505.
6 H. S. OLCOTT AND O. H. EMERSON, *J. Am. Chem. Soc.*, 59 (1937) 1008.
7 J. C. DRUMMOND, E. SINGER AND R. J. MACWALTER, *Biochem. J.*, 29 (1936) 2510.
8 H. M. EVANS, O. H. EMERSON AND G. A. EMERSON, *J. Biol. Chem.*, 113 (1936) 319.
9 A. R. TODD, F. BERGEL AND T. S. WORK, *Biochem. J.*, 31 (1937) 2257.
10 P. KARRER, H. SALOMON AND H. FRITZSCHE, *Helv. Chim. Acta*, 20 (1937) 1422.
11 W. JOHN, *Z. physiol. Chem.*, 250 (1937) 11.
12 E. FERNHOLZ, *J. Am. Chem. Soc.*, 59 (1937) 1154.
13 C. S. MCARTHUR AND E. M. WATSON, *Science*, 86 (1937) 35.
14 E. FERNHOLZ, *J. Am. Chem. Soc.*, 60 (1938) 700.
15 W. JOHN, E. DIETZEL, P. GÜNTHER AND W. EMTE, *Naturwiss.*, 26 (1938) 366.
16 L. I. SMITH, H. E. UNGNADE AND W. W. PRITCHARD, *Science*, 88 (1938) 37.
17 P. KARRER, H. FRITZSCHE, B. H. RINGIER AND H. SALOMON, *Helv. Chim. Acta*, 21 (1938) 520.
18 P. KARRER AND V. DEMOLE, *Schweiz. med. Wochschr.*, 68 (1938) 954.
19 L. I. SMITH AND H. E. UNGNADE, *J. Org. Chem.*, 4 (1939) 298.
20 L. I. SMITH, H. E. UNGNADE, H. H. HOEHN AND S. WAWZONEK, *J. Org. Chem.*, 4 (1938) 311.
21 L. I. SMITH, H. E. UNGNADE, J. R. STEVENS AND C. C. CHRISTMAN, *J. Am. Chem. Soc.*, 61 (1939) 2615.
22 W. JOHN AND H. PINI, *Z. physiol. Chem.*, 273 (1942) 225.
23 L. I. SMITH AND J. A. SPRUNG, *J. Am. Chem. Soc.*, 65 (1943) 1276.
24 O. H. EMERSON, *Science*, 88 (1938) 40.
25 L. I. SMITH AND H. C. MILLER, *J. Am. Chem. Soc.*, 64 (1942) 440.
26 M. TISHLER AND N. L. WENDLER, *J. Am. Chem. Soc.*, 63 (1941) 1532.
27 P. KARRER, H. SALOMON AND H. FRITZSCHE, *Helv. Chim. Acta*, 21 (1938) 309.
28 W. JOHN, *Z. physiol. Chem.*, 252 (1938) 222.
29 O. H. EMERSON, *J. Am. Chem. Soc.*, 60 (1938) 1741.
30 F. BERGEL, A. M. COPPING, A. JACOB, A. R. TODD AND T. S. WORK, *J. Chem. Soc.*, i (1938) 1382.
31 O. H. EMERSON AND L. I. SMITH, *J. Am. Chem. Soc.*, 62 (1942) 1869.
32 P. KARRER AND H. FRITZSCHE, *Helv. Chim. Acta*, 21 (1938) 1234.
33 P. D. BOYER, *J. Am. Chem. Soc.*, 73 (1951) 733.
34 C. MARTIUS AND H. EILINGSFELD, *Biochem. Z.*, 328 (1957) 507.
35 H. A. MATTILL, in W. H. SEBRELL, JR. AND R. S. HARRIS (Eds.), *The Vitamins*, Vol. III, Academic Press, New York, 1954, p. 483.

Chapter VIII

Vitamins K

ROBERT S. HARRIS

Massachusetts Institute of Technology, Cambridge, Mass. (U.S.A.)

The chemistry of the K vitamins was elucidated by three groups working independently under the leadership of Dam, Doisy and Karrer. Two pure vitamin K compounds were isolated in 1939 from alfalfa (vitamin K_1)[1] and from putrified fish meal (vitamin K_2)[2]. The structure of vitamin K_1 was proven by oxidative degradation and by synthesis. The structure of vitamin K_2 was long considered to have the same ring system as K_1, but with 6 rather than 4 isoprene groups, and a more unsaturated side chain. However, Isler *et al.*[3,4] showed that the side chain of K_2 consists of seven isoprene groups, or one more than was formerly accepted. Thus the vitamin K_2 (m.p. 54°) of Doisy[2] has formula II (Table I). Isler *et al.*[3,4] isolated from the mother liquors of vitamin K_2 a small amount of a compound with a structure (formula III) first assigned to vitamin K_2. Dam[5] has proposed that the two compounds be designated as vitamin $K_{2(35)}$(II) and vitamin $K_{2(30)}$(III) so as to permit concise designation of all homologs which may be encountered in nature. Though menadione and its derivatives (which have no side chain in the 3-position) have vitamin K activity, they cannot perform all of the functions of vitamin K.

1. Vitamin K_1

(i) Isolation

Vitamin K, has been found in all green leafy tissues, and was first isolated from alfalfa by the Doisy and Karrer groups independently[5-8].

(ii) Properties

A yellow, viscous oil; $d_{25}^{25} = 0.967$; m.p. $= -20°$; decomposes on heating above $100-120°$, but distills practically unchanged in a high vacuum (10^{-3} mm) at $140-5°$; $n_D^{25} = 1.5250$; absorption max. 243, 248, 261, 270 and 328 mμ; $E_{1cm}^{1\%} = 328$ at 248 mμ; $[a]_D^{20} = -0.4°$ (57.5% in benzene); in-

TABLE I

FORMULAE OF PRINCIPAL VITAMINS K

(I)

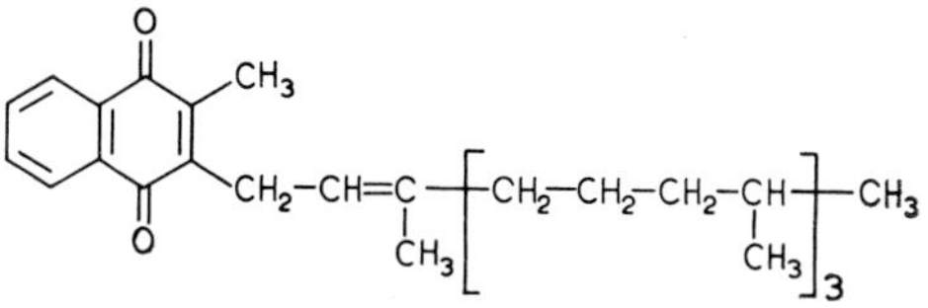

Vitamin K_1, $C_{31}H_{46}O_2$, 2-methyl-3-phytyl-1,4-naphthoquinone.

(II)

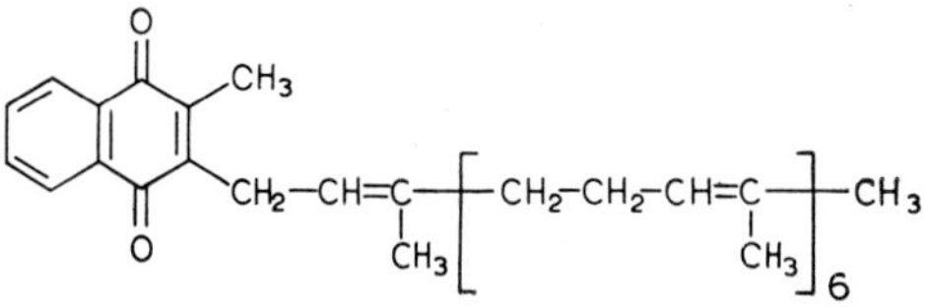

Vitamin $K_{2(35)}$, $C_{46}H_{64}O_2$, 2-methyl-3-(all-*trans*-farnesylgeranylgeranyl)-1,4-naphtho-quinone.

(III)

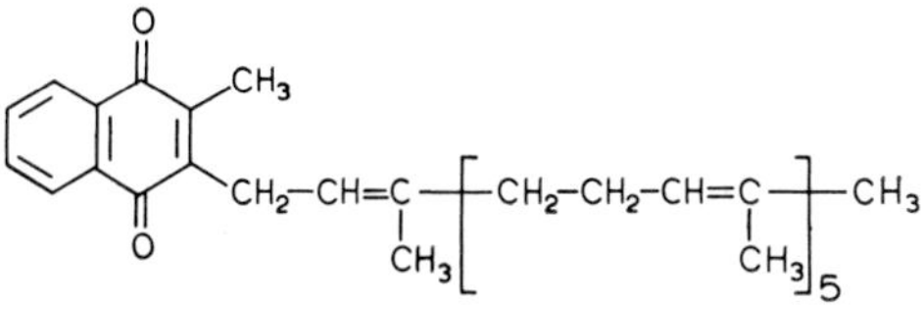

Vitamin $K_{2(30)}$, $C_{41}H_{56}O_2$, 2-methyl-3-farnesylfarnesyl-1,4-naphthoquinone.

(IV)

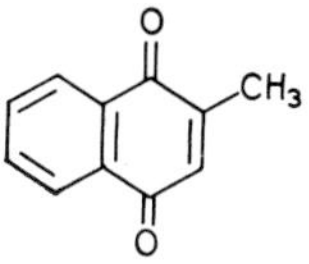

Menadione, $C_{11}H_8O_2$, 2-methyl-1,4-naphthoquinone.

soluble in water; sparingly soluble in methanol; soluble in ethanol, acetone, benzene, petroleum ether, hexane, dioxane, chloroform, ether, other fat solvents, and in vegetable oils; stable to air and moisture; decomposes in sunlight; not affected by dilute acids, but is destroyed by solutions of alkali hydroxides and by reducing agents.

(iii) Synthesis

In September 1939, three independent syntheses of vitamin K_1 were reported. In these syntheses phytyl bromide and menadione[9], phytyl bromide and the monosodium salt of menadiol[10], and phytol and menadiol[11], respectively, were used as starting material. The most efficient syntheses have been made by reacting menadiol 1-mono-esters with phytol in the presence of boron trifluoride etherate, aluminum chloride or potassium acid sulfate as catalyst[12-14].

Racemic vitamin K_1 has been synthesized from isophytol and menadiol[15,16], or from isophytol and menadiol 1-monobenzoate[14]. Other methods of synthesis have been discussed by Isler and Wiss[17].

[14]C-labeled vitamin K_1 is useful for the elucidation of the function and metabolic fate of this factor. However, it has been noted that radioactive vitamin K_1 decomposes relatively rapidly due to its own radiation[18].

The vitamin K_1 series with isoprenologs from 0 to 5 has been synthesized[19] and the properties of each were compared with corresponding compounds of the vitamin $K_{2(35)}$ series.

2. Vitamin $K_{2(35)}$

(i) Isolation

Vitamin K_2 was isolated from putrefying fish meal after extraction with petroleum ether, treatment with decalso, crystallization at $-5°$, and repeated recrystallization[20]. This compound was also isolated from the autolyzed cells of *B. brevis*[21]. Vitamin K_2 was proven to have 7 rather than 6 isoprene groups, by comparing the melting points, absorption spectra and R_F values of vitamin K_2 and its dihydro diacetate with synthetically prepared 2-methyl-3-(all-*trans*-farnesylgeranylgeranyl)-1,4-naphthoquinone[3,4].

It is important to note that vitamin K_2 is produced by bacteria in widely varying amounts depending upon strain and the composition of the culture media. It can be produced by bacteria on artificial media containing aspartic acid, ammonium citrate and glucose[22].

(ii) Properties

Light-yellow crystalline plates (from petroleum ether); m.p. $= 54°$; b.p.$_{0.0002} = 200°$ (with some decomposition); absorption maximum (hexane) 243, 249, 260, 269 mμ; $E_{1cm}^{1\%} = 520$ at 249 mμ; slightly less soluble than vitamin K_1 in the same organic solvents.

(iii) Synthesis

Isler *et al.*[3,4] have described the synthesis of the vitamin $K_{2(35)}$ side chain using acetone and menadione as starting materials.

3. Vitamin K$_{2(30)}$

Isolation

It was noted during the purification of vitamin K$_{2(35)}$ that the melting point (54°) could be obtained only after repeated recrystallization from different solvents[17], and that the lower-melting preparations had higher extinction coefficients than the pure crystals. By paper chromatography methods, Green and Dam[23] detected a faster-moving component in these preparations. Using a chromatogram lasting several weeks, a new vitamin K$_2$ compound (m.p. 50°) was isolated from the first fractions passing through the column during the 4th and 5th days. All further fractionations consisted of vitamin K$_{2(35)}$. The new factor was shown to be identical to 2-methyl-3-(all-*trans*-farnesylfarnesyl)-1,4-naphthoquinone. It is evident that bacteria produce relatively larger amounts of vitamin K$_{2(35)}$ than of vitamin K$_{2(30)}$.

A naphthoquinone derivative has been reported in mycobacteria[24]. This seems to be the compound from which phthiocol is synthesized[25,26]. It has been prepared in crystalline form (m.p. 58–59°) from *Mycobacterium tuberculosis*[27]. Physical, chemical and spectroscopic data indicate that it is a higher isoprenolog of vitamin K$_{2(35)}$, and has a C$_{50}$ side chain.

4. Menadione

Menadione is a synthetic naphthoquinone derivative which has many, but not all, of the physiologic properties of natural vitamin K. It has been prepared from β-methylnaphthalene by mild oxidation with chromic oxide[28]. It is equally as active as vitamins K$_1$ and K$_2$ on the molecular basis, but is more than twice as active on the gravimetric basis.

Properties

Bright yellow crystals; acrid odor; stable in air but decomposes in light; m.p. = 105–107°; insoluble in water; soluble in alcohol (1.7%), benzene (10%), vegetable oils (2%); moderately soluble in chloroform and carbon tetrachloride; no decomposition when heated to 120°; destroyed by alkalies and reducing agents.

Menadiol diacetate, menadiol diphosphate, menadione monoxime, menadione sodium bisulfite, menadoxime, as well as menadione, are synthetic substances which have been used clinically in the treatment of hypoprothrombinemia.

5. Related substances

Martius[29] isolated vitamin K$_{2(20)}$ from the tissues of rats which had received ^{14}C-labeled menadione. The structural similarity between vitamin K$_1$ and α-tocopherol, and especially α-tocopheroylquinone, was noted in 1939. The ubiquinones are a newly discovered class of ubiquitous benzoquinones which contain polyisoprene side chains[30-33].

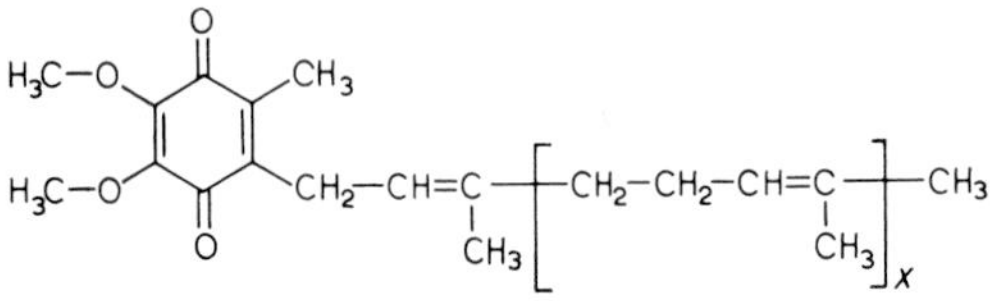

Ubiquinones: $x = 5-9$

The best-known ubiquinone was isolated from pig and beef heart muscle, and contains a C_{50} side chain. Others have been isolated from yeast (C_{30}) and bacteria (C_{35}, C_{40}, C_{45}). It is significant that the side chains of the ubiquinones are structurally the same as those of the vitamin K group.

Kofler has described a benzoquinone which occurs with vitamin K_1 in all green leaves. It is an *ortho*-dimethylbenzoquinone derivative and has a C_{45} side chain[35,36].

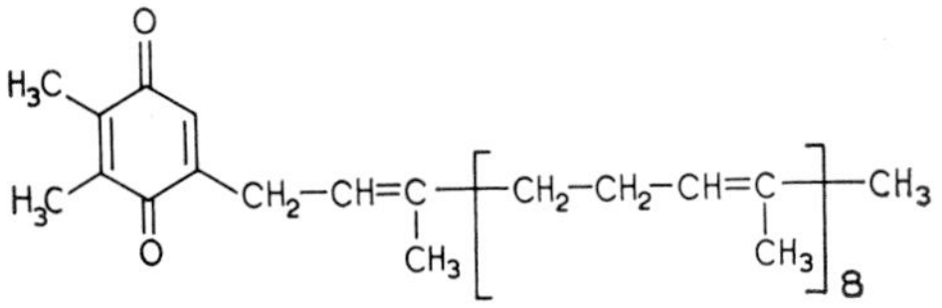

Kofler's quinone

6. Chemical structure and vitamin K activity

The general occurrence of vitamin K activity in substituted naphthoquinones strongly suggests that the common factor of reversible oxidation–reduction is concerned with their function. Fieser et al.[37] studied the activities of a number of compounds and made the following generalizations: (*a*) naphthoquinone has feeble activity, (*b*) introduction of a methyl group in the 2-position produces (menadione) a very potent compound, (*c*) any change in this structure brings about a diminution of activity, (*d*) introduction of a second methyl group in the 3-position causes great decrease in potency, (*e*) with one methyl group and a second side chain, the potency increases as the length of the side chain increases, until it is a phytyl group and then decreases as the side chain becomes still longer, (*f*) substitution of an ethyl or propyl group for a methyl group reduces the potency by 1000, (*g*) the double bond in the

β,γ position in the side chain is important for activity, (*h*) a double bond in any other position on the side chain has no effect on potency, (*i*) any substitution in the aromatic ring of the naphthoquinone nucleus results in inactivity.

It has been suggested[38] that the structure necessary for vitamin K activity is expressed by the following formulae:

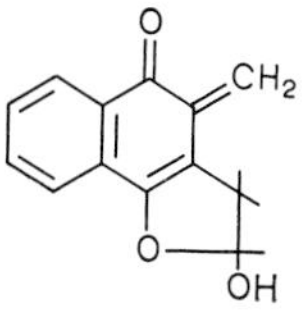

I a 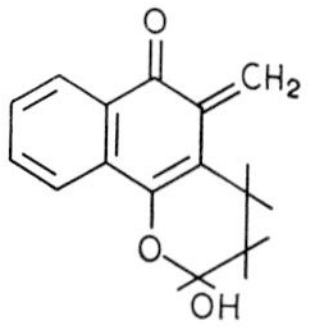   I b

in which the *ortho*-quinoid group

$$O=C-C=CH_2$$

acts as an active center, while the semiketal group combines the active molecule with the protein part of the enzyme. In biological systems, the molecules represented by formula Ia might result from the oxidation of the phytyl or difarnesyl chain of the vitamins K.

Substances which are easily oxidized to quinones may have antihemorrhagic activity, presumably because of oxidation in the body tissues. Diacetates of vitamin K_1 and K_2 are half as active, but are more stable. Water-soluble forms may be made by combining with dibasic or tribasic acids and making the sodium salts. Apparently the disulfates, diacetate and disuccinate esters are less active, and the diphosphates are equally as active, as the natural vitamins.

It is interesting to note that compounds in which the methyl groups of active coagulants are replaced by chlorine are hemorrhagic[39]. Furthermore, 2,3-dichloronaphthoquinone is a strong fungicide, the activity of which is antagonized by menadione[40]. The quinone derived from α-tocopherol caused hemorrhage in the gonads of mice and reproductive failure[41]; an effect which was antagonized by menadione, but not by α-tocopherol acetate. Possibly the most interesting antimetabolite of vitamin K is dicoumarol, a substance present in clover and other plant materials. Studies with radioactive dicoumarol have shown that vitamin K displaces this poison, preventing it from combination in the liver[42].

References p. 198

REFERENCES

1 R. W. McKee, S. B. Binkley, D. W. MacCorquodale, S. A. Thayer and E. A. Doisy, *J. Am. Chem. Soc.*, 61 (1939) 1295.

2 D. W. MacCorquodale, S. B. Binkley, R. W. McKee, S. A. Thayer and E. A. Doisy, *Proc. Soc. Exptl. Biol. Med.*, 40 (1939) 482.

3 O. Isler, R. Rüegg, L. H. Chopard-dit-Jean, A. Winterstein and O. Wiss, *Chimia (Switz.)*, 12 (1958) 69.

4 O. Isler, R. Rüegg, L. H. Chopard-dit-Jean, A. Winterstein and O. Wiss, *Helv. Chim. Acta*, 41 (1958) 786.

5 H. Dam, A. Geiger, J. Glavind, P. Karrer, W. Karrer, E. Rothschild and H. Salomon, *Helv. Chim. Acta*, 22 (1939) 310.

6 S. B. Binkley, L. C. Cheney, W. F. Holcomb, R. W. McKee, S. A. Thayer, D. W. MacCorquodale and E. A. Doisy, *J. Am. Chem. Soc.*, 61 (1939) 2558.

7 P. Karrer and A. Geiger, *Helv. Chim. Acta*, 22 (1939) 945.

8 P. Karrer, A. Geiger, R. Legler, A. Rüegger and H. Salomon, *Helv. Chim. Acta*, 22 (1939) 1464.

9 H. J. Almquist and A. A. Klose, *J. Biol. Chem.*, 130 (1939) 791.

10 D. W. MacCorquodale, S. B. Binkley, S. A. Thayer and E. A. Doisy, *J. Am. Chem. Soc.*, 61 (1939) 1928.

11 L. F. Fieser, *J. Am. Chem. Soc.*, 61 (1939) 2559.

12 R. F. Hirschmann, R. Miller and N. L. Wendler, *J. Am. Chem. Soc.*, 76 (1954) 4592.

13 V. Kvita, J. Weichet and V. Trčka, *Coll. Czech. Chem. Communs.*, 22 (1957) 583.

14 H. Lindlar, *U.S. Patent 2,839,570* (1958).

15 O. Isler and K. Doebel, *Angew. Chem.*, 65 (1953) 264.

16 O. Isler and K. Doebel, *Helv. Chim. Acta*, 37 (1954) 225.

17 O. Isler and O. Wiss, *Vitamins and Hormones*, 17 (1959) 53.

18 R. J. Woods and J. D. Taylor, *Canad. J. Chem.*, 35 (1957) 941.

19 O. Isler, R. Rüegg, A. Studer and R. Jürgens, *Z. physiol. Chem.*, 295 (1953) 290.

20 R. W. McKee, S. B. Binkley, S. A. Thayer, D. W. MacCorquodale and E. A. Doisy, *J. Biol. Chem.*, 131 (1939) 327.

21 M. Tishler and W. L. Sampson, *Proc. Soc. Exptl. Biol. Med.*, 68 (1948) 136.

22 A. Winterstein and A. Studer, Unpublished results cited by O. Isler and O. Wiss (1959).

23 J. P. Green and H. Dam, *Acta Chem. Scand.*, 8 (1954) 1341.

24 J. Francis, J. Madinaveitia, H. M. MacTurc and G. A. Snow, *Nature*, 163 (1949) 365.

25 R. J. Anderson and M. S. Newman, *J. Biol. Chem.*, 101 (1933) 773.

26 R. J. Anderson and M. S. Newman, *J. Biol. Chem.*, 103 (1933) 197.

27 H. Noll, *J. Biol. Chem.*, 232 (1958) 919.

28 L. F. Fieser, *J. Biol. Chem.*, 133 (1940) 391.

29 C. Martius, *Deut. med. Wochschr.*, 83 (1958) 1701.

30 R. A. Morton, G. M. Wilson, J. S. Lowe and W. M. F. Leat, *Chem. & Ind. (London)*, i (1957) 1649.

31 R. A. Morton, U. Gloor, O. Schindler, G. M. Wilson, L. H. Chopard-dit-Jean, F. W. Hemming, O. Isler, W. M. F. Leat, J. F. Pennock, R. Rüegg, U. Schwieter and O. Wiss, *Helv. Chim. Acta*, 41 (1958) 2343.

32 R. A. Morton, G. M. Wilson, J. S. Lowe and W. M. F. Leat, *Biochem. J.*, 68 (1958) 16P.

33 R. L. Lester, F. L. Crane and Y. Hatefi, *J. Am. Chem. Soc.*, 80 (1958) 4751.

34 D. E. Wolf, C. H. Hoffmann, N. R. Trenner, B. H. Arison, C. H. Shunk, B. O. Linn, J. F. McPherson and K. Folkers, *J. Am. Chem. Soc.*, 80 (1958) 4752.

35 M. Kofler, A. Langemann, R. Rüegg, L. H. Chopard-dit-Jean, A. Rayroud and O. Isler, *Helv. Chim. Acta*, 42 (1959) 1283.

36 N. R. Trenner, B. H. Arison, R. E. Erickson, C. H. Shunk, D. E. Wolf and K. Folkers, *J. Am. Chem. Soc.*, 81 (1959) 2026.

37 L. F. Fieser, M. Tishler and W. L. Sampson, *J. Biol. Chem.*, 137 (1941) 659.

[38] I. Chmielewska and J. Ciéslak, *Tetrahedron*, 4 (1958) 135.
[39] P. Meunier, C. Mentzer and N. P. Buu-Hoi, *Bull. Soc. Chim. Biol.*, 27 (1945) 191.
[40] D. Woolley, *Proc. Soc. Exptl. Biol. Med.*, 60 (1945) 225.
[41] D. Woolley, *J. Biol. Chem.*, 159 (1945) 59.
[42] C. C. Lee, L. W. Trevoy, J. W. T. Spinks and L. B. Jaques, *Proc. Soc. Exptl. Biol. Med.*, 74 (1950) 151.

Chapter IX

Quinones

R. A. MORTON

Johnston Professor of Biochemistry, The University of Liverpool (Great Britain)

1. Introduction

Quinones are diketones derived from dihydro aromatic compounds in which the two carbonyl groups are connected by a system of conjugated double bonds

$$O=\overset{|}{C}-(\overset{|}{C}=\overset{|}{C})_n-\overset{|}{C}=O$$

The two ketonic groups in polycyclic compounds may be in the same ring or in different rings.

Easy reducibility (SO_2, Zn in acid, alkaline hydrosulphite) to aromatic dihydroxy compounds is characteristic of *o*- and *p*-quinone and intermediate compounds or pseudo-quinols are known.

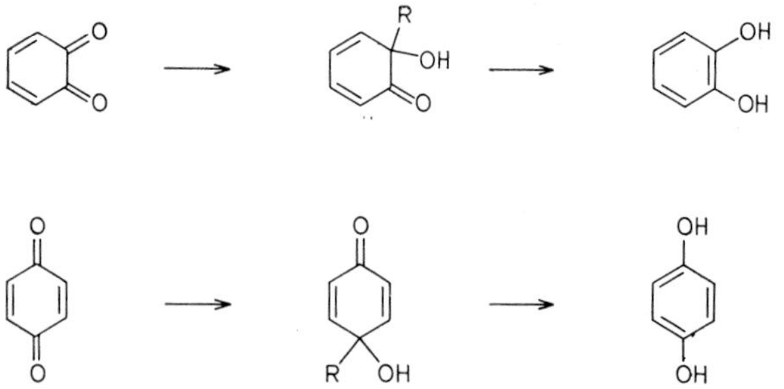

The diphenols are often readily oxidised to quinones (moist Ag_2O, ferric salts, chromic acid in acetic acid). In solution the semiquinone half-way compound may be studied as a free radical, *i.e.* an odd-electron, paramagnetic compound with characteristic spectroscopic properties. Quinhydrones are double compounds in which one molecule of quinol and one of quinone are united to form a diamagnetic complex.

The oxidation–reduction potentials of quinones are important in many biochemical systems and it should be noted that for example the oxidation of hydroquinone results in loss of H^+ ions and of electrons.

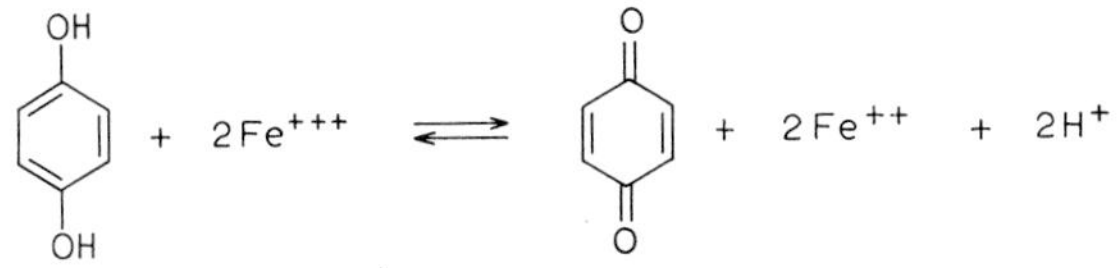

$$HQ \rightleftharpoons Q + 2e + 2H^+$$

$$E = E_0 + \frac{RT}{2F} \ln \frac{[Q]}{[HQ]} + \frac{RT}{F} \ln [H^+]$$

So that

$$E = E_0 \text{ when } [Q] = [HQ] \text{ and } [H^+] = 1.0$$

and

$$E = E_0 + 0.03 \, ^{10}\log \frac{[Q]}{[HQ]} - 0.06 \, pH$$

A convenient medium consists of 95% ethanol made 0.2 N with respect to hydrogen chloride and 0.2 N with respect to lithium chloride.

Table I shows the redox potentials of a few compounds and it will be seen that the introduction of methyl and methoxyl groups tends to reduce E_0 while hydroxyl groups raise it.

TABLE I

NORMAL ELECTRODE POTENTIALS OF SOME QUINONES[3]

Quinone	$E_0(alcohol)$ volts
Diphenoquinone	0.954
o-Benzoquinone	0.792
p-Benzoquinone	0.715
Ubiquinone (50)	0.542
1,2-Naphthoquinone	0.576
1,4-Naphthoquinone	0.484
2-Methyl-1,4-naphthoquinone	0.422
Lawsone (2-hydroxy-1,4-naphthoquinone)	0.358
Phthiocol (2-methyl-3-hydroxy-1,4-naphthoquinone)	0.299
2-Methoxy-3-methyl-1,4-naphthoquinone	0.381
5,6,7,8-Tetrahydro-1,4-naphthoquinone	0.585
Anthraquinone	0.154

2. Naturally occurring quinones

Out of the very large number of naturally occurring quinones[1] space will only allow reference to a few, selected because they seem at present of special interest to biochemists.

Methoxybenzoquinone and the 2,6-dimethoxy compound have been isolated from wheat germ to the extent of about 0.53 and 0.066 g/kg respectively.

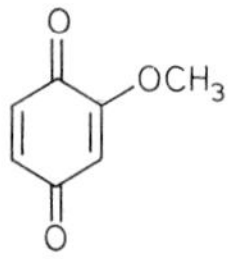

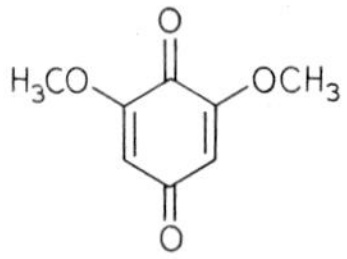

They seem to be derived from the naturally occurring methoxyquinol glucosides which seem to have a role, still to be fully elucidated, in germination. Dough made from flour rich in germ is liable to turn pink as a result of the formation of methoxyquinone. Certain flour beetles produce toluquinol and ethylquinol which also give rise to quinones capable of "spoiling" the flour.

It should be noted that these quinones are essentially artifacts and do not of necessity possess biological importance as such. This may not be true for the plant *Adonis vernalis* L. which is also a source of 2,6-dimethoxy-1,4-benzoquinone.

A number of interesting benzoquinone derivatives have been isolated from *Aspergillus fumigatus* Fres.[4] and from *Gliocladium* species[5-7].

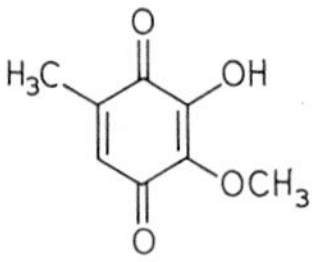

Fumigatin

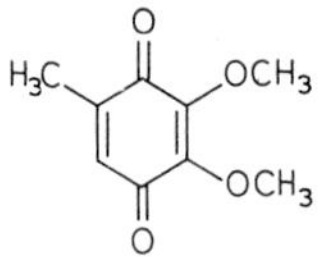

Fumigatin-methyl ether
(made from fumigatin)

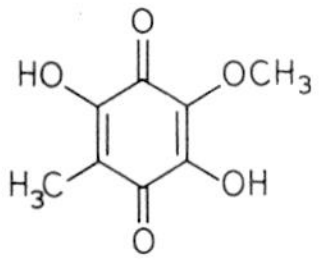

Spinulosin

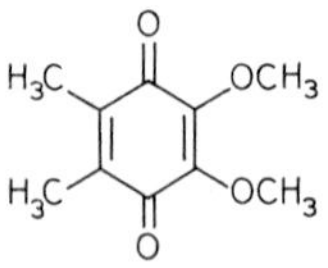

Aurantiogliocladin

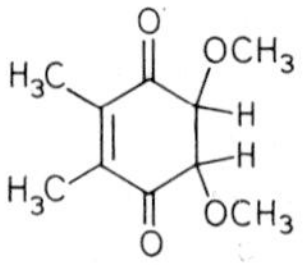

Gliorosein

Rubrogliocladin is a dark red double compound made up of one molecule of aurantiogliocladin for one of the corresponding quinol.

Embelin and rapanone are 2,5-dihydroxy-1,4-benzoquinones with C_{11} and C_{13} substituents respectively.

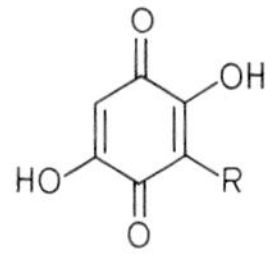

R = $C_{11}H_{23}$ or $C_{13}H_{27}$

Other naturally occurring *o*-hydroxyquinones are perezone and pedicinin.

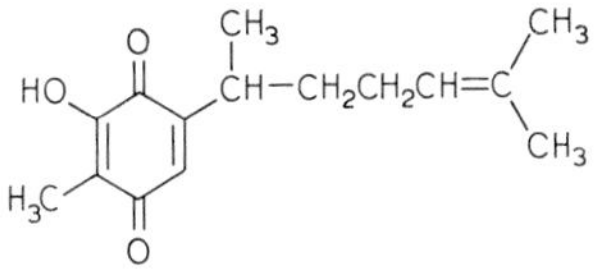

Perezone

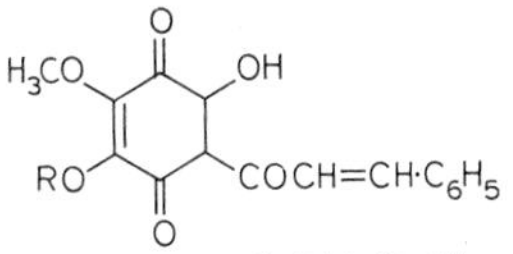

Pedicinin (R=H)
Methyl pedicinin (R= CH₃)

Fully methylated pedicinin can be reduced to the quinol and cyclised to a flavonone.

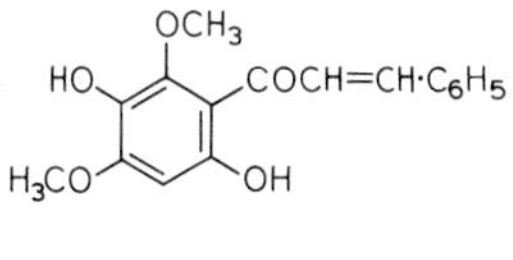

Pedicin

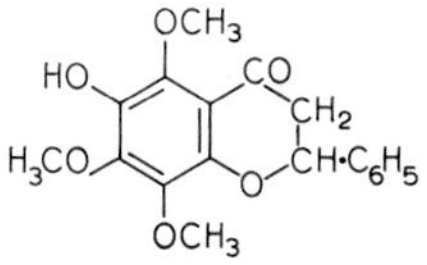

iso–Pedicin

Plant products also yield many interesting naphthoquinones, *e.g.*:

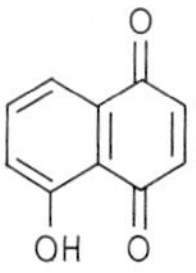

Juglone

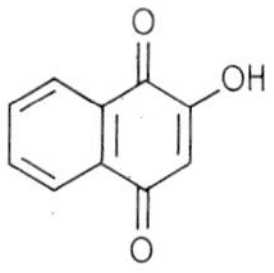

Lawsone

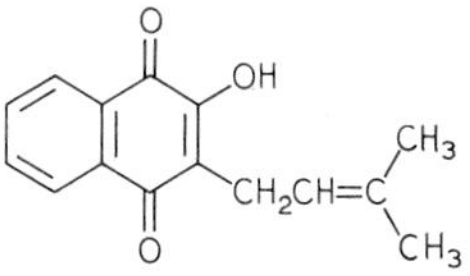

Lapachol

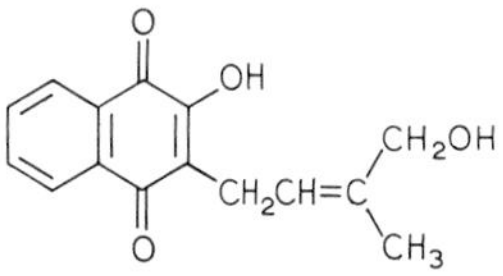

Lomatiol

All green parts of walnut trees (*Juglandaceae*), especially the green shells, contain a juglone precursor, namely the 5-glucoside of 1,4,5-trihydroxy-naphthalene. Lawsone, from the leaves of *Lawsonia* species is the 2-hydroxy analogue of juglone. It is weakly anti-haemorrhagic, and it is bacteriostatic towards *Mycobact. tuberculosis* and it accelerates respiration of red cells (rabbit). Phthiocol (2-methyl-3-hydroxy-1,4-naphthoquinone) obtained from the human type *M. tuberculosis* is presumably derived from a vitamin K_2.

Lapachol undergoes interesting transformations presaging recent work on solanachromene and ubichromenol (p. 208).

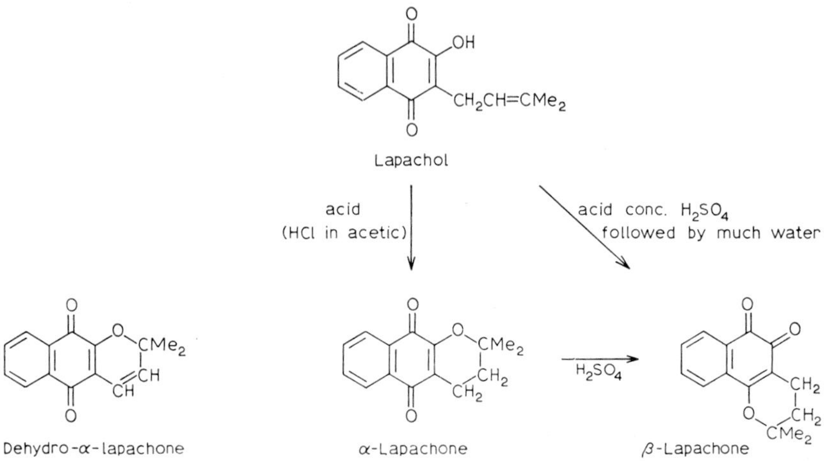

Lapachol

acid
(HCl in acetic)

acid conc. H_2SO_4
followed by much water

Dehydro-α-lapachone

α-Lapachone

H_2SO_4

β-Lapachone

After a lengthy pause there has been renewed activity in the vitamin K field. It will be recalled that the classical work of Dam, Doisy and of Almquist seemed to leave the chemical aspects at least, in a very tidy state.

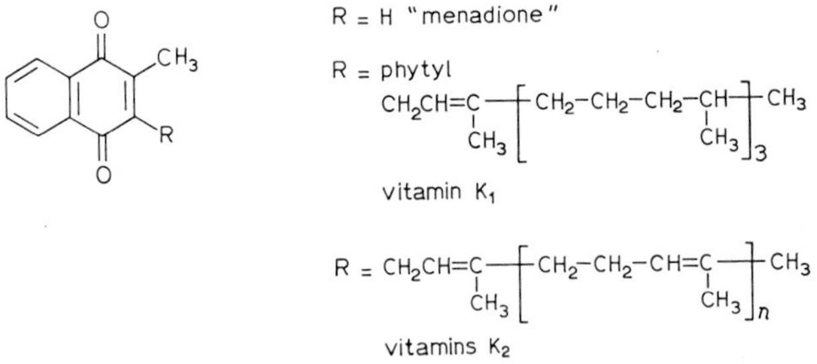

R = H "menadione"

R = phytyl
$CH_2CH=C$—$[CH_2-CH_2-CH_2-CH]$—CH_3
            CH_3 CH_3]$_3$

vitamin K_1

R = $CH_2CH=C$—$[CH_2-CH_2-CH=C]$—CH_3
                CH_3 CH_3]$_n$

vitamins K_2

Martius[2] has isolated from animal tissues a vitamin K_2 with a $C_{20}H_{33}$ side chain ($n = 3; 4$ unconjugated double bonds) and Francis et al.[8] and Noll[9] have obtained from M. tuberculosis a vitamin K_2 with a $C_{45}H_{73}$ side chain (9 isoprenoid groups with 9 unconjugated double bonds). Isler et al.[10] have shown that Doisy's classical vitamin K_2 has a $C_{35}H_{57}$ side chain but there is a small amount of a congener with a $C_{30}H_{49}$ side chain. There are at least 4 natural vitamins K_2 ($K_2(20)$, $K_2(30)$, $K_2(35)$ and $K_2(45)$) and all the other isoprenologues from $K_2(5)$ to $K_2(50)$ have been synthesised. (See also Chapter VIII.)

The tocopherols are readily oxidised to tocopherylquinones which in turn are easily reducible to the tocopheryl hydroquinones, *e.g.*:

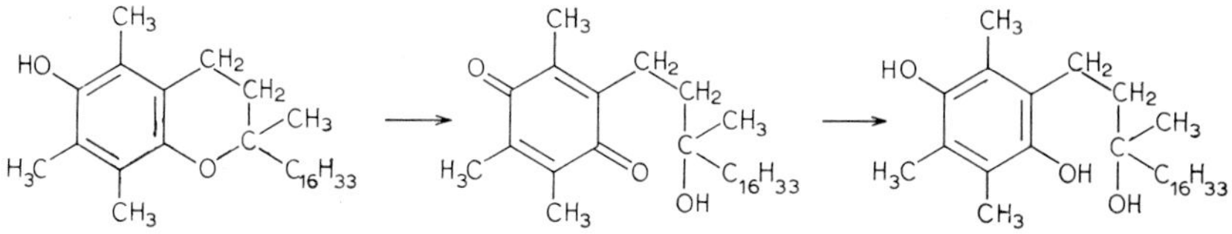

There is evidence that α-tocopherylquinone occurs as such in animal tissues but some workers are unconvinced.

Rowland *et al.*[11] isolated from tobacco a highly unsaturated alcohol *solanesol*, thought at first to have the formula $C_{50}H_{81}OH$ but now known (Isler[2], Folkers[2]) to be $C_{45}H_{73}OH$:

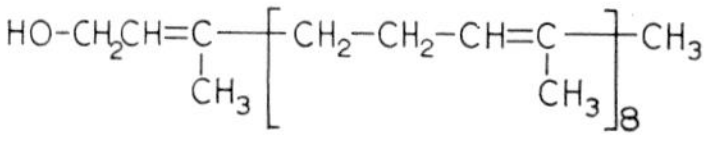

$$HO-CH_2CH=C \underset{CH_3}{\overset{}{|}} \left[CH_2-CH_2-CH=C \underset{CH_3}{\overset{}{|}} \right]_8 CH_3$$

When condensed with 2-methyl-1,4-dihydroxynaphthalene it gives the reduced form of vitamin $K_2(45)$ identical with Noll's product already referred to.

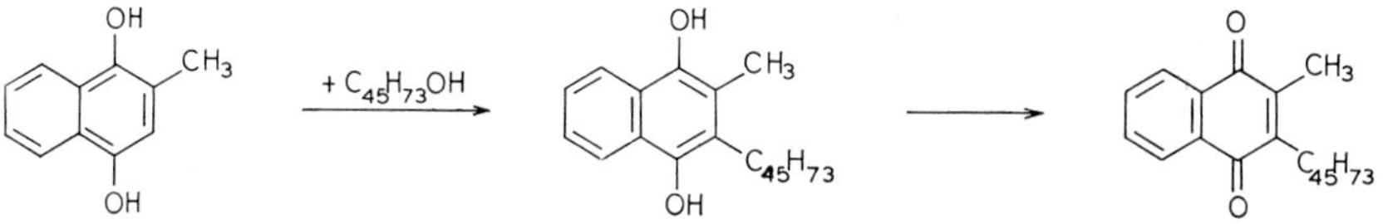

3. Ubiquinones

Kofler[12] isolated from leaves a substituted *p*-benzoquinone which was clearly of potential biochemical significance. Its constitution is now known and Crane has obtained the compound from chloroplasts.

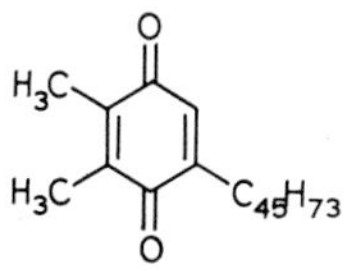

Kofler's quinone
Crane's Q254 or
plastoquinone[13]

This quinone may be synthesised (Isler, Folkers) from 2,3-dimethylhydroquinone and solanesol. Crane believes that his Q254 (λ_{max} 254 mμ), identical with the "synthetic" product, plays an important part in photosynthetic phosphorylation.

The history[14] of the new class of substances known as ubiquinones or coenzymes Q goes back to 1950 when a substance (SA) was obtained from horse intestinal mucosae with λ_{max} 272 mμ, $E_{1cm}^{1\%}$ ca. 200 (cyclohexane as solvent). This could be obtained both from the mucosal *lipid* or the tissue unsaponifiable fraction by adsorption chromatography on alumina. A substance very similar to SA was obtained from yeast.

The material was also obtained from liver and there was a considerable increase in the concentration in liver from vitamin A-deficient rats. A congener, designated SC (λ_{max} 233, 275, 283 and 332 mμ in cyclohexane) was also obtained from these deficient livers. In fact the *concentrations* of both SA and SC rose as the deficiency advanced, the former progressively and the latter more markedly in the terminal stages. The best source of SC was "normal" human kidney but SC could not be found in nephritic kidney.

SA was obtained also from pig liver and heart and crystallised ($E_{1cm}^{1\%}$ 272 mμ = 167). It was also prepared from ox heart mitochondria (Crane *et al.*[15]). The distribution of "SA" seemed to justify the name ubiquinone (see Morton[14]). Structural work established the formula (10 unconjugated double bonds).

Ubiquinone (50) or SA
Coenzyme Q_{10} or Q275

Reduction yielded a quinol (λ_{max} 291 mμ, $E_{1cm}^{1\%}$ 52) and infrared spectra showed the replacement of C=O absorption by —OH absorption. The oxidation–reduction potential suggested a substituted quinone.

Perbenzoic acid titrations and catalytic hydrogenation revealed the presence of considerable aliphatic unsaturation. Molecular weight determination gave conflicting results but indicated the presence of a long side chain or chains. When fully reduced to per-hydro-SA a quinone could be formed by oxidation which had *almost* exactly the same ultraviolet absorption as SA itself. The new quinone however took up only 1/11 of the hydrogen absorbed by SA. This result implied that SA took up 10 molecules of hydrogen in the side chain and used one molecule in reducing quinone to quinol. The molecular weight was thus fixed by an indirect process. The absorption spectrum of SA was compared with that of aurantiogliocladin (p. 202) and related substances. These considerations, supported by unambiguous analyses and degradations (Morton *et al.*[16]; Wolf *et al.*[17]) established the structure where $n=9$ for the product from most animal tissues

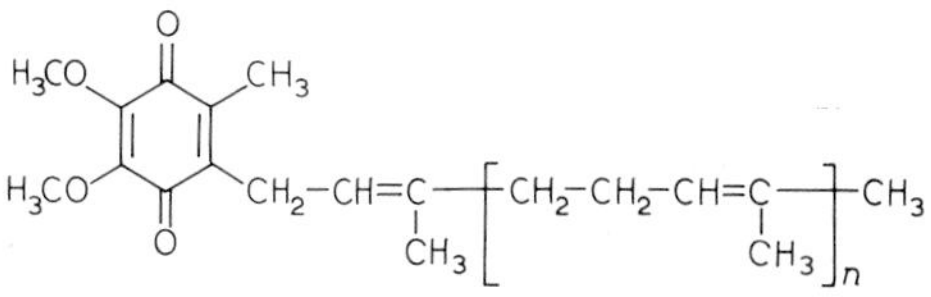

and $n=8$ for the rat liver product

and $n=5$ for the baker's yeast material (Gloor et al.).

Crane, Lester and Hatefi[15] were studying the lipids of heart muscle mitochondria with reference to possible co-factors functioning in oxidative electron transport sequences. They attributed to their quinone (Q275) a role justifying the designation "coenzyme Q". Aided by Folkers and his associates they independently proved the structure and found isoprenologues in which the side chain could have 30, 35, 40, 45 or 50 carbon atoms.

TABLE II

UBIQUINONES OR COENZYMES Q

Source	Designation
Heart, liver, kidney	Ubiquinone (50) or coenzyme Q_{10}
Rat liver; torula yeast	Ubiquinone (45) or coenzyme Q_9
Rat liver; *Azotobacter vinelandii*	Ubiquinone (40) or coenzyme Q_8
Torula yeast	Ubiquinone (35) or coenzyme Q_7
Baker's yeast	Ubiquinone (30) or coenzyme Q_6

In some assay systems the minimum length of side chain is 10 carbon atoms (Q_2) for biological activity to occur.

Ubiquinone (50) is still relatively scarce. The Basle group led by Isler obtained 120 g of the pure compound from 3200 kg of pig heart. Ubiquinone (45) is more accessible since it can be synthesised from solanesol (p. 205).

Human kidney (46.5 kg) was used[18] to obtain SC as it is so far the best source, yielding 0.45 g of crude SC and 0.15 g of the pure substance. Standard methods of characterisation supported by the results of ultraviolet, infrared and nuclear magnetic resonance spectra indicated that SC was a cyclic isomeride of ubiquinone (50) with the structure:

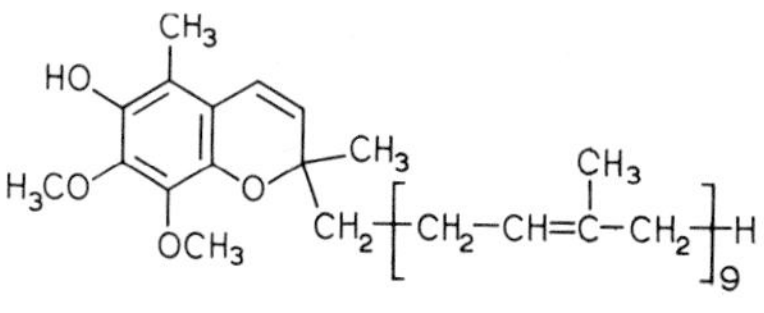

Ubichromenol (50) or SC

Ubichromenol can also be obtained from ubiquinone by chemical methods but the product is racemic whereas that from tissue is optically active[2].

The structure of ubichromenol recalls that of solanachromene[19] from tobacco and it is evident that solanachromene is related to

Solanachromene n=8

Kofler's quinone in the same manner as ubichromenol is to ubiquinone.

Isler's group have synthesised all the vitamins K_2 and the ubiquinones with polyisoprenoid side chains from 5 to 50 carbon atoms. Folker's group discovered that under certain defined conditions the methoxy groups of the ubiquinones could be replaced by ethoxy groups. If it is necessary to saponify a raw material the risk of producing artifacts is diminished by adding pyrogallol to the mixture before heating and the use of *methanolic* potash instead of *ethanolic* potash is obviously wise.

The biochemistry of the ubiquinones will be discussed elsewhere in these volumes but a brief and tentative account is necessary now. Lynen[2] has indicated a general route for terpenoid biosynthesis via [1-^{14}C]-isopentenyl pyrophosphate. In yeast extracts this can lead to long-chain terpenylpyrophosphates.

When yeast is grown aerobically it contains 5 – 10 times as much ubiquinone as anaerobic yeast provided that the medium to be aerated contains glucose (Sugimura and Rudney[20]). Under these conditions of adaptation to aeration [^{14}C]-formate provides carbon for methoxyl groups. [^{14}C]-Acetate has been used with [^{14}C]-mevalonic acid to study the *in vivo* synthesis of ubiquinones by rats[23]. The biosynthesis is relatively slow but the carbon of methoxyls can be incorporated from formate and that of the side chain from acetate or mevalonate.

In the rat the specific activity of ubiquinone (45) was $1/3$ to $1/2$ that of cholesterol but 25–35 times that of ubiquinone (50), suggesting that the lower isoprenologue is the functioning form in the rat. Wiss *et al.*[2] found incorporation from mevalonate into both ubiquinones; if the rats were vitamin A-deficient, liver cholesterol biosynthesis from mevalonate was reduced but that of squalene and ubiquinone was increased. Solanesol was found to occur in animal tissues but in rats given [^{14}C]-mevalonate it was not radioactive.

Packter and Glover[22] have found that *Aspergillus fumigatus* Fres. grown on a medium enriched with *l*-leucine produces ubichromenol apparently at the expense of fumigatin.

There is no doubt that the discovery of Q275 (ubiquinone, coenzyme Q) in mitochondria has resulted in a new phase in the study of electron transport systems[2]. From many points of view the "damaged" mitochondria of the Keilin–Hartree heart-muscle preparation are very suitable for detailed study although the systems which work are non-phosphorylating.

Analyses show that in the preparation the cytochromes are present in the relative molecular concentrations:

$$a + a_3, 2.0; \qquad b, 1.5; \qquad c + c_1, 1.0$$

On this scale the amount of ubiquinone (50) is about 11. Succinate reduces 90% and DPNH about 70% of the endogenous ubiquinone of this particulate preparation but the oxidation of substrate is faster than the reduction of ubiquinone. Some of the ubiquinone is in a bound form but becomes extractable by organic solvents if a Tris buffer is used. The oxidation of ubiquinol is inhibited by cyanide, antimycin A and by BAL (British anti-lewisite). The two latter have no effect on the rate or extent of reduction of ubiquinone.

The biochemistry of the ubiquinones is being actively studied and there is still much to be done before any arguments can be accepted as conclusive, particularly perhaps in the difficult field of electron transport.

Fig. 1 is probably consistent with the present state of knowledge.

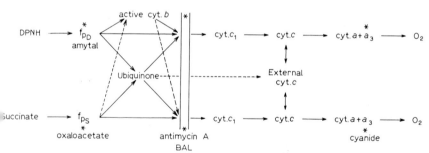

Fig. 1. Probable sequence of electron carriers (Keilin–Hartree heart-muscle preparation). * inhibitors; f_p = flavoprotein; f_{PD} = flavoprotein accepting H from DPNH; f_{PS} = flavoprotein accepting H from succinate.

There are still many problems to be faced over the fate of the ubiquinones, and the functions of ubichromenols, tocopherols and the vitamins K_2 must all be fitted into a pattern.

The recent discovery of a new class of long-chain unsaturated alcohols of which dolichol[21] $C_{100}H_{161}OH$ with 20 unconjugated double bonds is the first member, opens up further possibilities since solanesol has proved to be a key compound.

REFERENCES

1 R. H. THOMSON, *Naturally Occurring Quinones*, Butterworth, London, 1957, 302 pp. [Covers much of the field before the ubiquinone work.]

2 *Ciba Symposium on Quinones in Electron Transport* contains contributions from most of the workers concerned with ubiquinones and coenzymes Q.

3 L. F. FIESER AND M. FIESER, *Organic Chemistry*, Heath, Boston, Mass., 1956, p. 712.

4 W. K. ANSLOW AND H. RAISTRICK, *Biochem. J.*, 32 (1938) 687.

5 E. B. VISCHER, *J. Chem. Soc.*, (1953) 815.

6 N. BAKER, J. F. W. MCOMIE AND D. MILES, *J. Chem. Soc.*, (1953) 820.

7 P. W. BRIAN, *Experientia*, 7 (1951) 266.

8 J. FRANCIS, J. MADINAVEITIA, H. M. MACTURC AND G. A. SNOW, *Nature*, 163 (1949) 365.

9 H. NOLL, *J. Biol. Chem.*, 232 (1958) 919.

10 O. ISLER, R. RÜEGG, L. H. CHOPARD-DIT-JEAN, A. WINTERSTEIN AND O. WISS, *Helv. Chim. Acta*, 41 (1958) 786.

11 R. L. ROWLAND, P. H. LATIMER AND J. A. GILES, *J. Am. Chem. Soc.*, 78 (1956) 4680.

12 M. KOFLER, *Festschrift für E. C. Barell*, Basle, 1946, p. 199.

13 F. L. CRANE, *Arch. Biochem. Biophys.*, 87 (1960) 198.

14 R. A. MORTON, *Nature*, 182 (1958) 1764.

15 F. L. CRANE, R. L. LESTER AND Y. HATEFI, *Biochim. Biophys. Acta*, 25 (1957) 220.

16 R. A. MORTON, U. GLOOR, O. SCHINDLER, G. M. WILSON, L. H. CHOPARD-DIT-JEAN, F. W. HEMMING, O. ISLER, W. M. F. LEAT, J. F. PENNOCK, R. RÜEGG, U. SCHWIETER AND O. WISS, *Helv. Chim. Acta*, 41 (1958) 2343.

17 D. E. WOLF, C. H. HOFFMANN, N. R. TRENNER, B. H. ARISON, C. H. SHUNK, B. O. LINN, J. F. MCPHERSON AND K. FOLKERS, *J. Am. Chem. Soc.*, 80 (1958) 4752.

18 D. L. LAIDMAN, R. A. MORTON, J. Y. F. PATERSON AND J. F. PENNOCK, *Biochem. J.*, 74 (1960) 541.

19 R. L. ROWLAND, *J. Am. Chem. Soc.*, 80 (1958) 6130.

20 T. SUGIMURA AND H. RUDNEY, *Biochem. Biophys. Acta*, 37 (1960) 560.

21 J. F. PENNOCK, F. W. HEMMING AND R. A. MORTON, *Nature*, 186 (1960) 470.

22 N. M. PACKTER AND J. GLOVER, *Nature*, 187 (1960) 414.

23 D. E. M. LAWSON, D. R. THRELFALL, J. GLOVER AND R. A. MORTON, *Biochem. J.*, 79 (1961) 201.

Volume 9

Part C

PHENOLIC PLANT CONSTITUENTS

Chapter X

Flavonoid Compounds, Tannins, Lignins and Related Compounds

T. A. GEISSMAN

Chemistry Department, University of California, Los Angeles, Calif. (U.S.A.)

The almost limitless abilities of plants to synthesize aromatic substances, most of which are phenols or their oxygen-substituted derivatives, affords so large and structurally varied a group of substances as to defy attempts to classify them in summary form. Their range of structural complexity runs from such simple substances as hydroquinone (1) (as the glucoside, arbutin) to such complex ones as the polycyclic dianthrone, hypericin (2).

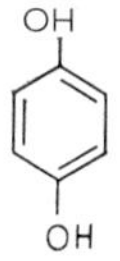

(1) 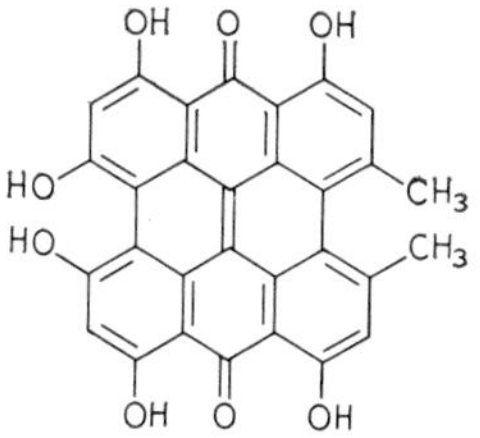   (2)

An examination of the known structural classes of naturally occurring phenols, coupled with present knowledge concerning the biogenetic origins of many plant substances, suggests that most of the compounds of this group can be placed in five main categories:

(*1*) Compounds having their origin from isoprenoid (terpenoid) precursors, modified by oxidation to produce hydroxylated aromatic compounds.

(*2*) Compounds of a class that may be regarded, either provisionally on structural grounds or on the basis of direct experimental evidence, as being derived by a linear combination of 2-carbon fragments ("acetate units"), through hypothetical poly-β-keto acids (*i.e.*, 3,5,7,...etc.-polyketoalkanoic acids) and thence, by cyclization, to benzenoid, naphthalenoid and anthracenoid ring systems[1].

(*3*) Compounds containing a substituted 1-phenylpropane structural unit and existing as monomeric (C_9), dimeric (C_{18}) or polymeric representatives of this fundamental unit. This class properly includes many compounds containing side chains of less than three (by degradation) and more than three (by extension) carbon atoms[2].

(*4*) Compounds formed by combinations of fragments derived by "acetate" pathways with those derived from phenylpropane units. This class, a very large and diverse one, comprises chiefly the so-called flavonoid substances and includes dimeric (biflavonyls) and polymeric (tannins) representatives[3-5].

(*5*) A large, diverse and heterogeneous group of substances, basically members of groups 1–4, but containing additional structural elements such as carbon-linked methyl groups introduced by biological methyl donors; isoprenoid (C_5) units attached as both oxygen- and carbon-linked substituents; glycosyl units attached by carbon–carbon linkages; and many compounds containing vestigial fragments of one of the chief structural units.

It should be emphasized that any attempt to erect a system of *a priori* classification based upon biosynthetic origin is hazardous because relatively few biosynthetic pathways in the field of the natural phenols have been firmly established by experimental means. One who attempts to classify upon this basis cannot escape the responsibility for making assumptions that are unsupported by direct evidence. For example, eugenone (3) and peonol (4) can safely be regarded as acetate-derived (group 2), and *p*-hydroxycinnamic acid (5) is a typical phenylpropane derivative (group 3). Shall *p*-hydroxyacetophenone (6), then, be classified as a member of the former group, or as derived by loss of a carbon atom from a phenylpropane precursor? The choice must be an arbitrary one, and is made even more difficult

by the fact that acetovanillone (7), which possesses the 3,4-dihydroxylation pattern characteristic of phenylpropane-derived compounds, is also a substance of natural origin (see also pungenin, p. 223). In the ensuing discussion, therefore, certain compounds will be found to be assigned to classes to which future studies may show that they do not belong.

1. Compounds with isoprenoid structures

The simple phenols, thymol (8), carvacrol (9), and *p*-cumenol (10) are well known naturally occurring compounds. Thymoquinone is also found naturally, possibly as an oxidative artifact. Perezone (11) (pipitzahuic acid) is a hydroxyquinone that is clearly of the sesquiterpenoid group, *cf.* farnesol (12).

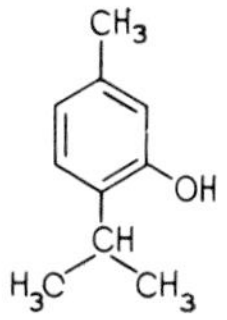

(8) 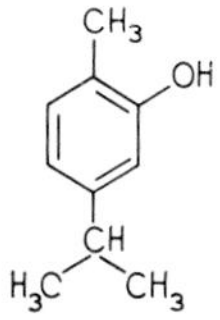   (9) 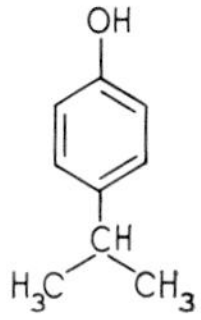   (10) 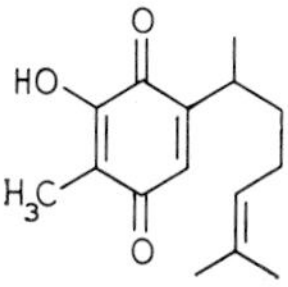   (11) 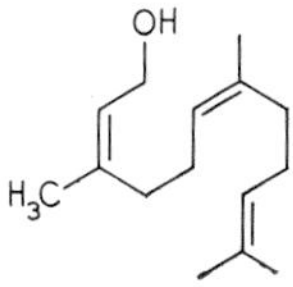   (12)

A complex sesquiterpenoid phenol is gossypol (13), the yellow coloring matter of cottonseed.

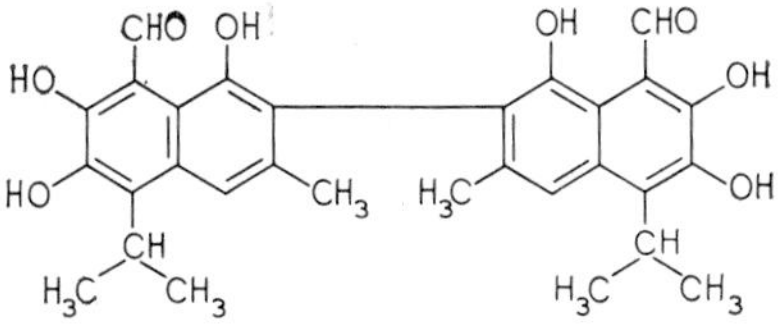

(13)

Diterpenoid phenols are represented by podocarpic acid (14), ferruginol (15), totarol (16), and sugiol (17).

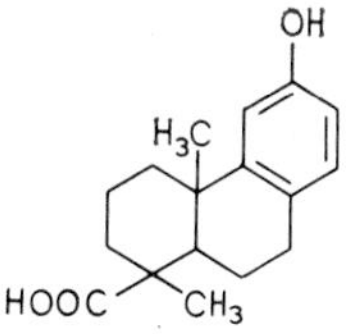

(14) 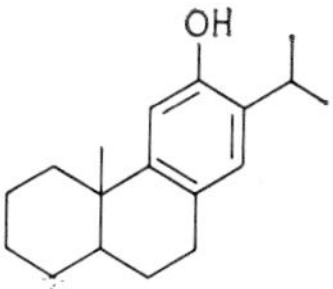   (15) 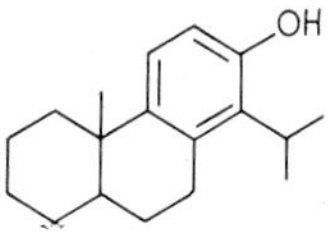   (16) 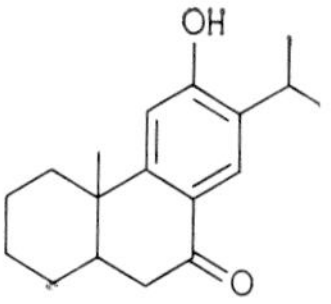   (17)

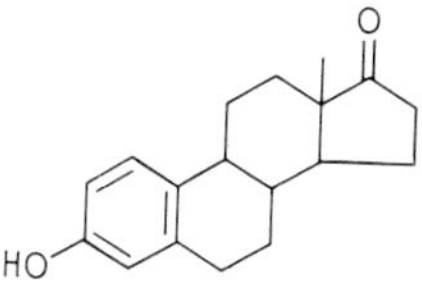

(18) 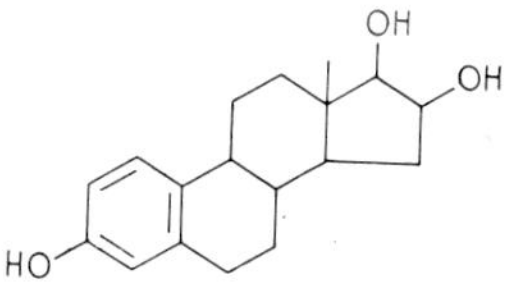   (19)

It is of interest to note that the steroidal phenols estrone (18) and estriol (19), which are typical of the animal kingdom, have been reported to occur in plants; the former was found in palm kernels, the latter in the willow[6].

In general, the production of aromatic compounds from terpenoid precursors is uncommon in nature. Most of the natural phenolic substances are those, discussed in the sequel, that have different biogenetic origins.

2. Phenolic compounds derived by linear condensation of two-carbon units

The idea of the origin of many phenolic plant products by the cyclization of linear polyketomethylene precursors, derived by the condensation of —CH_2—CO— units, was first suggested by Collie[7] and later developed along speculative and experimental lines by Robinson[8] and Birch and Donovan[1]. In its simplest form it can be represented by the formation of orcinol (20) and orsellinic acid (21) from four "acetate units".

The depsides and depsidones found in lichens (Asahina and Shibata[9]) represent examples of compounds that are clearly of the same origin, some of them orsellinic acid derivatives such as lecanoric acid (22) and erythrin (23) (the

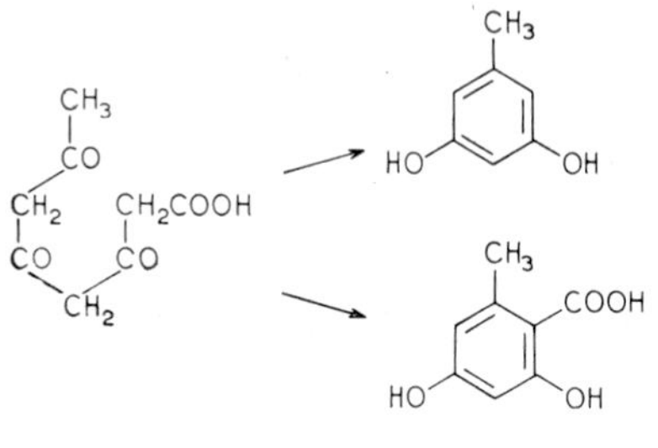

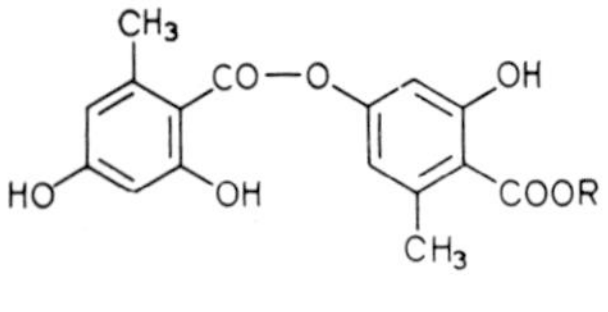

(22) R = H
(23) R = CH$_2$CHOHCHOHCH$_2$OH

erythritol ester of (22)), but many of them bearing *n*-alkyl or *n*-alkanoyl groupings in place of the methyl groups of (22) and (23). Some examples of these are divaricatic acid (24), sphaerophorin (25), anziaic acid (26) and olivetoric acid (27).

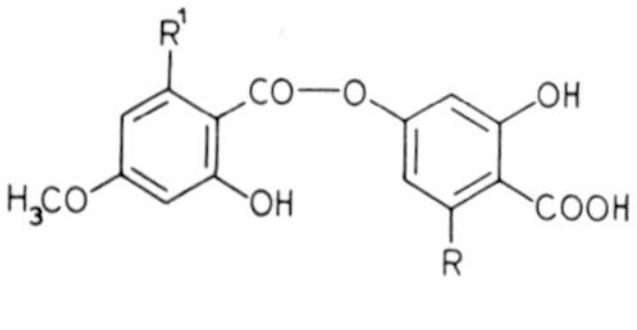

(24) R^1 = R = CH$_2$CH$_2$CH$_3$
(25) R^1 = CH$_3$, R = CH$_2$CH$_2$CH$_2$CH$_2$CH$_2$CH$_2$CH$_3$
(26) R^1 = R = CH$_2$CH$_2$CH$_2$CH$_2$CH$_3$
(27) R^1 = CH$_2$COCH$_2$CH$_2$CH$_2$CH$_2$CH$_3$
R = CH$_2$CH$_2$CH$_2$CH$_2$CH$_3$ (and OH for OCH$_3$)

It is apparent that compounds of the type exemplified by (27) represent the cyclization products of an extended chain of 2-carbon units, as in (28), in

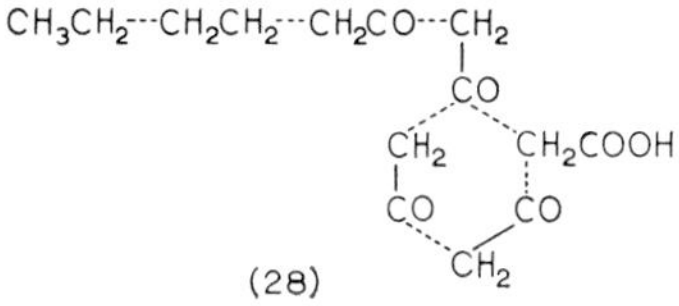
CH3CH2---CH2CH2---CH2CO---CH2
CO
CH2
CH2COOH
CO
CO
CH2

(28)

which partial reduction of some of the carbonyl groups has occurred. The relationship of a compound such as that formed in (28) to a fatty acid is apparent.

Examples of natural phenols related structurally to the lichen acids are the group of substances found in the *Anacardiaceae*, represented by urushiol (29), anacardic acid (30), and cardol (31). Of particular interest in this class of compounds are those found[10] in Tigaso oil (*Campnosperma brevipetiolata*). Besides campnospermonol (32) the optically active hydroxyketone (33) is found.

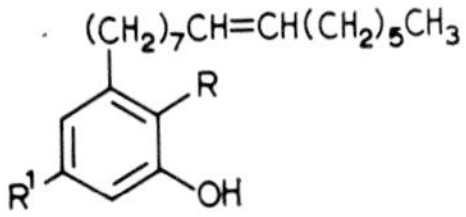
(CH2)7CH=CH(CH2)5CH3
R
R1
OH

(29) R = OH, R^1 = H
(30) R = COOH, R^1 = H
(31) R = H, R^1 = OH

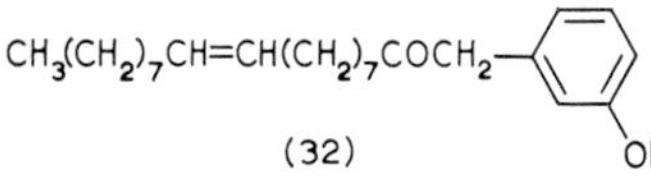
CH3(CH2)7CH=CH(CH2)7COCH2
OH

(32)

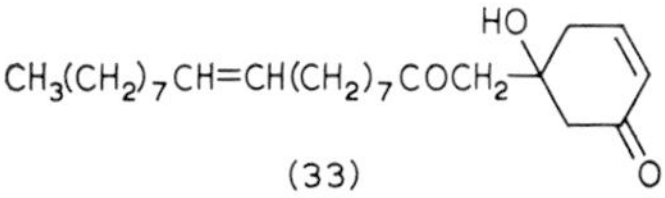
HO
CH3(CH2)7CH=CH(CH2)7COCH2
O

(33)

Dehydration of the ketone (33) would yield (32); and (33) is clearly the cyclic acid aldol of the hypothetical intermediate (34) or its decarboxylation product.

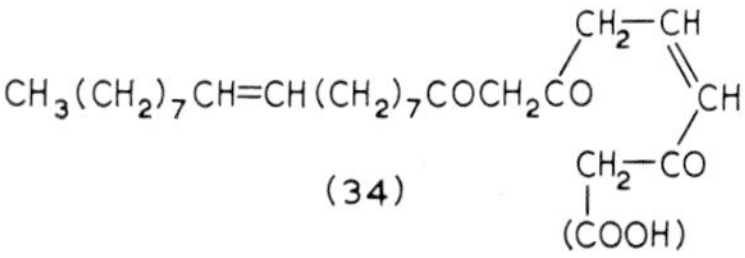
CH2—CH
CH3(CH2)7CH=CH(CH2)7COCH2CO
CH
CH2—CO
(COOH)

(34)

There is an obvious structural relationship between compounds such as (32) and (33) to oleic acid; but whether their genesis is by way of an extension of oleic acid itself or by elaboration of the heptadecenyl side chain at some other stage in the process is not known. It will be noted later that extension of phenylpropane-derived phenolic precursors by the addition of acetate units (methysticin, shogaol, zingiberone and flavonoid compounds) is a well-recognized path of synthesis.

References p. 250

$$CH_3(CH_2)_7CH=CH(CH_2)_7COOH + 4(CH_2CO) \longrightarrow (34)$$

A group of compounds which have no close resemblance to those already discussed, but which are regarded[1] as derived by cyclization of polyketomethylene precursors, are the naturally occurring stilbenes, represented by pinosylvin (35) and hydroxyresveratrol (36).

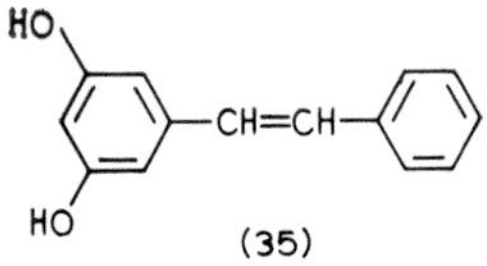

(35) 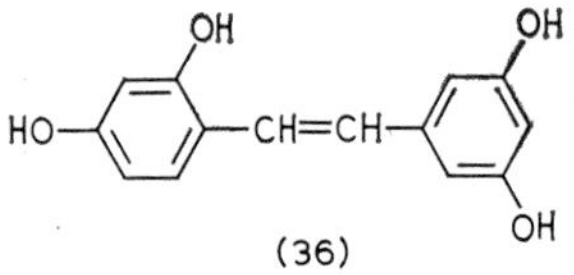   (36)

Again, the 1,3-relationship of the hydroxyl groups suggests their origin from the structural unit —CH_2COCH_2CO—, as, in the case of (36).

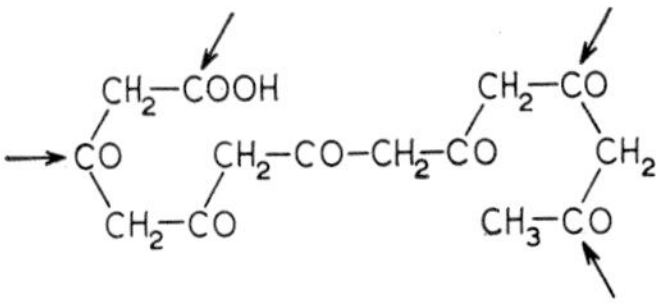

(→ indicates site of final OH group)

Naphthalene and anthracene derivatives

Numerous phenols possessing naphthalene and anthracene nuclei—commonly as quinones — occur as plant constituents[11]. The simple compound 2,6-dimethoxy-p-benzoquinone occurs in a higher plant, while numerous benzoquinones are produced by fungi (e.g., Penicillium and Aspergillus spp.). Hydroxylated 1,4-naphthoquinones abound in the plant kingdom. Juglone (37), lawsone (38) and flaviolin (39) are examples.

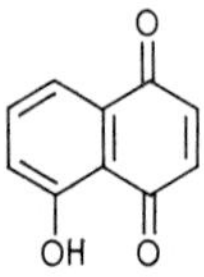

(37) 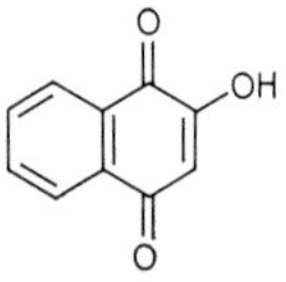   (38) 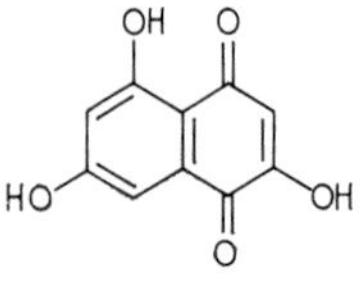   (39) 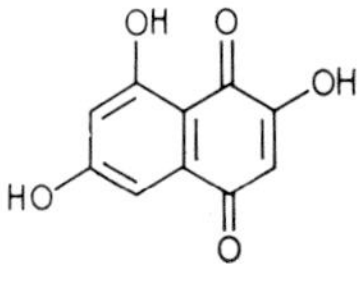   (40)

That these substances are members of the polyketomethylene class is suggested by the fact that of the alternative structures (39) and (40) for flaviolin, (39) was regarded as the more likely (see 41) on the basis of the acetate hypothesis, and was shown to be correct by synthesis of its trimethyl ether[12].

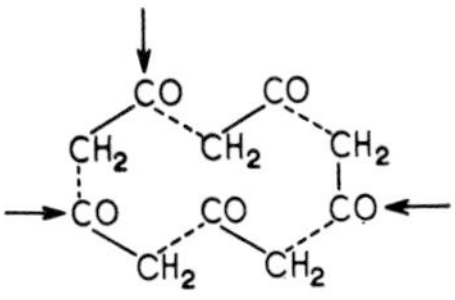

(41)

The derivation of more complex naphthalene derivatives which include additional skeletal atoms, and cyclizations in other ways to produce anthracene derivatives, enlarges this class of polynuclear compounds. Eleutherin (42) is an example of a compound of the first of these groups, in which the hypothetical precursor can be discerned as in (43).

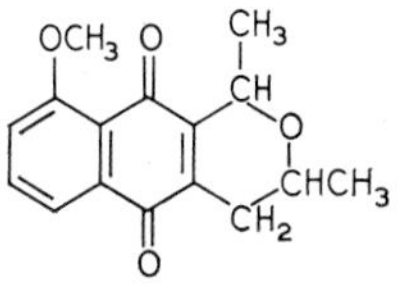

(42)

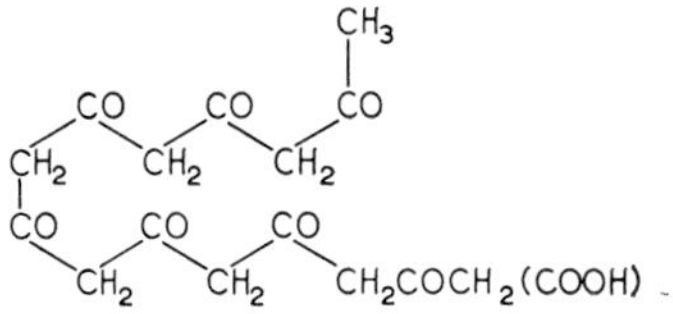

(43)

Lapachol (44), lomatiol (45) and shikonin (46) are naphthoquinones further elaborated by the introduction of isopentyl (isoprenoid) fragments into the fundamental C_{10} unit.

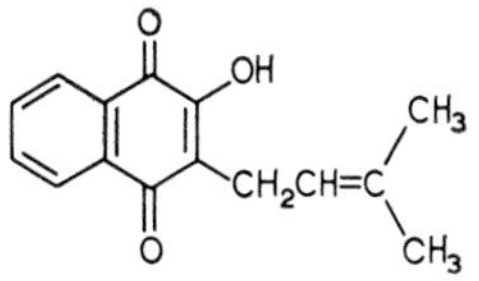

(44)

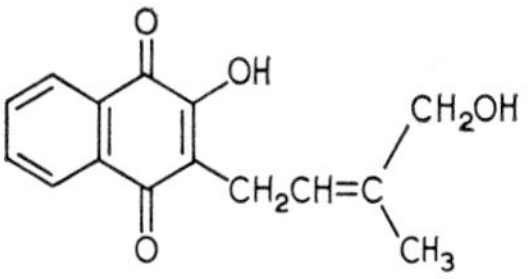

(45)

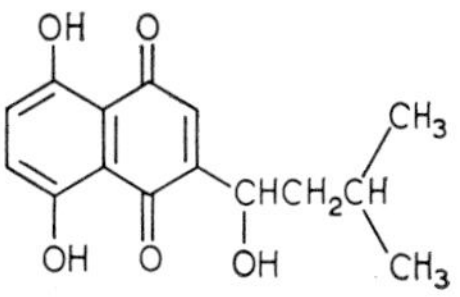

(46)

Vitamin K, also an isoprenoid-substituted naphthoquinone derivative, is dealt with in Chapter VIII.

Anthraquinones are found in nature as the products of the metabolism of fungi, lichens and higher plants. The simplest representatives, 2-hydroxy-(47) and 1,2-dihydroxyanthraquinone (48), are plant products; the latter, alizarin, is the once-important dyestuff in madder (*Rubia tinctorum* L.).

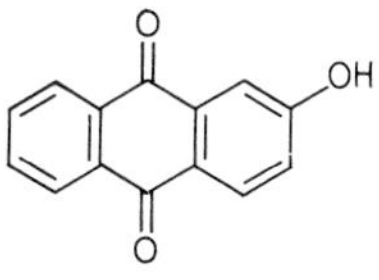

(47)

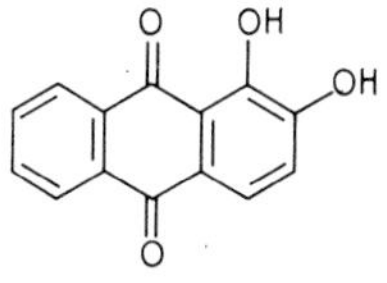

(48)

Homologues of hydroxyanthraquinones, containing methyl, hydroxymethyl and carboxyl groups as nuclear substituents, are widely distributed in nature, usually (in higher plants) as glycosides. They form a class of useful purgative drugs commonly obtained from senna (*Cassia* spp.), *Rhamnus* spp., aloes and several rubiaceous plants. The lichens also elaborate numerous compounds of this class.

Endocrocin (49) is perhaps the most striking illustration of the "regular" derivation from eight acetate units (51) of a complex anthraquinone.

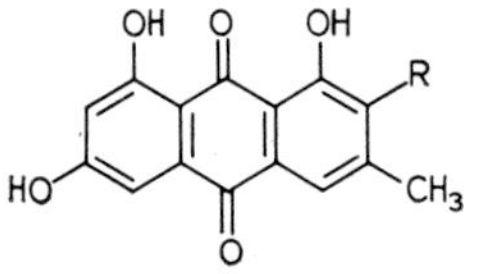

(49) R = COOH
(50) R = H

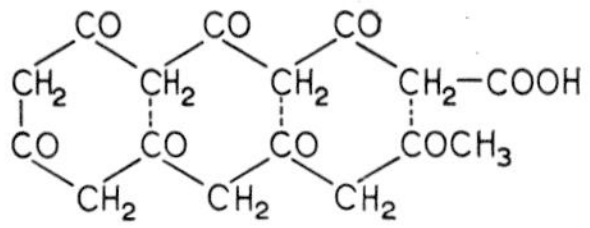

(51)

Emodin (50), is an anthraquinone of higher plants, occurring in several glycosylated forms. Some other anthraquinones of plants whose structures depart from the ideal prototype (49) are rubiadin (52), morindadiol (53), aloeemodin (54) and rhein (55).

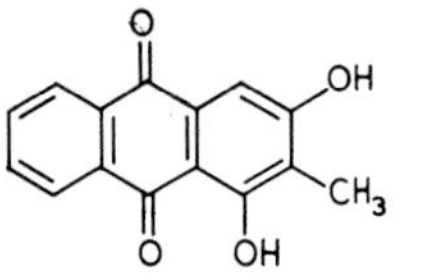

(52)

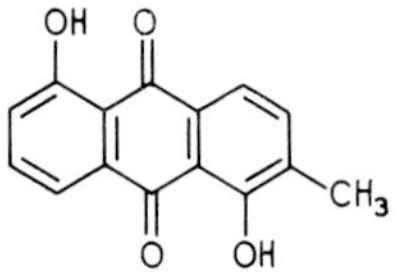

(53)

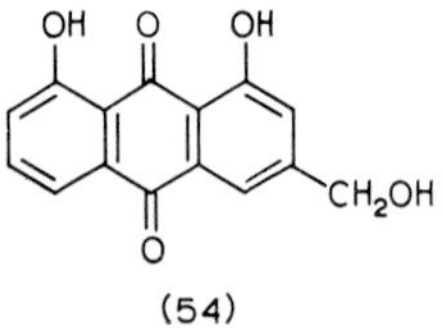

(54)

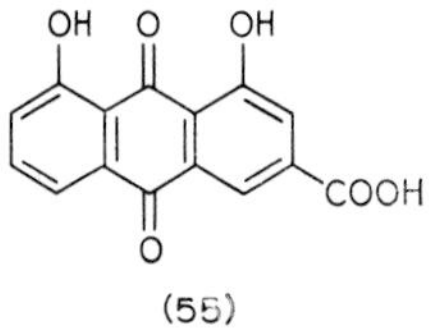

(55)

An interesting structural departure from the anthraquinones (50, 52–55) is carminic acid, elaborated by the cochineal insect. Carminic acid has been assigned the structure (56).

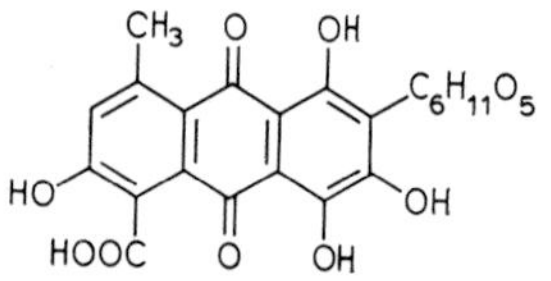

(56)

The C_6-side chain appears to be a carbohydrate residue, but it is carbon–carbon linked to the aromatic nucleus. Other examples of C–C-linked carbohydrate-like residues are found in bergenin (57) (an isocoumarin) and vitexin (58) (a flavone).

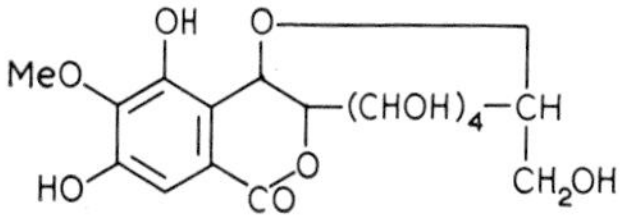

(57) 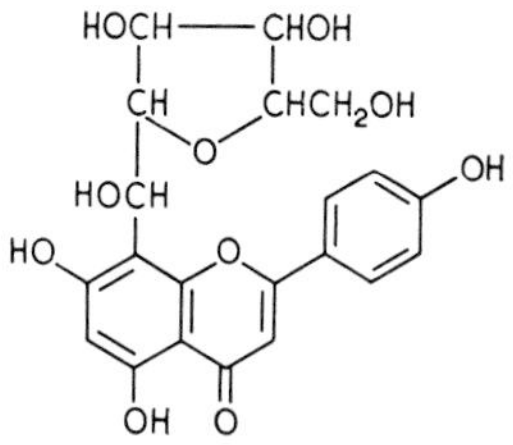   (58)

Reduced forms of the anthraquinone glycosides are found in nature as the corresponding anthrones, and in the form of the *meso*-naphthodianthrone exemplified by hypericin (2), the photodynamic pigment of St. John's wort (*Hypericum perforatum*).

3. Phenylpropane-derived compounds

Compounds containing the structural unit represented by (59) abound in nature[2]; indeed, when one considers those substances in which the C_6–C_3 unit occurs alone, in dimeric and polymeric combination, and in combination with acetic acid-derived and terpenoid-derived fragments, the total includes the major part of the known natural phenols.

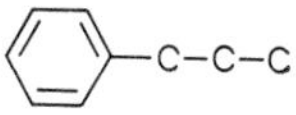

(59)

(a) Cinnamic acids

The highest oxidation state in which the C_3-side chain commonly occurs is in cinnamic (60), *p*-hydroxycinnamic (*p*-coumaric) (61), caffeic (62), ferulic (63), sinapic (64) and 3,4,5-trimethoxycinnamic (56) acids.

Many compounds possessing C_3-side chains at a lower level of oxidation are found in nature. Those in which no oxygen atoms are present in the side chain possess sufficient volatility to permit their isolation by distillation processes and thus to characterize them as members of the class of "essential

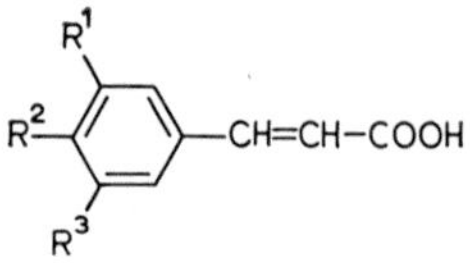

(60) R¹ = R² = R³ = H

(61) R¹ = R³ = H; R² = OH

(62) R¹ = H; R² = R³ = OH

(63) R¹ = H; R² = OH, R³ = OCH₃

(64) R¹ = R³ = OCH₃; R² = OH

(65) R¹ = R² = R³ = OCH₃

oils." Typical and familiar members of this group are eugenol (66), chavicol (67), safrol (68), and elemicin (69).

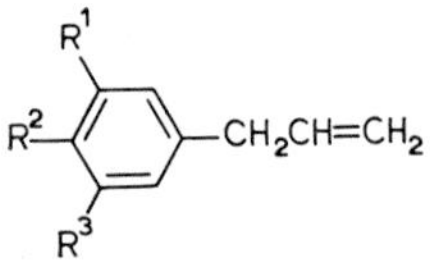

(66) R¹ = H; R² = OH; R³ = OCH₃

(67) R¹ = R³ = H; R² = OH

(68) R¹ = R² = —OCH₂O—; R³ = H

(69) R¹ = R² = R³ = OCH₃

While the 4-, 3,4-, and 3,4,5-hydroxylation patterns are by far the commonest in this group of compounds (and, as will become apparent, in all of the natural phenylpropane derivatives), there occur in some plants, notably in the *Umbelliferae*, compounds hydroxylated* in the 2,3,4- and 5-positions. Apiole (70) and dillapiole (71) are examples.

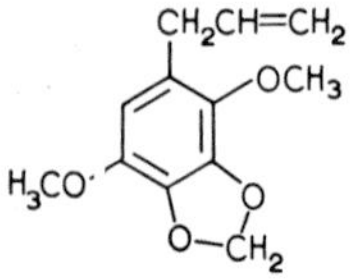

(70) 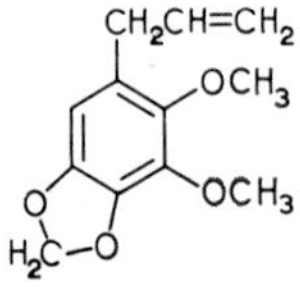   (71)

* Phenol ethers are regarded as equivalent to the corresponding phenols so far as nuclear hydroxylation is concerned.

Additional examples of departures from the 4- or 3,4- or 3,4,5-hydroxylation pattern are found in myristicin (72), *trans*-asarone (73) and croweacin (74).

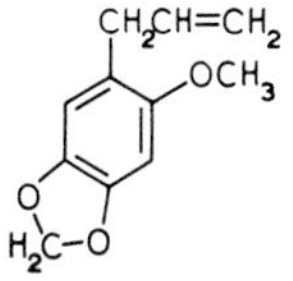

(72) 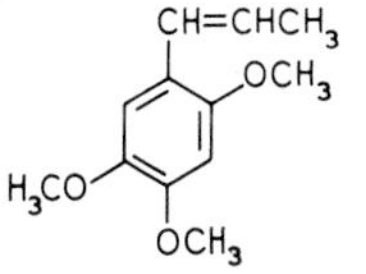   (73) 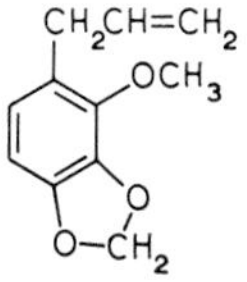   (74)

It is to be noted that in *trans*-asarone (73) the side chain is the 1-propenyl grouping; the more common C_3-unit is the allyl grouping (72, 74).

(b) Compounds with side chains of less or more than 3 carbon atoms

Numerous compounds are known that contain a side chain of less than three carbon atoms. While the relationship of these to the C_6–C_3 compounds is not known in all cases, it has been shown[13] that pungenin, the glucoside of 3,4-dihydroxyacetophenone (75) in *Picea pungens* owes its origin to a C_6–C_3 precursor.

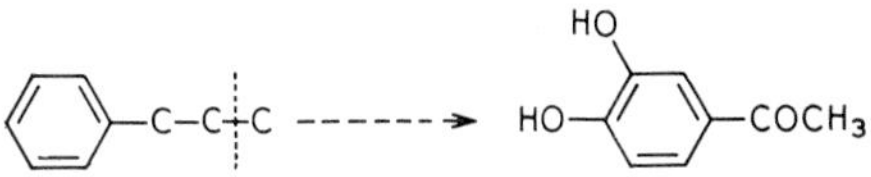

(75)

The biogenesis of certain other hydroxyacetophenones has not yet been established by experiment. While it is probable that picein, the aglucon of which is *p*-hydroxyacetophenone (76) owes its formation to the phenyl-propanoid pathway, it is by no means apparent whether paeonol (77) and xanthoxylin (78) are phenylpropane- or acetate-derived. The latter appears

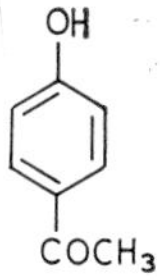

(76) 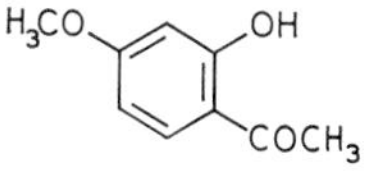   (77) 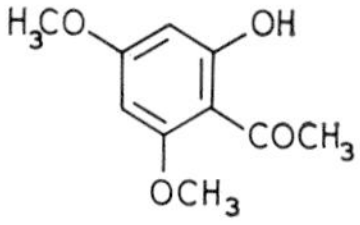   (78)

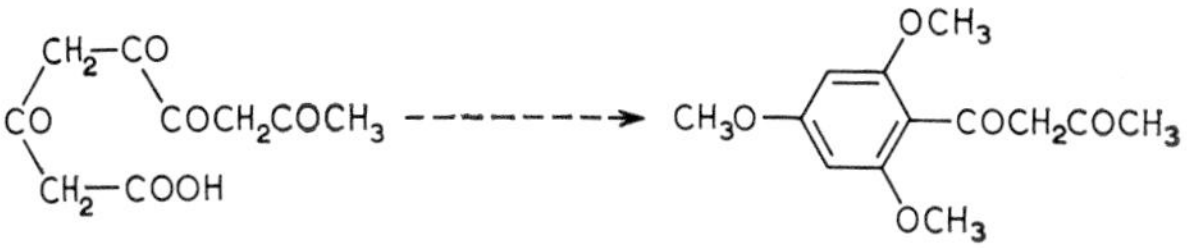

(79)

to be the more likely. The occurrence in nature of eugenone (79), which appears to be the product of the condensation of five C_2 units, would support the supposition that (78), at least, is derived from a different route from that which gives rise to (75). Acetophenone itself occurs in *Stirlingia latifolia*.

Benzaldehyde, benzoic acid and benzyl alcohol are all plant products, and numerous phenolic derivatives of them are well known: salicin, the glucoside of *o*-hydroxybenzyl alcohol; salicylaldehyde, vanillin, piperonal, anisaldehyde, salicylic acid, *p*-hydroxybenzoic acid, gallic and protocatechuic acids, and esters and glycosides of these occur naturally.

Extension of the side chain, probably by the addition of C_2 units, of phenylpropanoid precursors leads to compounds that possess the typical 3,4-dihydroxyphenyl ring attached, not to a C_3 fragment, but to a longer chain. Zingerone (80) and shogaol (81), both of which are found in plants of the *Zingiberaceae*, are interesting examples.

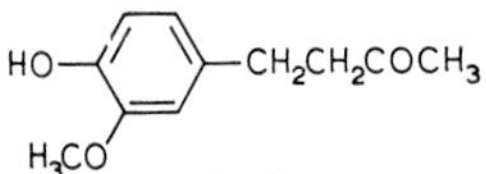

$$\text{HO}-\text{C}_6\text{H}_3(\text{H}_3\text{CO})-\text{CH}_2\text{CH}_2\text{COCH}_3$$
(80)

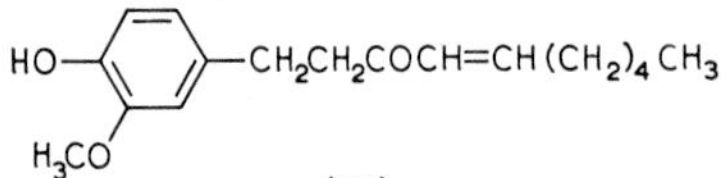

$$\text{HO}-\text{C}_6\text{H}_3(\text{H}_3\text{CO})-\text{CH}_2\text{CH}_2\text{COCH}=\text{CH}(\text{CH}_2)_4\text{CH}_3$$
(81)

Curcumin (82) is another example of a phenylpropane-derived compound possessing an extended side chain. It is interesting to note that *Curcuma* is a genus of the *Zingiberaceae*.

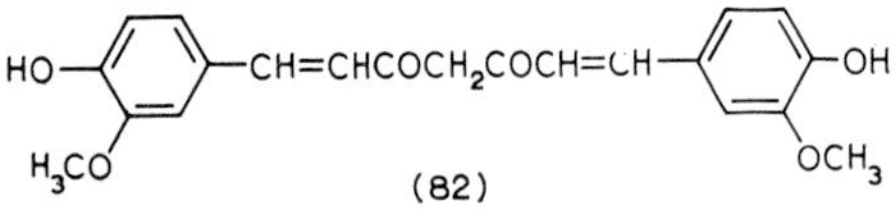

$$\text{HO}-\text{C}_6\text{H}_3(\text{H}_3\text{CO})-\text{CH}=\text{CHCOCH}_2\text{COCH}=\text{CH}-\text{C}_6\text{H}_3(\text{OCH}_3)-\text{OH}$$
(82)

The substituted 6-styryl-α-pyrones, kawain (83) and methysticin (84), and the related yangonin (85) belong to this same class.

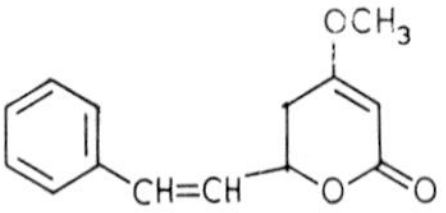

(83) 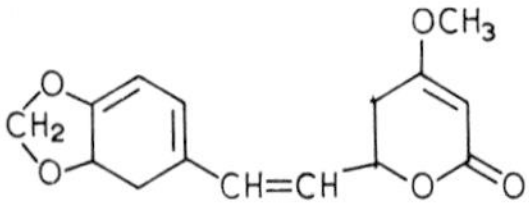   (84) 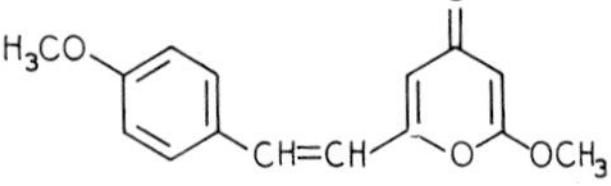   (85)

Yangonin (85) is an ether of the cyclized form of the hypothetical precursor (86), which can be regarded as having arisen by the union of a phenylpropane derivative with two C_2 units.

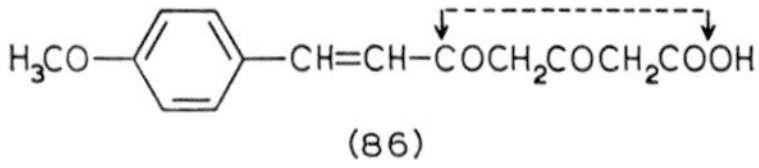

$$\text{H}_3\text{CO}-\text{C}_6\text{H}_4-\text{CH}=\text{CH}-\text{COCH}_2\text{COCH}_2\text{COOH}$$
(86)

It is apparent from the above examples that degradation and extension of the side chain can modify a C_6–C_3 precursor to produce a wide variety of compounds. The hallmark of the phenylpropanoid substances is the presence of the 3,4-dihydroxyl grouping in the aromatic ring. The 4-hydroxy- and the 3,4,5-trihydroxy substitution patterns can be referred with considerable assurance to the same origin; but when 2,4- or 2,4,6-hydroxylation is present biogenetic origins cannot in all cases be assumed with safety.

(c) *Lignin and lignanes*

The structure of the complex polymer "lignin" has been a subject of inquiry for a great many years, and up to the present time no positive conclusions have been reached regarding the total structure of this widely distributed and important substance. It is generally agreed that lignin arises by the polymerization (probably oxidative) of a phenolic phenylpropane derivative, with the formation of a complex cross-linked macromolecule in which carbon–carbon and carbon–oxygen bonds have formed during the condensation process.

Extensive experiments by Freudenberg[14] have led him to the conclusion that the central role in lignin formation is played by coniferin (87), the glucoside of coniferyl alcohol (88).

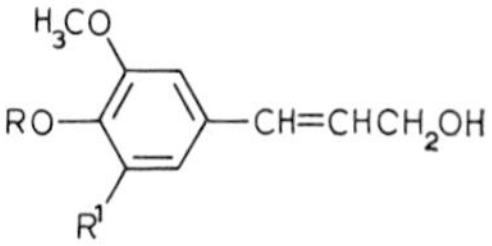

(87) R = D-glucopyranosyl, R^1 = H

(88) R = H, R^1 = H

(89) R = H, R^1 = OCH₃

It has been found that coniferyl alcohol, with the agency of an enzyme (peroxidase) and either hydrogen peroxide or atmospheric oxygen, can be converted, through a number of identifiable intermediate oligomers, into a polymeric substance that has all of the chemical and physical characteristics of lignin. Whether the "synthetic" material is indeed identical with natural lignin has been a matter of some dispute among workers in the field, since in the isolation of lignin some alteration of its structure from the "native" condition undoubtedly occurs, and the establishment of the identity of two amorphous, polymeric substances is difficult to achieve[15].

Coniferyl alcohol is an extremely sensitive substance and is readily oxidized, while coniferin, present in the cambial sap of conifers, is a substance relatively stable to oxidation. The relationship of coniferin to phenylpropanoid compounds of other kinds is shown by the demonstration that phenylalanine is converted into coniferin in spruce saplings. Freudenberg has proposed the following outline of the events that lead to lignin formation.

Shikimic acid route → coniferin (cambial tissue)

↓ β-glucosidase of xylem

coniferyl alcohol

↓ xylem oxidase

lignin

The details of the oxidation process that leads to lignin formation as the final result are still not clear, but certain indications of the nature of the transformation can be gained from the observations that coniferin and 3,4-dimethoxycinnamyl alcohol are not susceptible to the ready oxidation to which the free phenol is subject; and that under controlled experimental conditions a variety of the products of less extensive oxidation and polymerization have been isolated.

It is relevant to the discussion to introduce at this point a class of widely occurring C_{18} compounds, known as lignans, which are dimers of C_6–C_3 units. These are known in a variety of forms, including diarylbutane derivatives such as guaiaretic acid (90), tetrahydrofuran derivatives such as olivil (91)

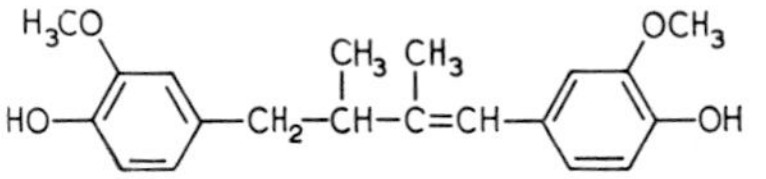

(90)

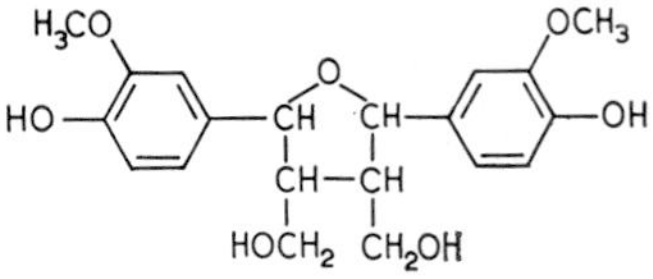

(91)

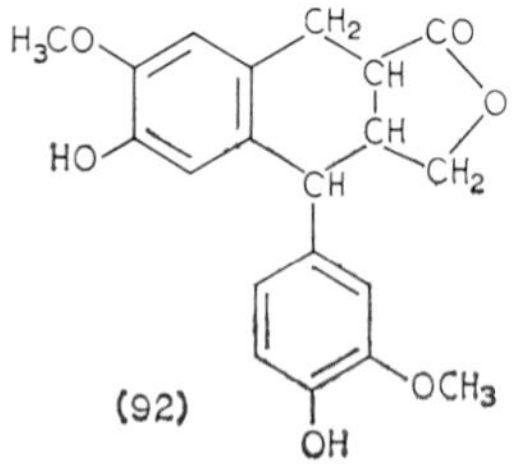

(92)

and α-phenyltetralin derivatives such as conidendrin (92). The examples (90–92) are only representative of a large number of lignans known in nature; numerous modifications in detail of these structural types occur. By far the largest number of the natural lignans possess the 4-hydroxy-3-methoxy-phenyl grouping seen in (90–92), and also characteristic of coniferyl alcohol. It was first suggested by Erdtman[16] that a rational scheme of biogenesis of this class of compounds can be devised, based upon an initial oxidation of a prototype substance (93) followed by condensations along recognized mechanistic lines. In the following demonstrations of a typical sequence illustrating this hypothesis a two-electron oxidation will be employed for convenience, although a completely analogous scheme can be based upon a one-electron change.

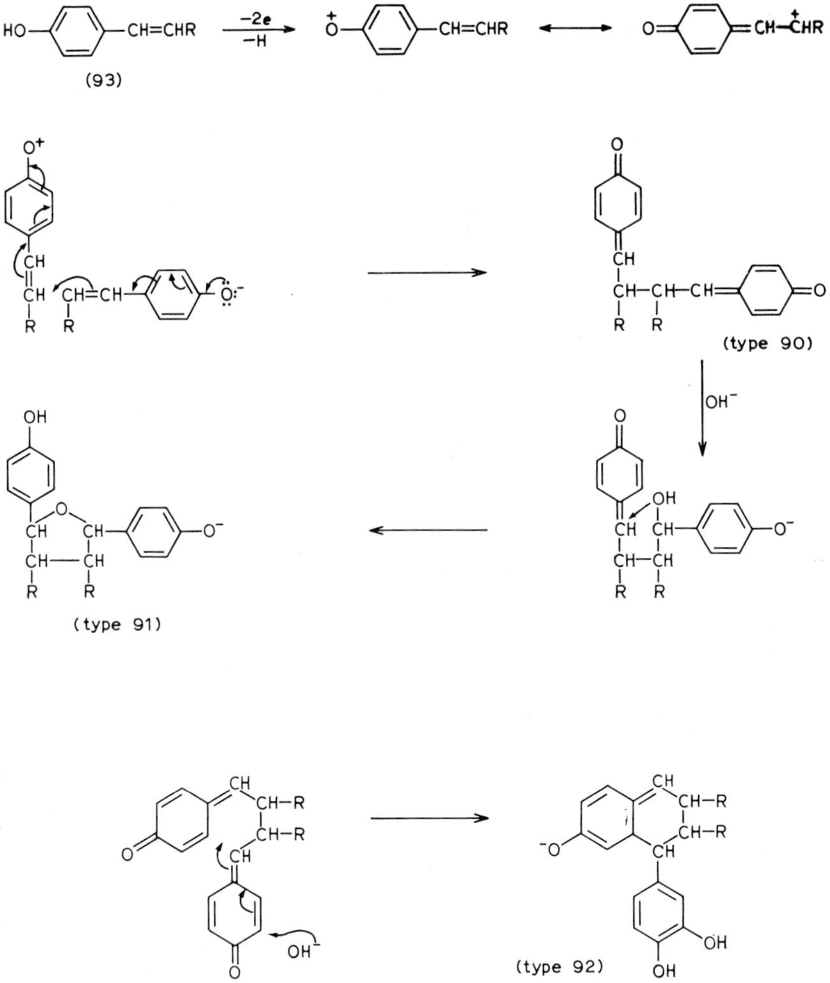

(93)

(type 90)

(type 91)

(type 92)

In Freudenberg's experiments in which coniferyl alcohol was oxidized in the presence of an enzyme preparation, a number of "intermediate" oxidation products have been isolated (95–98).

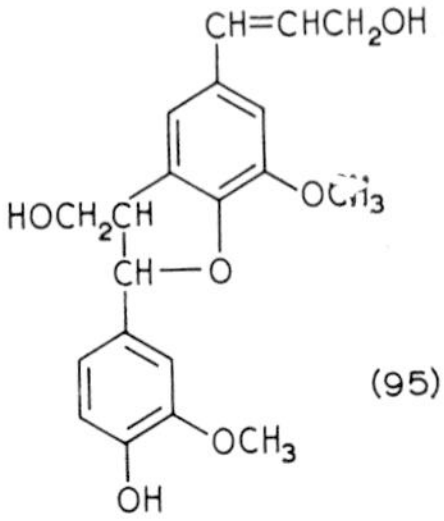

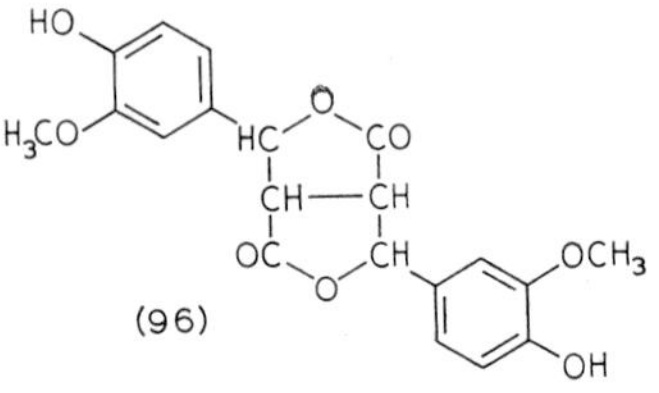

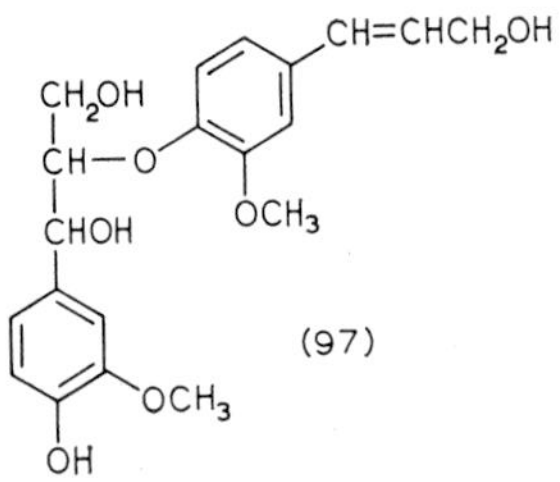

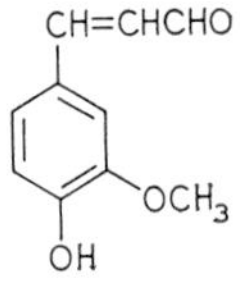

The derivation of these by way of an initial oxidation of coniferyl alcohol is readily formulated; for example, (95) and (97).

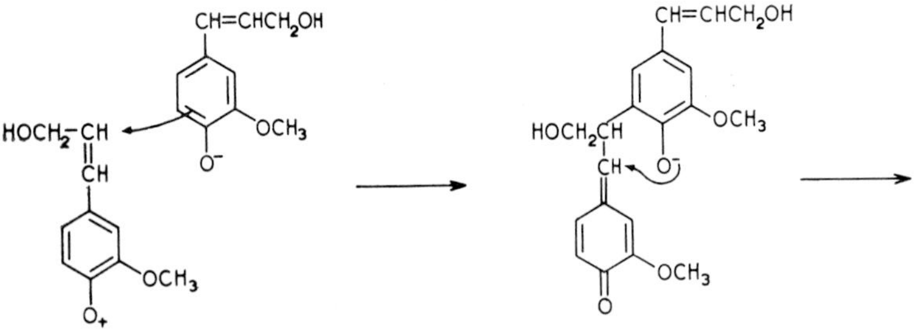

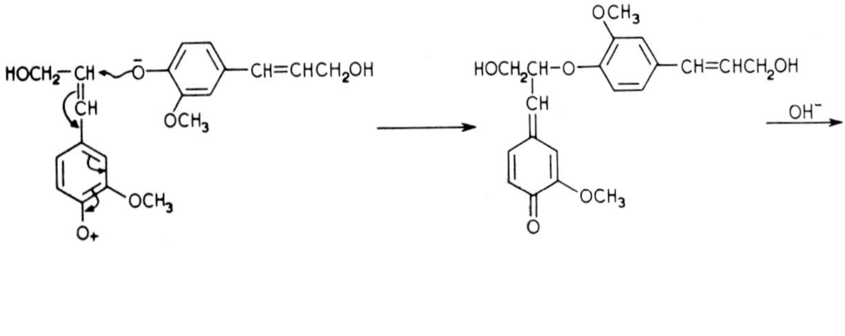

That the continuation of processes of oxidation and condensation such as those described above is the probable source of lignin is indicated by the facts that (a) coniferyl alcohol is enzymatically oxidized to a polymer indistinguishable from lignin; (b) oxidation of methylated lignin leads to isohemipinic acid; and (c) the number of hydroxyl groups in lignin is less than one per C_6–C_3 unit. The production of as much as 25% of vanillin by the oxidation of spruce wood indicates that the 3-methoxy-4-hydroxyphenyl residue exists in lignin or is readily freed in the oxidation procedure.

While there is no proper basis at the present time for writing a "complete" structural formula for the lignin molecule, some essays in this direction have been made. Adler[17] has written a structure for a portion of the molecule of a

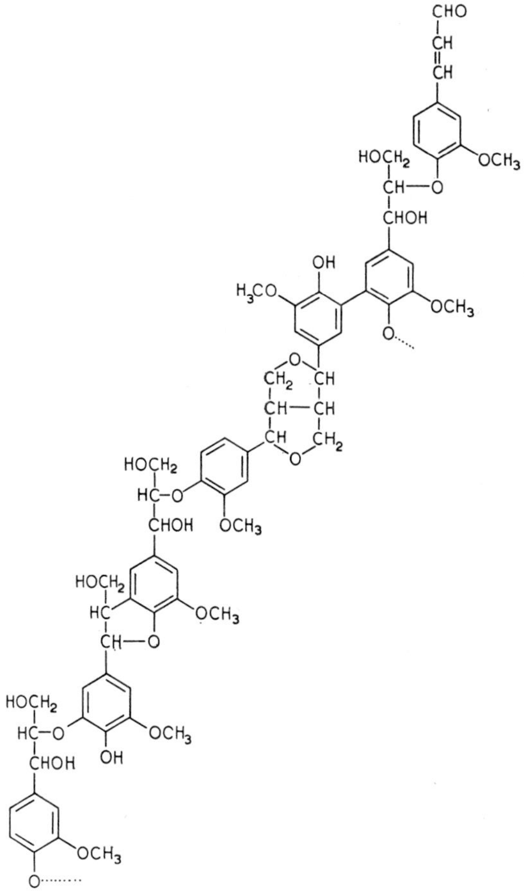

Fig. 1. Suggested partial structure for gymnosperm lignin.

gymnosperm lignin (98) that is based upon some of the observations discussed in the foregoing pages (Fig. 1).

Lignins based structurally upon a coniferyl alcohol monomer are characteristic of gymnosperms. Angiosperm lignin, on the other hand, contains
residues derived from syringyl alcohol (89). The exact nature of the process
by which syringyl alcohol might be incorporated into a co-polymer with
coniferyl alcohol is not known. It has been observed that syringyl alcohol is
not polymerized by enzymatic oxidation as is coniferyl alcohol; the presence
of the additional methoxyl group in the ring would prevent those condensation steps such as that leading to type (95) products. Nevertheless, when
coniferyl alcohol is polymerized in the presence of syringyl alcohol, the latter
is incorporated into the final "lignin."

It should be emphasized that the picture of lignin formation that has
been presented must be regarded as hypothetical, for although coniferyl
alcohol is incorporated into lignin in the living plant and is converted into
a synthetic lignin *in vitro*, this cannot be regarded as proof that coniferyl
alcohol is the obligatory precursor of lignin in nature. The evidence that it
is indeed the true precursor is, however, substantial; and no alternative
suggestions have been supported by convincing evidence. Agreement upon
the exact nature of the process of lignin formation is not complete, but the
present state of our information supports the views that (*a*) the precursor
of lignin is a phenylpropane derivative derived from the shikimic acid pathway; (*b*) the polymerization of the C_6–C_3 precursor probably involves an
oxidative process that may be regarded as a phenol dehydrogenation reaction;
and (*c*) an excellent case can be made that coniferyl alcohol is indeed the
precursor, although the exact point at which the methoxyl groups of lignin
are introduced has not been established with certainty. No acceptable
"total" structure of lignin can be written. The molecular size of lignin in
the plant is not known with certainty, although molecular weights of
Freudenberg's "synthetic" lignins have been determined.

4. Flavonoid and related compounds

The union of a C_6–C_3 unit with an aromatic ring leads to the structural unit
(99), known as the "flavonoid" structure because its occurrence in nature is
most common in the flavones (100).

(99)   (100)

The naturally occurring flavonoid compounds are, except for flavone itself, hydroxylated (phenolic) substances; and their hydroxylation patterns give a clue, substantiated in recent years by direct evidence, to their origins and interrelationships.

By far the greatest number of flavonoid compounds possess two distinct patterns of hydroxylation in the two aromatic nuclei: one, designated as the A ring (see 100), is most commonly 2-, 2,4- or 2,4,6-hydroxylated — that is, in the typical "acetate-derived" pattern. The other, the B ring, is most commonly 4-, 3,4- or 3,4,5-hydroxylated — that is, in the pattern characteristic of the phenylpropane derivatives that arise via the shikimic acid pathway. Some of these patterns are exemplified in the structures of chrysin (101), apigenin (102), luteolin (103), fisetin (104), butein (105), epiafzelechin (106), myricetin (107) and delphinidin (108).

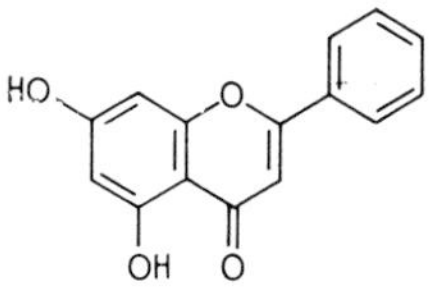

(101) 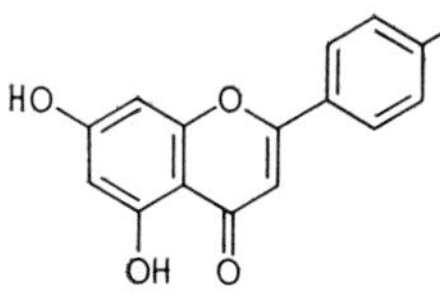   (102) 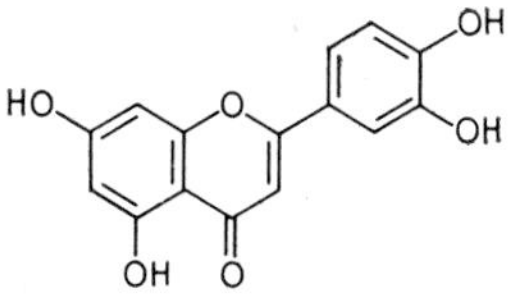   (103)

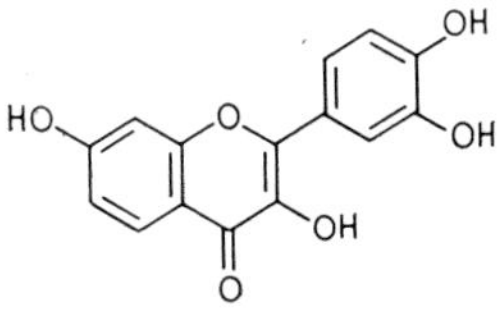

(104) 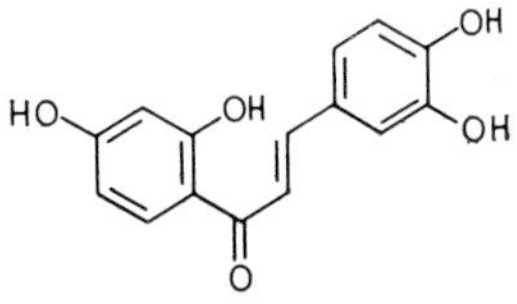   (105)

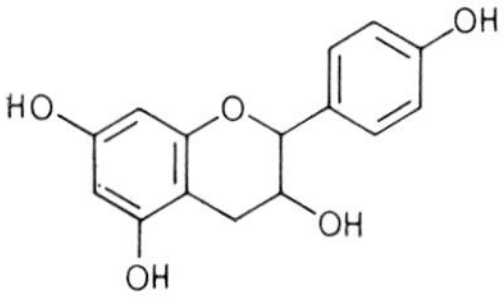

(106) 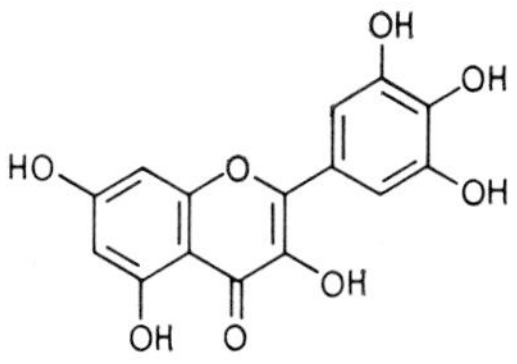   (107) 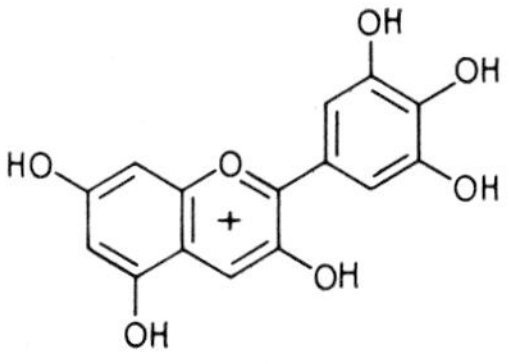   (108)

These various examples of flavonoid compounds are given to point out another feature of the structural differentiation between them; that is, the state of oxidation of the C_3 unit that joins the A and B rings. The forms in which flavonoid substances occur in nature range from the most highly reduced C_3 unit found in the catechins (flavan-3-ols) and dihydrochalcones to the most highly oxidized in the flavonols*:

A—CH₂—CHOH—CHOH—B	flavan-3-ols (catechins)
A—CO—CH₂—CH₂—B	hydrochalcones
A—CO—CH=CH—B	chalcones
A—CO—CH₂—CHOH—B	flavanones
A—CHOH—CHOH—CHOH—B	leucoanthocyanidins (flavan-3,4-diols)
A—CO—CH₂—CO—B	flavones
A—CH₂—CO—CO—B	anthocyanidins
A—CO—CO—CH₂—B	benzalcoumaranones (aurones)
A—CO—CHOH—CHOH—B	flavanonols
A—CO—CO—CHOH—B	flavonols

The lowest oxidation level, represented by the structure (109), is not known in nature.

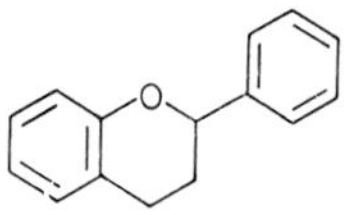

(109)

(a) Chalcones and flavanones

Polyhydroxychalcones that occur free in nature have a resorcinol-derived A ring: that is, they do not possess a 2,4,6-trihydroxy A ring. If more than two hydroxyl groups are present in the A ring, the third is found in the 3- or

---

* In all of the above structures, the A ring is assumed to carry an *ortho*-hydroxyl group which engages in ring closure to form the chromanol, chromanone, etc., ring. Enolization, loss of the elements of water or flavylium salt formation are processes that do not affect oxidation level, and thus flavones, anthocyanidins and aurones, of quite different structures, all possess the equivalent of two —CO— and one —CH₂— groups. To illustrate this, the formal conversion of the type A—CH₂COCO—B to the usual anthocyanidin structure is as follows:

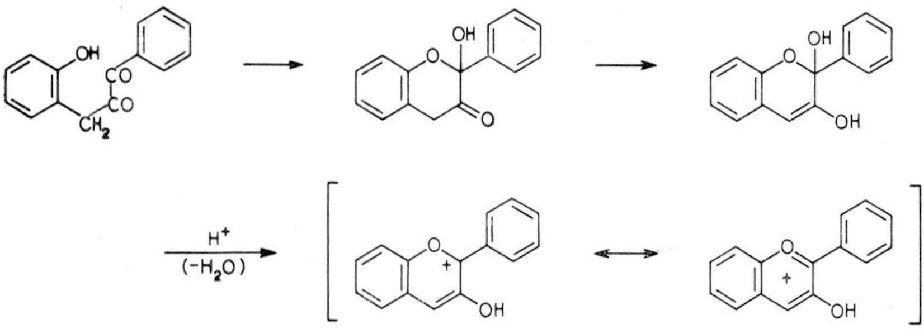

5-position. Examples of known chalcones are butein (105), stillopsidin (110) and okanin (111).

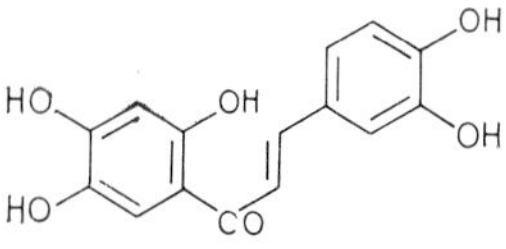

(110) 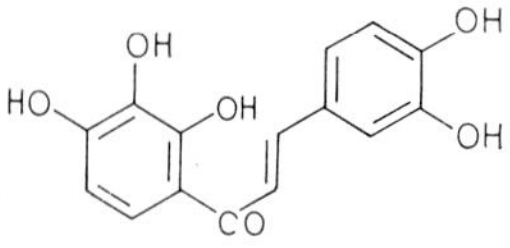   (111)

This is not to say that the *pattern* of the chalcone (112) does not occur in nature; but this hypothetical chalcone always occurs in the form of the isomeric flavanone (113). The non-existence of the chalcone is to be ascribed to the stabilization afforded to the cyclic isomer by hydrogen bonding between the 4-carbonyl and 5-hydroxyl group (113).

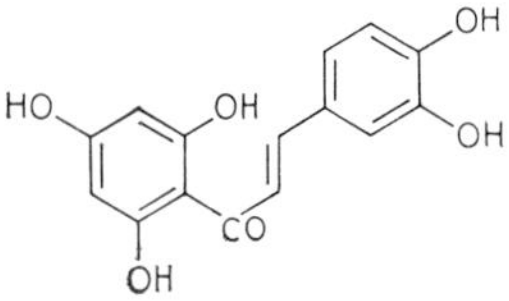

(112) 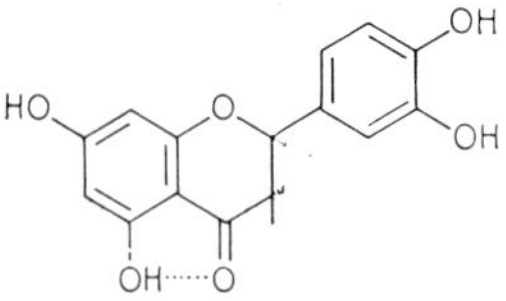   (113)

Equilibria between chalcone and flavanone exist in other cases; butein can be readily converted by dilute acid to the corresponding flavanone, butin, and indeed there is no good evidence on the question of whether, in such cases, both isomers exist in the plant. In the case of phloroglucinol-A ring compounds (112,113) the chalcone is not free in the plant, except when one of the hydroxyl groups *ortho* to the carbonyl group is attached to a sugar, as in salipurposide (114), and thus is not available for hydrogen bonding.

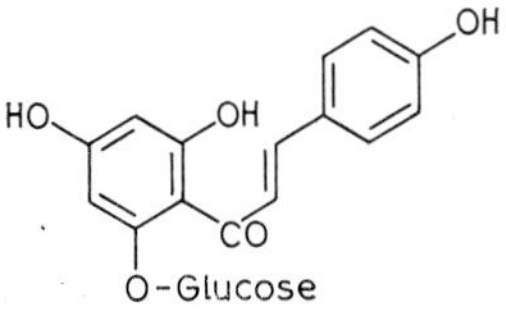

(114)

The occurrence of chalcones in nature is rather limited, but flavanones are numerous and common. Both of these classes of compounds occur in most, but not all, cases as glycosides, in which the sugar is usually attached to the

7-hydroxyl group (4'-hydroxyl as chalcones are numbered). Typical examples are coreopsin (115) and hesperidin (116).

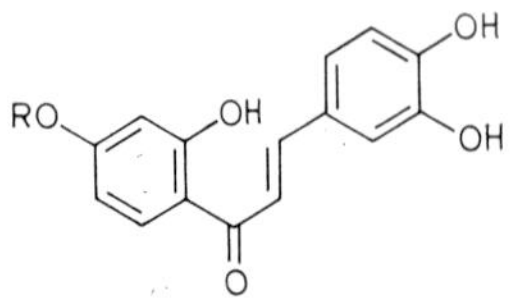

(115)
R = glucosyl

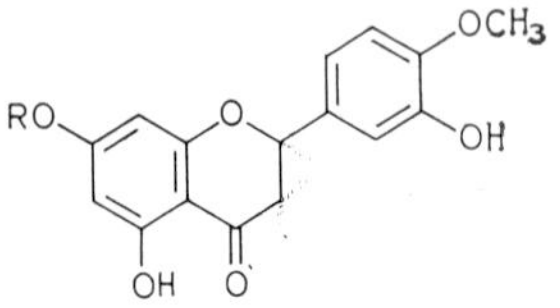

(116)
R = rhamnoglucosyl (rutinosyl)

Glycosylation is known in other positions as well: butrin is the 3',7-di-glucoside of butin (the flavanone isomeric with butein), and the flavanone corresponding to (114), naringenin 5-glucoside, occurs along with the chalcone. It is to be noted that methylation of the phenolic hydroxyl groups also occurs (see 116): many cases of O-methylation will be encountered in other flavonoid compounds to be dealt with in this chapter.

Dihydrochalcones are rare. The best known is the important glucoside phlorizin (117), occurring in the root bark of *Malus* spp. Phlorizin is of

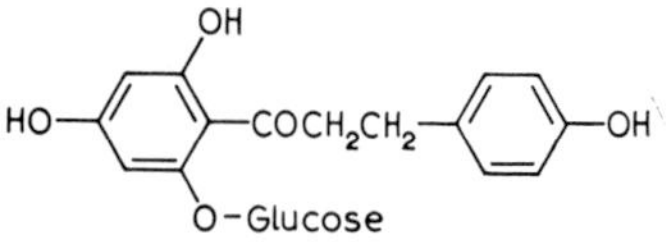

(117)

special interest by reason of its power to produce glucosuria in animals by inhibiting the reabsorption of glucose in the renal tubules.

(b) Flavones, aurones and flavonols

Examples of flavones and flavonols have been given (101, 104, 107). Aurones, isomeric with flavones, and typified by sulfuretin (118), are of uncommon occurrence, and deserve comment on two matters. Both the resorcinol-A

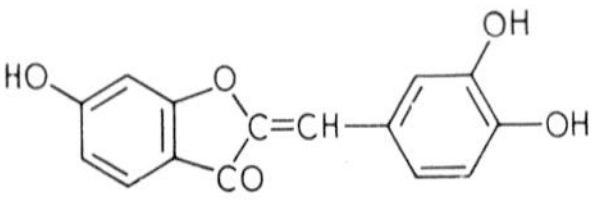

(118)

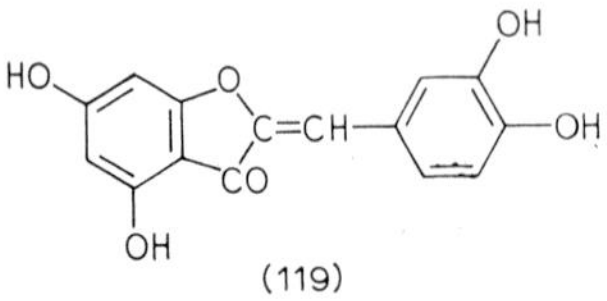

(119)

ring type exemplified by (118) and the phloroglucinol-A ring type as in aureusidin (119) are known in the natural aurones. The former are invariably found in association with the corresponding chalcones (*e.g.*, sulfuretin with butein, etc.), and in view of the ready conversion of chalcones (such as butein) into aurones (such as sulfuretin) by oxidation (even in air in alcohol solution, but more rapidly at higher pH) it is quite likely that the aurones are formed by the direct oxidation of chalcones in the plant.

It is interesting to note that the oxidation of (105) to (118) can be formulated most simply by postulating an initial oxidation that resembles the first step in the conversion of coniferyl alcohol to the dimeric oxidation products described earlier.

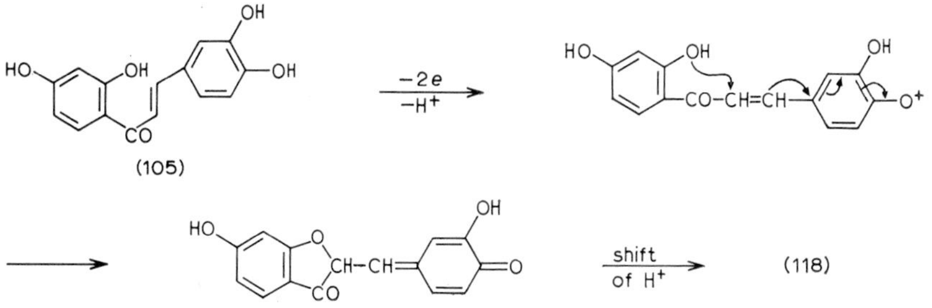

(105)

(118)

Although aurones and flavones are isomeric, the latter are widespread in their distribution in nature while the aurones are found in a relatively few plants. This suggests that there is some fundamental difference in the early stages of their formation; but what this difference is, or, indeed, what the actual immediate precursors of the flavones are, is unknown. However, since it is likely that chalcones are converted to aurones it seems probable that the flavone structure is derived from a compound in which the heterocyclic ring is already present before the final stages of oxidation.

Flavones are known in nature with no hydroxyl groups (flavone itself) and with hydroxylation as high as that in nobiletin, 3',4',5,6,7,8-hexa-methoxyflavone (120).

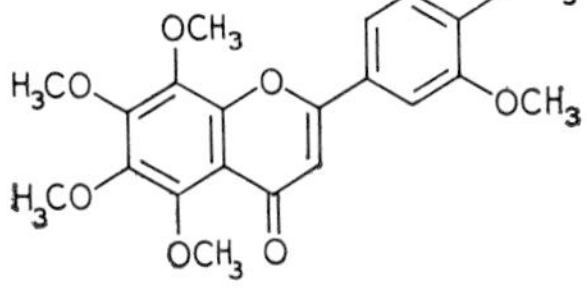

(120)

Certain metabolic peculiarities of higher plants are indicated by the chemical structures of the compounds they elaborate. The *Rutaceae*, for example, are notable for the prevalence in plants of this family of highly O-methylated flavones. Nobiletin (120) is one example; others are auranetin (121), pon-kanetin (122) and meliternatin (123).

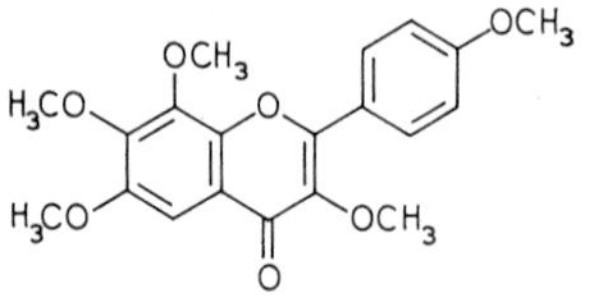

(121) 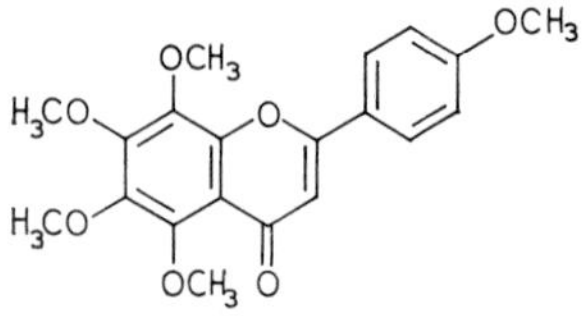   (122)

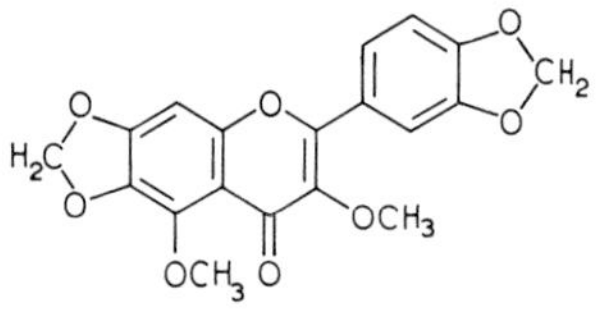

(123)

Flavonols, or 3-hydroxyflavones, are represented by quercetin (124), the various glycosides of which (quercitrin, isoquercitrin, rutin, hyperin, quer-cimeritrin and others) are found widely in nature. Kampferol (125) and myricetin (126), also in various glycosidic combination, are well known:

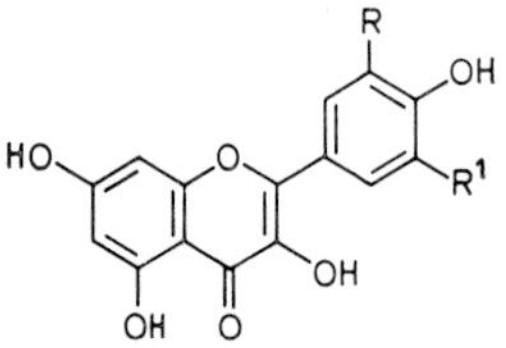

(124) R = OH, R¹ = H
(125) R = R¹ = H
(126) R = R¹ = OH

The biosynthetic origin of the flavonoid compounds has been clearly de-monstrated in recent years by a number of studies. The results of these can be summarized in the following scheme:

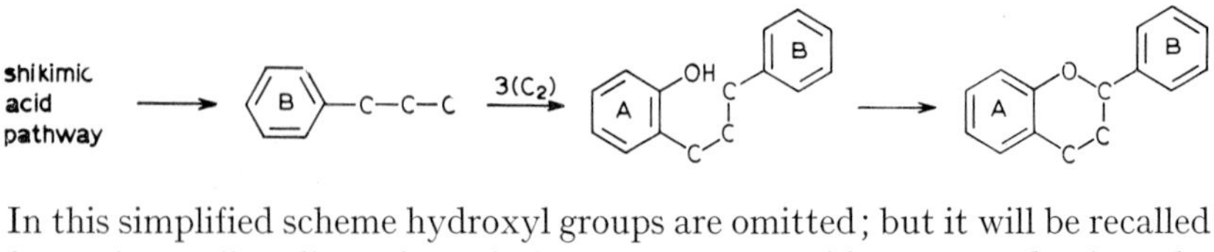

In this simplified scheme hydroxyl groups are omitted; but it will be recalled from the earlier discussion of the phenylpropanoid compounds that the B ring is typically 3,4-dihydroxylated (as in quercetin), and the acetate-derived A ring is most commonly 2,4,6-trihydroxylated. It is apparent from the examples that have been given that hydroxyl groups can be introduced or removed (relative to the "typical" pattern), and thus a very large number of different compounds can be formed.

The influence of flavones and flavonols upon plant (in particular, flower) coloration is relatively slight. These compounds and their glycosides are seldom deeper in color than yellow, and thus their pigmenting power in the low concentrations in which they are present in plant tissues is usually minor. Most yellow flowers are pigmented by carotenoids. Since heavy metal salts (usually chelated) of 3- and 5-hydroxylated flavones and flavonols are more intensely colored than the free compounds, it has been suggested that flavone–metal complexes may play a part in the pigmentation of some yellow flowers. Support for this idea is found in the fact that anthocyanin–metal complexes are known to occur in some flowers and probably increase the blueness of their colors.

The chalcones and aurones form a special class of plant pigments. The deeply yellow flowers of many species of composites (for example, in *Dahlia*, *Coreopsis*, *Bidens*, *Cosmos*) contain pigments of these classes, as do yellow *Antirrhinum* flowers.

(c) Anthocyanins

The anthocyanins are the most striking and conspicuous pigments of the plant world. They provide the pink, red, blue and purple colorations of most flowers, fruits and leaves. Anthocyanins, being both salts and glycosides, are quite water soluble and are readily extracted from plant tissues by aqueous acids, from which they can be precipitated as picrates or lead salts and eventually obtained crystalline as the chlorides.

Anthocyanins are glycosides of anthocyanidins[18]. The latter form a surprisingly small group of structural types that are variations of a relatively simple fundamental nucleus. Most of the known anthocyanins are glycosides (usually at 3 or at 3 and 5) of one of the aglycons (127–133).

pelargonidin (127): R = R¹ = H
cyanidin   (128): R = H, R¹ = OH
delphinidin (129): R = R¹ = OH
peonidin   (130): R = H, R¹ = OCH₃
petunidin   (131): R = OH, R¹ = OCH₃
malvidin   (132): R = R¹ = OCH₃
hirsutidin   (133): R = R¹ = OCH₃; —OCH₃ at 7

The wide variations in, for example, flower colors can be understood when it is noted that (*a*) monosides, biosides and dimonosides of these, at the 3- or 3,5-hydroxyl groups can exist; (*b*) mixtures of several anthocyanins can occur together; and (*c*) changes in cellular pH or in the content of heavy metal ions can exist in various plants or even in the same plant under different growing conditions. In general, pelargonidin glycosides are found in scarlet, cyanidin glycosides in crimson and delphinidin glycosides in blue flowers. Methoxyl groups endow the pigments with redder shades than the corresponding unmethylated compounds: peonidin is likely to be redder than cyanidin (in a flower petal), malvidin redder than delphinidin, etc.

An additional variation in anthocyanin structure is introduced by the attachment of an acyl group to one of the hydroxyl groups of a sugar residue. These "complex anthocyanins" yield, on alkaline hydrolysis, an anthocyanidin glycoside and an organic acid; on acid hydrolysis, an anthocyanidin, sugar(s) and the organic acid. For example, delphinin chloride yields delphinidin (chloride), 2 mols of glucose and 2 mols of *p*-hydroxybenzoic acid; gentianin is a *p*-hydroxycinnamoyl derivative of a delphinidin glucoside; and monardaein (chloride) yields pelargonidin, glucose, *p*-hydroxycinnamic acid and malonic acid on hydrolysis. Gallic and syringic acids have also been found as constituents of other complex anthocyanins.

(*d*) Catechins and flavan-3,4-diols

The most reduced form of the C_3 unit in the natural flavonoid compounds is found in the catechins (*e.g.*, 106). Catechin itself (134) possesses the common 5,7,3',4'-hydroxylation pattern, and gallocatechin (135) is also known.

(134) R = H

(135) R = OH

The stereoisomers of (134) and (135) are also known: these are epicatechin and epigallocatechin. It can be seen that the structure (134, 135) of the catechins contains two asymmetric carbon atoms at C-2 and C-3. Thus, the aryl residue and the hydroxyl group can occupy positions *cis* or *trans* to each other, and it is known that in the *epi*-series the compounds are of the *cis*-configuration. The earliest evidence for this structural assignment was the catalytic reduction of cyanidin chloride to ($\pm$) epicatechin — a reaction that is to be expected to lead to the *cis* introduction of the hydrogen atoms. Later evidence of other kinds has confirmed this conclusion.

The flavan-3,4-diols are of special interest for a number of reasons. They are often called by the trivial name* of "leucoanthocyanidins" because upon heating with mineral acids they are converted into flavylium salts. "Leucocyanidin" (140) yields cyanidin under these conditions, "leucodelphinidin" (141) yields delphinidin (as the chlorides, if hydrochloric acid is used). It is of interest to note that among the flavan-3,4-diols are found a number of compounds of which the corresponding anthocyanidin is not a natural pigment. Robinetindiol (142) and melacacidin (143) are examples.

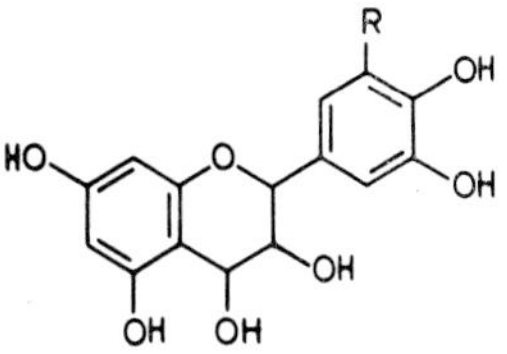

(140) R = H
(141) R = OH

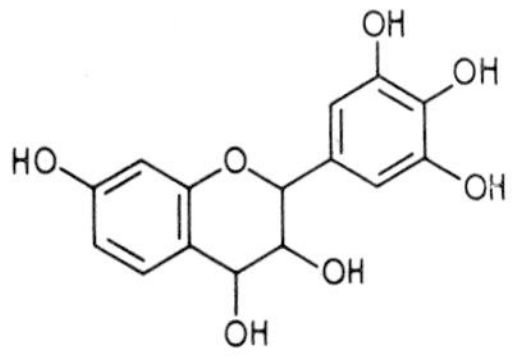

(142)

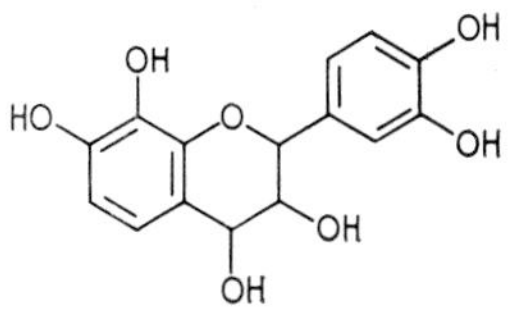

(143)

The flavan-3,4-diols corresponding to a number of the "natural" anthocyanidins—for example, "leucocyanidin" (5,7,3′4′-tetrahydroxyflavan-3,4-diol) — have also been discovered in nature.

The polyhydroxyflavan-3,4-diols occur in many natural sources, but seem to be most characteristic of woody tissues. They have been identified as the substances chiefly responsible for the puckering and astringent taste of certain materials, properties that have usually been ascribed to the "tannin" content[19].

(e) Flavonoid tannins

Both the catechins and the flavan-3,4-diols are commonly associated in nature with condensed, polymeric phenolic substances that are known under the general, but undefinitive, name of "tannins." Tannins are so called not by reason of their inclusion within any well-defined structural class of compounds, but because of their ability to "tan" leather or precipitate gelatin from solution. Tannins may be grouped into two broad categories: the "hydrolyzable" tannins, which consist of esters of gallic acid, and compounds derived from it, with sugars; and "condensed" tannins, which are polymeric substances derived from flavonoid monomers. Along with the condensed,

---

* FREUDENBERG AND WEINGES, *Tetrahedron*, 8 (1960) 336, have proposed a new system of nomenclature for flavonoid compounds and suggest the term "proanthocyanidins" for this class of compounds.

or flavonoid, tannins are found complex phenolic substances of ill-defined nature that are also polymeric, called "phlobaphenes."

The manner in which the condensed tannins are formed from the mono-meric flavan-3-ols and flavan-3,4-diols is not known with certainty. Indeed, there is no agreement as to the extent to which simple (acid-catalyzed) condensation polymerization, on the one hand, or oxidative condensation, on the other, occurs. Experimental studies on the monomeric flavan deriva-tives have shown that they are very susceptible to polymerization under the influence of heat (in aqueous solution) or acids. Studies of a series of model compounds in these series have shown that the hydroxyl groups at 3,5 and 3' (144) are not essential for these self-condensations but that those at 7 and 4', and in view of what is to be said, that at 4, are chiefly responsible for acid-catalyzed self-condensation (145).

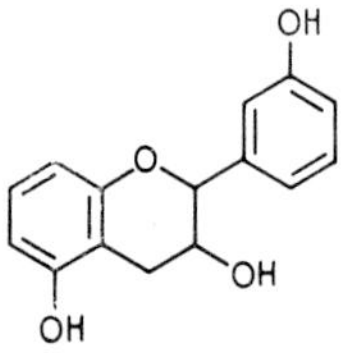

(144) 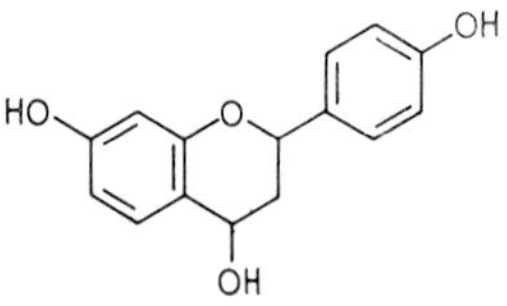   (145)

The hydroxyl groups in the 7,4- and 4'-positions lend to these compounds the reactive characteristics of p-hydroxybenzyl alcohol, which may be re-garded as the simplest prototype of (145), and which is known to undergo exceedingly ready polymerization under the influence of acids. Indeed, an even simpler prototype would be the condensation of phenol with formal-dehyde, which is known to yield polymeric products.

Experiments by Freudenberg and his collaborators on the self-condensa-tion of catechin have led to the isolation of a crystalline dimer which has been named "dicatechin." Dicatechin has the properties of a tannin, while catechin itself has not. From the properties and analytical data of dicatechin, the structure (146) has been proposed.

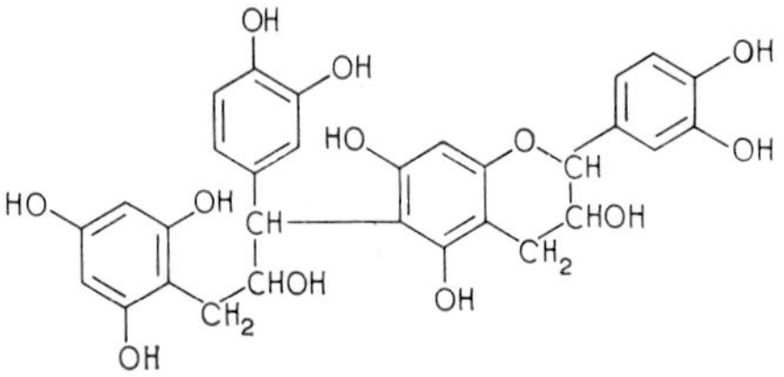

(146)

The formation of (146) is readily comprehensible if one regards it as the result of acid-catalyzed formation of the carbonium ion (147), followed by normal electrophilic substitution of this into the reactive 6- (or 8-) position of another catechin molecule.

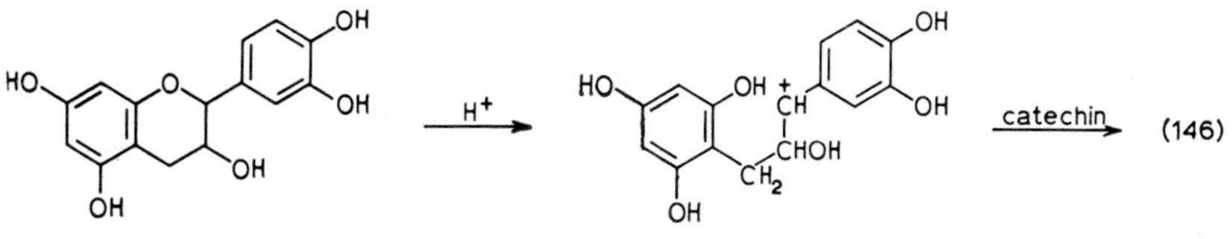

(147)

A continuation of this process by substitution either at the 2-position of the catechin residue of (146), or into the phloroglucinol ring, can lead to complex phenolic polymers. In the case of the flavan-3,4-diols another reactive, benzyl alcohol-like position is available, and condensation at this, the 4-position, is also to be anticipated (148).

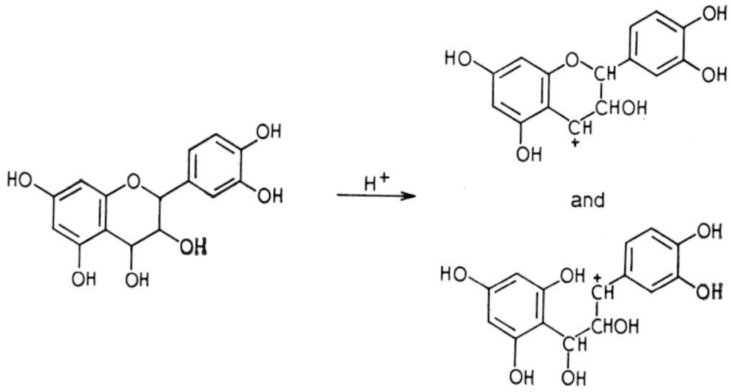

and

(148)

The summary of this view of tannin formation is that the flavan derivatives, formed in sites of metabolic activity (leaves, cambial tissue), are transported to woody tissue where they are deposited, and in time undergo condensation to polymeric polyphenols.

An alternative view is that tannin formation is an oxidative process that proceeds by way of quinone formation and subsequent polymerization. Natural processes of this sort are well known; perhaps the most pertinent is the browning of plant tissues by the action of oxygen upon suitable polyphenols under the influence of polyphenol oxidases.

Perhaps the truth of the matter is that both processes occur, and that the highly polymeric phlobaphenes, which are dark in color, represent the result of both oxidative and non-oxidative polymerization. Certainly it can be said that in view of the facts that compounds such as catechin and the corresponding flavan-3,4-diol are clearly susceptible to the ionic condensation processes described, and are very sensitive to oxidation, both points of view can be strongly supported by persuasive argument. It will require further experimental evidence to demonstrate the true nature of the processes of tannin formation. What seems to be generally accepted is that the polyhydroxyflavan-3-ols and -flavan-3,4-diols are the forerunners of the polymeric end-products.

(f) Hydrolyzable tannins

A widely distributed structural entity found in plants is the 3,4,5-trihydroxyphenyl grouping. It is found as a part of the structures of such compounds as delphinidin (108), myricetin (107), and gallocatechin. It is much more widespread, however, as gallic acid (149) itself, esterified with sugar molecules and as ellagic acid (150), also present in esterified form as the diacid, attached to sugars. These gallic and ellagic acid esters[20] are the "hydrolyzable tannins".

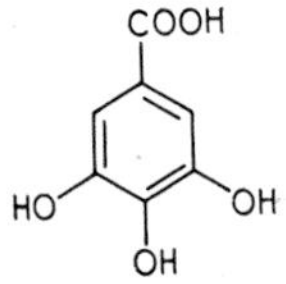

(149) 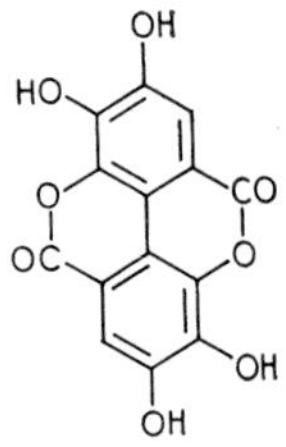   (150)

Hamamelitannin, the tannin of *Hamamelis virginica*, is a digallic ester of a hexose, which yields gallic acid and hamamelose (151) on hydrolysis.

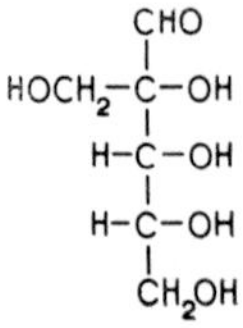

(151) 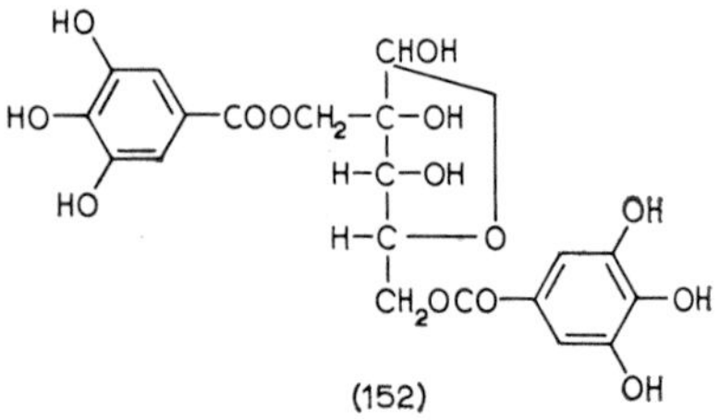   (152)

The structure (152) has been assigned to the tannin, although final confirmation of this is still lacking.

Chinese gallotannin is a penta-(*m*-digalloyl)-β-glucose with the probable structure (153).

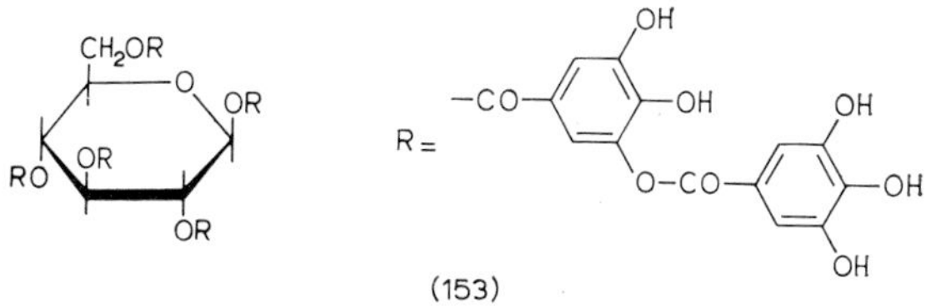

(153)

Structure (153) is somewhat idealized, however, since the tannin as isolated is undoubtedly a mixture in which there is an average of somewhat less than 10 mols of gallic acid per mol of glucose.

The ellagitannins form a group of substances closely allied to (and probably derived in nature from) the polygalloylglucoses. A typical tannin of this class is corilagin, for which the structure (154) has been established (a β-glucoside).

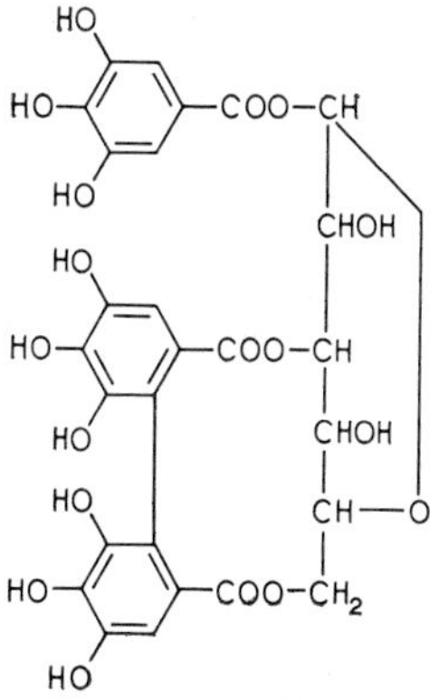

(154)

Hydrolysis of corilagin yields gallic acid, ellagic acid and glucose. When corilagin is first methylated, hydrolysis yields gallic acid trimethyl ether and hexamethoxydiphenic acid. The formation of the latter shows that the ellagic acid is not present as such in the tannin, but is formed by lactonization of the hexahydroxydiphenic acid released by hydrolysis.

Chebulinic acid, the tannin of myrobalans, is hydrolyzed to glucose, three mols of gallic acid and one of chebulic acid (155). Mild hydrolysis yields gallic and chebulic acids and 3,6-digalloylglucose. Chebulic acid has been shown to have the structure (155) by oxidative degradation to 1-butanol-

1,2,3,4-tetracarboxylic acid (lactone), and the recognition (in other ways) of the presence of a pyrogallol nucleus.

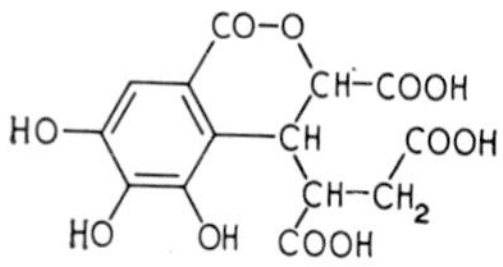

(155)

It is evident that the aliphatic tricarboxylic acid portion of the molecule of chebulic acid represents the residue of a degraded reduced pyrogallol nucleus (or of a quinic acid nucleus).

The total structure assigned to chebulinic acid is (156) (where the sugar configuration is that of a β-glucopyranoside).

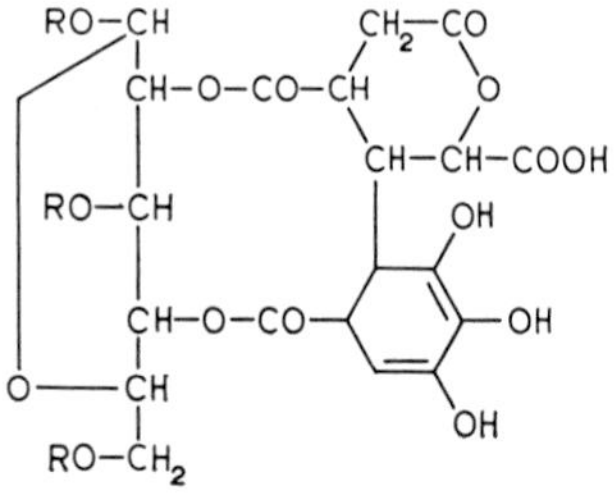

(156)   R = Galloyl

In chebulagic acid, the two galloyl residues of (156) at 3 and 6 are modified by oxidative coupling to a hexahydroxydiphenic acid residue (as in 154). Brevilagin, a tannin from *Caesalpinia brevifolia*, is hydrolyzed to glucose and ellagic acid and a new acid, brevifolin carboxylic acid (158), which readily loses carbon dioxide to give brevifolin (157).

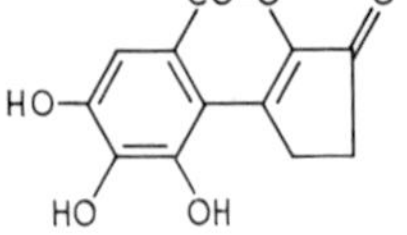

(157) 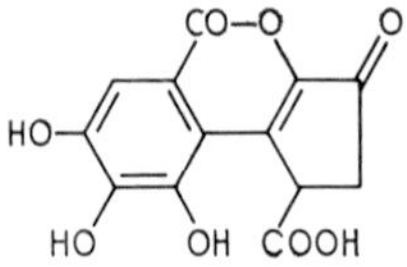   (158)

Another oxidation product derived from ellagic acid and gallic acid is valoneic acid dilactone (159), a hydrolysis product of the tannin of valonea (*Quercus* spp.). A simpler compound of related structure, derived from chestnut tannin, is dehydrogallic acid (160).

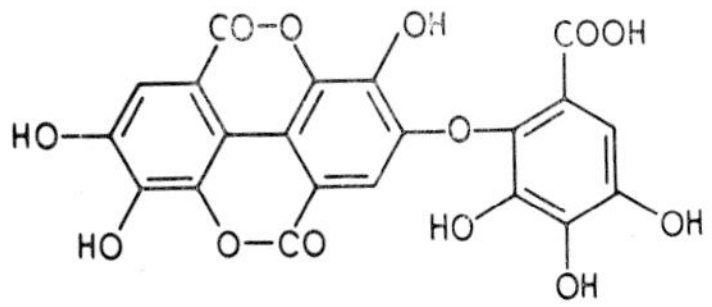

(159) 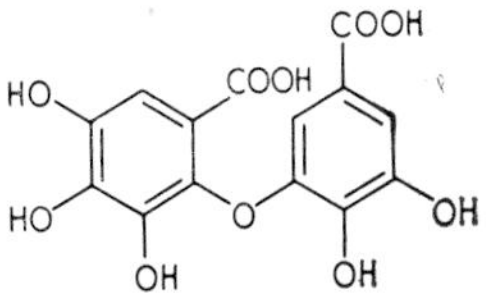   (160)

5. Miscellaneous compounds

The presence in most plants of the synthetic mechanisms and starting materials for the production of isoprenoid-, acetate-, or phenylpropanoid-derived structures leads to the synthesis of a wide variety of compounds of which a mixed origin is apparent. In addition to these "main" routes of synthesis the methyl-donating systems of living cells are also called into play, with the result that the inclusion of single-carbon fragments can further modify carbon skeletons to produce substances that do not fit neatly into one of the regular schemes.

(a) Isoprenoid modifications

The addition of isoprenoid units by what appears to be nuclear alkylation or acylation of a phenolic ring is very common. A general formulation of this process, using as likely reagents the mevalonic acid-derived precursors of isoprenoid chains and an activated senecioic acid (162), can be represented as follows:

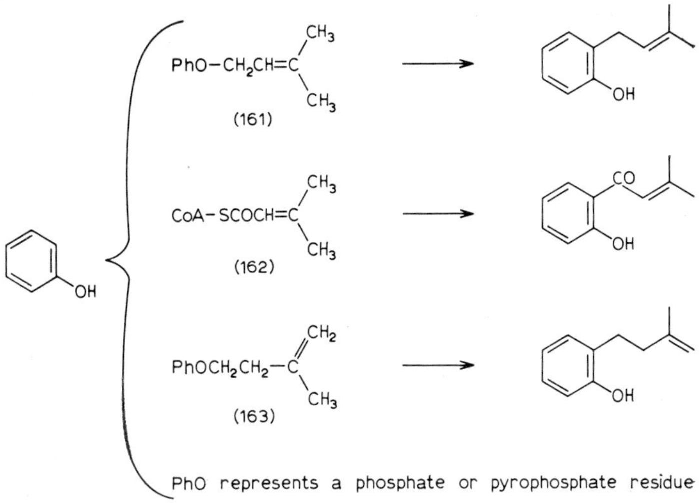

PhO represents a phosphate or pyrophosphate residue

Rutaceous and umbelliferous plants are noted for their content of substances containing furan- and isopropylfuran-derived compounds. Many of these are furocoumarins, of which the simplest example is psoralene (164). Coumarin

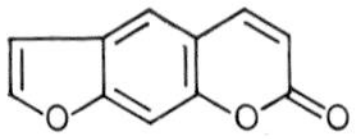

(164)

has recently been shown to be phenylpropanoid in origin, that is, formed by ring closure of a C_6-C_3 compound. The insertion of an isoprenoid side chain into the benzene ring followed by degradation prior or subsequent to furan ring closure, will lead to (164). That the furan ring is indeed isoprenoid in derivation is inferred from the occurrence, often in the same plant and commonly in the same family, of compounds in which the complete C_5 unit is retained. Examples of this are oreoselone (165) and athamantin (166).

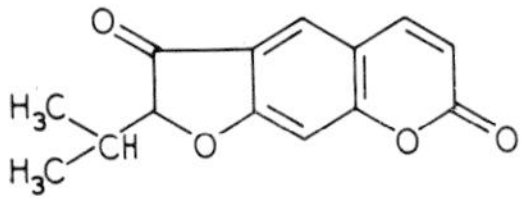

(165) 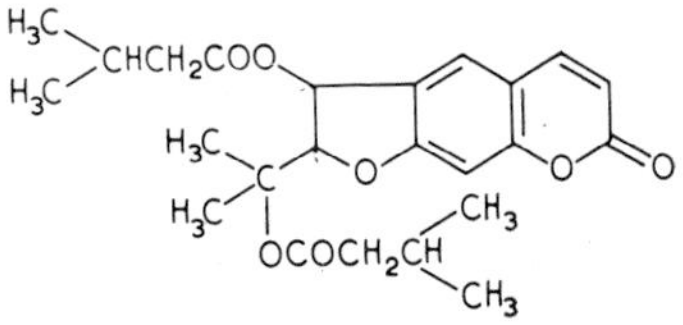   (166)

Athamantin (166) is of additional interest because it contains acyl groups derived from senecioic acid, an observation that supports the view that the acylating species (162) is available for synthesis.

In the coumarin suberosin (167) the isoprenoid fragment is unaltered, while in xanthyletin (168) a different manner of ring closure has occurred.

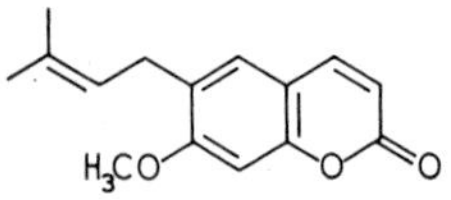

(167) 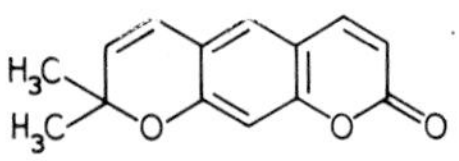   (168)

The introduction of isoprenoid substituents is not confined to the coumarins. The flavones phellamurin and amurensin (169) contain this unit, and the furanoflavones, which as karanjin (170), contain the residual furan ring:

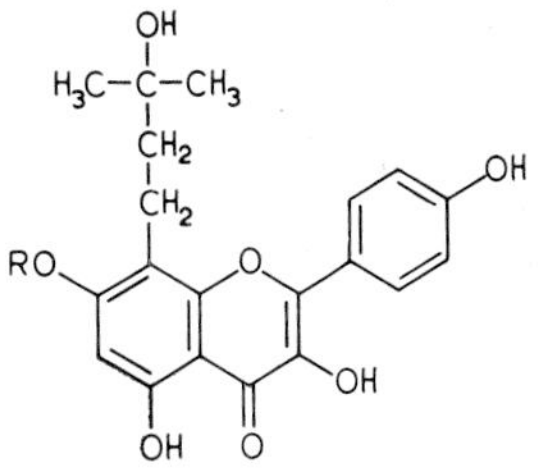

(169)   R=glucosyl 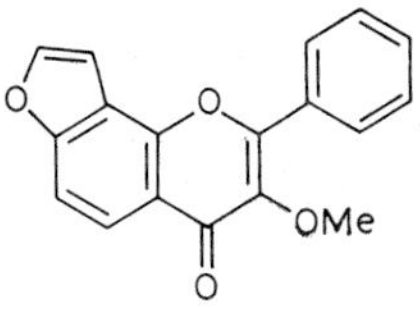   (170)

(b) Methylation

The carbon-alkylation of phenolic nuclei, presumably by single-carbon donor systems, is common in nature. The wild clove, *Eugenia caryophylla* L., contains the group of closely related compounds eugenin (171), eugenitin (172), isoeugenetin (173), and isoeugenitol (174).

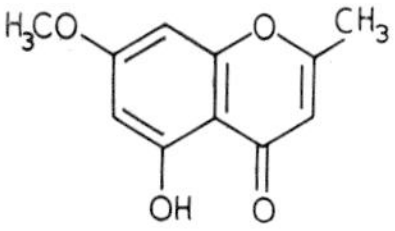

(171) 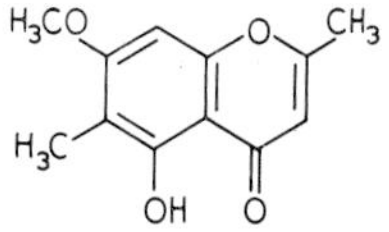   (172) 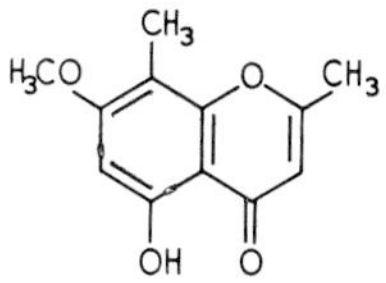   (173) 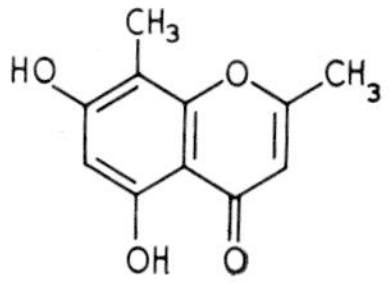   (174)

These compounds are clearly acetate-derived and can be seen to be closely related to eugenone (79).

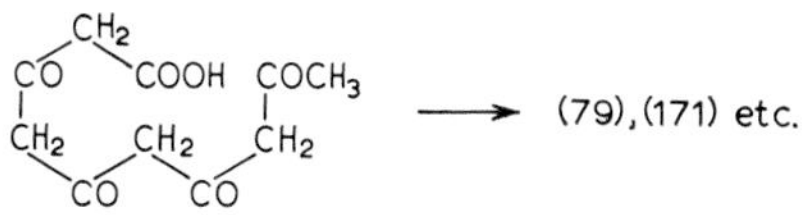

The introduction of the carbon-linked methyl groups in (172), (173) and (174) could take place prior to or after the formation of the aromatic ring: both the hypothetical β-diketonic precursor and the phloroglucinol-derived final compounds are types that are known to be readily susceptible to C-alkylation.

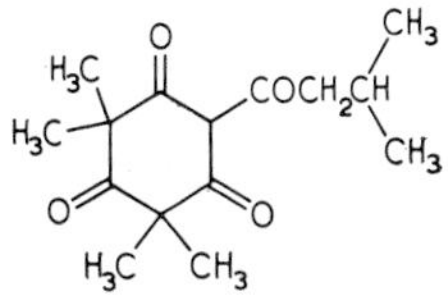

(175) 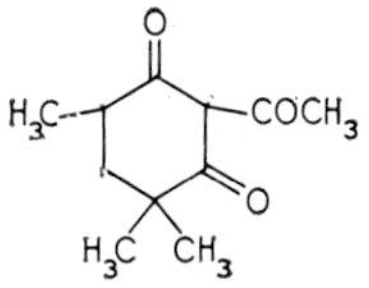   (176)

The non-phenolic compounds leptospermone (175) and angustione (176) are illustrative of how extensively C-methylation can proceed.

It should be noted that leptospermone is a C_{15} compound and thus might be regarded as sesquiterpenoid, particularly in view of the presence of —$C(CH_3)_2$ groupings in the molecule. It seems more probable, however, that, while the side chain is indeed isoprenoid, the methylated ring is derived from the acetate pathway.

Numerous additional examples of C-alkylation of aromatic rings are known among the natural phenolic substances, but the examples given above suffice to indicate the scope of this process.

(c) Single-carbon incorporation into ring systems

The addition of a carbon atom from a one-carbon donor often leads to the formation of unusual structures differing from members of a well-known class by one carbon atom. The rotenoid compounds, for example, can be looked upon as related to furano-isoflavones by the addition of a methylene group. In rotenone itself (177), the carbon atom marked by the asterisk is this "extra" carbon atom.

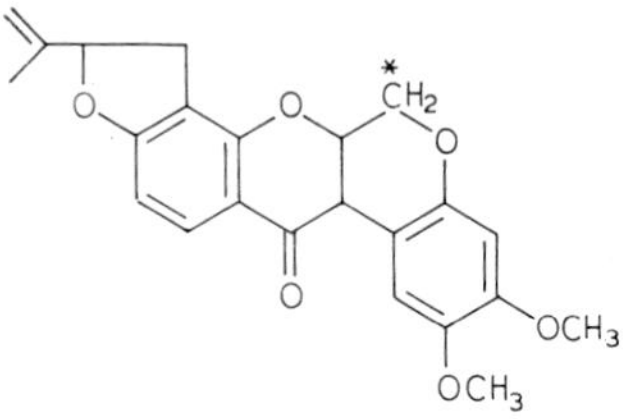

(177)

An interesting compound, recently discovered[21], may be the "missing link" in rotenoid biogenesis; this is munduserone (178).

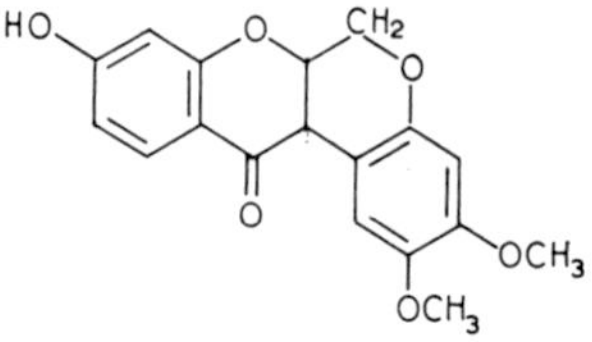

(178)

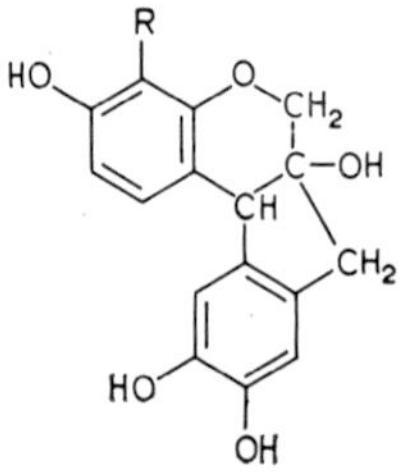

(179)   R = H
(180)   R = OH

Brazilin (179) and hematoxylin (180), are also $C_9 + C_6 + C$ compounds in which still a different arrangement is found.

6. Conclusion

The foregoing discussion has presented what must be regarded as only a fragmentary summary of the host of phenolic compounds produced by plants. What can be perceived in these widely various structural types are certain fundamental modes of biosynthesis that are common to many and different families and genera of plants. Superimposed upon these basic themes are variations played by species differences. Studies of the control of biochemical processes by genetic factors have given sufficient information to permit the generalization that these superficial modifications of basic structural patterns are the consequences of evolutionary changes in genetic make-up. As more information is gained about the detailed chemical structures of plant constituents it is to be expected that the outlines of biosynthetic processes will become clearer and more readily susceptible to rigorous experimental proof. Perhaps taxonomic relationships can continue to be studied by the use of chemical methods, as has been done for coniferous plants. The reciprocal relationship between chemistry and biology is also apparent in the use that can often be made of taxonomic relationships in aiding the process of structure elucidation of plant products. Further study of the chemistry of plant constituents will continue to serve both chemistry and biology.

REFERENCES

1 A. J. BIRCH AND F. W. DONOVAN, *Australian J. Chem.*, 6 (1953) 360.
2 T. A. GEISSMAN in K. PAECH AND M. V. TRACEY (Eds.), *Modern Methods of Plant Analysis*, Springer, Berlin, 1955, p. 543.
3 T. A. GEISSMAN AND E. HINREINER, *Botan. Rev.*, 18 (1952) 77.
4 T. A. GEISSMAN in K. PAECH AND M. V. TRACEY (Eds.), *Modern Methods of Plant Analysis*, Springer, Berlin, 1955, p. 450.
5 W. MAYER in W. RUHLAND (Ed.), *Encyclopedia of Plant Physiology*, Springer, Berlin 1958, p. 354.
6 E. H. RODD (Ed.), *The Chemistry of Carbon Compounds*, Vol. IIB, Elsevier, Amsterdam, 1953, p. 878.
7 J. N. COLLIE, *J. Chem. Soc.*, 91 (1907) 1896.
8 R. ROBINSON, *Structural Relations of Natural Products*, Oxford University Press, 1955.
9 Y. ASAHINA AND S. SHIBATA, *The Chemistry of Lichen Substances*, Japan Soc. Prom. Science, Ueno, Tokyo, 1954.
10 L. K. DALTON AND J. A. LAMBERTON, *Australian J. Chem.*, 11 (1958) 46.
11 O. HOFFMANN in K. PAECH AND M. V. TRACEY (Eds.), *Modern Methods of Plant Analysis*, Springer, Berlin, 1955, p. 359.
12 J. E. DAVIES, F. E. KING AND J. C. ROBERTS, *J. Chem. Soc.*, (1955) 2782; A. J. BIRCH AND F. W. DONOVAN, *Chem. & Ind. (London)*, (1954) 1047.
13 A. NEISH, *Can. J. Biochem. Physiol.*, 35 (1957) 161.
14 K. FREUDENBERG in K. PAECH AND M. V. TRACEY (Eds.), *Modern Methods of Plant Analysis*, Springer, Berlin, 1955, p. 499.
15 J. M. HARKIN, *Experientia*, 16 (1960) 80.
16 H. ERDTMAN in K. PAECH AND M. V. TRACEY (Eds.), *Modern Methods of Plant Analysis*, Springer, Berlin, 1955, p. 428.
17 E. ADLER, *Tappi*, 40 (1957) 294.
18 F. BLANK in W. RUHLAND (Ed.), *Encyclopedia of Plant Physiology*, Springer, Berlin, 1958, p. 300.
19 E. C. BATE-SMITH, *Qualitas Plant. Mater. Vegetabiles*, 3–4 (1958) 440.
20 O. TH. SCHMIDT in K. PAECH AND M. V. TRACEY (Eds.), *Modern Methods of Plant Analysis*, Springer, Berlin, 1955, p. 517.
21 N. FINCH AND W. D. OLLIS, *Proc. Chem. Soc.*, (1960) 176.

SUBJECT INDEX

COMPREHENSIVE BIOCHEMISTRY

SECTION II (VOLUMES 5–11)

Chemistry of Biological Compounds

PRINTED IN THE NETHERLANDS BY
NEDERLANDSE BOEKDRUK INRICHTING N.V.